FractalVision: Put Fractals to Work for You

FractalVision: Put Fractals to Work for You

Dick Oliver

SAMS
PUBLISHING

A Division of Prentice Hall Computer Publishing
11711 North College, Carmel, Indiana 46032 USA

International Standard Book Number: 0-672-30248-9

Library of Congress Catalog Number: 92-74182

95 94 93   4 3 2

Interpretation of the printing code: the rightmost double-digit number is the year of the book's printing; the rightmost single-digit, the number of the book's printing. For example, a printing code of 92-1 shows that the first printing of the book occurred in 1992.

Composed in AGaramond and MCPdigital by Prentice Hall Computer Publishing

Printed in the United States of America

Trademarks

Publisher

Richard K. Swadley

Acquisitions Manager

Jordan Gold

Acquisitions Editor

Gregory Croy

Development Editor

Ella Davis

Editors

Fran Hatton
Hugh Vandivier
Mary Corder
Grant Fairchild
Gayle Johnson
Tad Ringo

Editorial Coordinators

Rebecca S. Freeman
Bill Whitmer

Editorial Assistants

Rosemarie Graham
Lori Kelley

Technical Editor

Jerry Fath

Cover Designer

Jean Bisesi

Production Director

Jeff Valler

Production Manager

Corinne Walls

Imprint Manager

Matthew Morrill

Book Designer

Michele Laseau

Production Analyst

Mary Beth Wakefield

Proofreading/Indexing Coordinator

Joelynn Gifford

Graphics Image Specialist

Dennis Sheehan

Production

Christine Cook
Dennis Clay Hager
Carla Hall-Batton
John Kane
R. Sean Medlock
Juli Pavey
Linda Quigley
Susan Shepard
Nancy Sixsmith
Tina Trettin
Alyssa Yesh

Indexer

Hilary Adams

Overview

Contents

Acknowledgements

This book owes its existence to (at least) five people besides myself. If you enjoy it, you should thank:

David Briars for asking me to write a fractal program for him while he tuned my piano,

Peter King for convincing me that geometry matters while juggling a hatchet, a quarter, and a knife on a unicycle,

Jeff Zack for sharing philosophy and algorithms while doing flips on the neighbor's trampoline,

Peter May for imagining a fractal human while picking ferns in the Vermont woods,

And Jan Oliver for keeping me and our daughter warm and well fed.

I would also like to thank the many publishers who gave permission to reprint the copyrighted material that appears in quotes at the beginning of each section, and the many authors whose words are quoted. You'll find specific references at the end of each quote, and in the annotated bibliography.

Dedication

To Erica Catherine Oliver
Born April 28, 1992

About the Author

Dick Oliver has been working with computer graphics and artificial life since 1978, and he has taught mathematics, computer literacy, and programming to all ages. He attended the University of Maine and the University of Michigan, and he developed an ecology data analysis system for the U.S. Bureau of Land Management. Dick is now president of Cedar Software, which he founded in 1989 to help people understand and use the new sciences of complexity. His house in Hyde Park, Vermont, is surrounded by maple trees and ferns.

Introduction

Take the Tour

Welcome to the real world. Fractal geometry and chaos theory are revolutionizing mathematics and science, providing us with a new way of seeing reality. With this book and the included FractalVision software, you can create graphical models of plants, rivers, clouds, weather data, snowflakes, earthquakes, and much more.

But don't stop there. Prepare to embark on a breathtaking journey into the fantastic world of fractal geometry. You'll learn to design your own spiralling vortexes of color, otherworldly plants, and dazzling portraits of infinity. Yet, as you unveil the beauty of pure mathematics, you will also reveal hidden connections to the everyday natural world.

Many books have been written on chaos science and fractal geometry, and a number of programs display mathematical fractals such as the famous Mandelbrot set. Most of these books are stuffed with mind-boggling set theory equations, and the programs are touted as hypnotizing "productivity destroyers."

This book puts fractal geometry, and the theories of chaos and complexity that lie behind it, to work for you. By the time you finish it, you will have a rock-solid understanding of the science, philosophy, and practical application of fractals and chaos—an understanding based on extensive firsthand experience. With FractalVision software, you can create realistic models by visually simulating the actual underlying forces within natural systems. Over 200 modifiable sample files are included, and a dozen bonus programs will turn your PC into a graphics laboratory for experimenting with chaos and complexity.

No programming is required to use any of the software, but programmers will not be disappointed. All bonus programs come with full C source code, and every equation and algorithm is completely explained. Source code for the FractalVision program is also available (see the registration/order form near the back of the book).

In short, this book gives you the conceptual tools you will require to cope with 21st century math and science. From geologists to astronomers, from weather forecasters to financial forecasters, from fine artists to pure mathematicians: virtually no field is left untouched by this radical shift in how we think, work, and create. You need to know.

What you don't need is convoluted rhetoric. This book is written in plain English that even your kids will understand. I've taught courses and workshops in computer science, mathematics, and programming to students from ages 7 to 70, and you'll get the same friendly, over-your-shoulder help that I offer them.

Part of the excitement surrounding fractals comes from the fact that serious science and math are once again working on a human scale. They have returned from a private universe of particle accelerators and chalkboards full of Greek letters to the macroscopic world we all see and touch. Hard science has become directly relevant, and comprehensible, to us mere mortals without PhDs.

If you're not careful, you might even have fun.

What Are Chaos and Fractals?

Science and mathematics have always sought order in a chaotic universe. Chaos science is the latest chapter in this story. So why call it "chaos"? Because it finds order in phenomena people previously saw as entirely chaotic, and yet these phenomena remain unpredictable and uncontrollable.

Until recently, we've used the line as a basic building block to understand the universe. Chaos science uses a different geometry called *fractals*. A few things that fractals model better are: plants, weather, fluid flow, geologic activity, planetary orbits, human body rhythms, animal group behavior, socioeconomic patterns...and the list goes on.

You'll have plenty of opportunities to get your hands dirty with fractals and chaos, but a quick summary of some key concepts will help you get started:

■ Even the simplest systems become richly complex and deeply beautiful when a process is *iterated* over and over, using the results of each step as the starting point of the next. This is how nature creates a magnificently detailed 300-foot redwood from a seed the size of your fingernail.

■ Most *iterated systems* are easily simulated (even on your PC), but very few are predictable and controllable. Why? Because a tiny influence, like a "butterfly flapping its wings," can strangely amplify to have major consequences, such as completely changing tomorrow's weather.

■ You can magnify fractals forever without loss of detail, so all our math that relies on straight lines is useless with them. *Fractal dimension* can measure the texture and complexity of everything from coastlines to storm clouds. What's more, we can now use fractals to store photographic-quality images in a tiny fraction (down to 1/10,000) of the space ordinarily needed.

■ While fractals win prizes at graphics shows, their chaotic patterns pop up in every branch of science. Physicists find beautiful artwork emerging from their plotters. *Strange attractors* with fractal turbulence appear in celestial mechanics. Biologists diagnose *dynamical diseases* when fractal rhythms fall out of sync. Even pure mathematicians go on tour with dazzling slide shows and videos of their research.

All this adds up to an entirely new way of observing and modeling complex phenomena. An arising cross-disciplinary science of complexity, coupled with the computational power of modern desktop computers, brings a wealth of new tools and techniques for working with real-world systems.

How to Use This Book

You can read this book by itself or use the included software to explore hands-on examples as you go. You'll find special sections marked **You Can Do It**, which guide you step-by-step through the computerized examples.

For those familiar with the C language, sections marked **For Programmers Only** give you working source code to use as a starting point in your own programming adventures.

A few of the **You Can Do It** boxes expect you to have a copy of FRACTINT software, which is not included on the disk. This freeware program is the fastest software available for displaying many types of abstract mathematical fractals, and is also capable of creating realistic 3-D models of mountains and planets. It's available from several sources:

1. If you have a modem, you can download FRACTINT from CompuServe or most other BBS systems. On CompuServe, type GO COMART and download FRAINT.EXE from section 15, fractals. (Be warned that the file is almost 500,000 bytes, which usually translates to well over an hour online at 2,400 baud.)

2. Most shareware/freeware distribution houses will send you a copy of the most recent version (17.2 as of this writing) for a small distribution fee. For example, Public Software Library offers FRACTINT as disk #7039 for $6.99 plus a $4.00 shipping and handling fee per order. The FRACTINT source code is also available on two additional disks.

3. **But the easiest way to get the latest version** is to simply check the FRACTINT box when you send in the FractalVision registration form in the back of this book. Please include $5 to cover disk duplication cost and shipping. If you also choose to order the complete FractalVision source code, you'll get a free copy of the FRACTINT source code with it.

You Can Do It: Introducing FractalVision Software

License Agreement

The enclosed copy of FractalVision software is licensed to one user, the person who bought this book. Like the book, you may transfer it between people as long as only one copy is in use at a time. There is no charge for the software beyond what you paid for the book.

Please be sure to send in the FractalVision software registration form in the back of the book. You will receive a free newsletter, notification of future updates, and information on related software, including my new 3-D fractal modeling system.

Installation

FractalVision and the accompanying bonus programs are compressed to fit on one 3 1/2-inch 720K disk. (If you need 5 1/4-inch diskettes, use the disk exchange coupon inside the back cover.) To use the software, you must decompress it to your hard drive by running the INSTALL batch file. You'll need approximately 1500K bytes (1.5 megabytes) free on your hard disk.

1. Place the disk in drive A. (If your 3 1/2-inch disk drive is drive B, simply type B: wherever you see A: in the instructions that follow.)

2. Type A: at the DOS prompt, and press Enter.

3. Type INSTALL C: \FRACTAL, and press Enter.

Note that there should be a space between the drive name C: and the directory name \FRACTAL. Everything will be automatically installed to the \FRACTAL directory on drive C. (If you want to install on a drive or directory other than C: and \FRACTAL, type that drive letter and directory name after INSTALL.)

If you have any problems, or would like more detailed instructions, refer to Appendix A.

Starting the FractalVision Program

To run the main FractalVision Program, go to the C:\FRACTAL subdirectory and enter FV. So you would type

```
C:
CD \FRACTAL
FV
```

pressing the Enter key after each line. (If you prefer to launch FV.EXE from the DOS shell or Windows, it will still work fine.)

When the list of video modes appears, press V to pick standard VGA 640x480 mode. (If you don't have a VGA or Super VGA, pick the best mode your hardware can do.)

In the unlikely event that you don't see the words "FractalVision" on your screen, refer to Appendix A for troubleshooting.

Finally, press any key except H to get the FractalVision main menu. (If you press H, you start the online help system—you should explore that on your own later.)

How to Load Sample Files

Notice the main menu on the left. Pressing each key listed under KEY performs the associated ACTION—or you can simply point and click with your mouse. For example, to Quit the program you could either press Q or

continues

click **Quit** with the left mouse button.

But don't quit yet! First, for some instantaneous gratification, let's see what this thing can do...

The shape in the lower middle of the screen is a *fractal template*. You'll learn the nitty gritty on how these work in the online help and throughout this book, but the basic idea is simple: the largest diamond is called the *seed shape*. Think of it as a single parent. The two smaller diamonds are slightly altered copies of it—its children.

1. Press D, or click **Draw** with the mouse.

The children have children and grandchildren and great-grandchildren. That, in a nutshell, is how fractals work. It's also how nature often works. To see an example, you can load a different template from the EXAMPLES directory:

2. Press L for **Load**, and T for **Template**.

A list of files appears. The ones preceded by a \ (backslash) are subdirectories. The EXAMPLES subdirectory contains all the examples.

Note:
The backslash simply indicates a directory name rather than a filename. It does not mean, as it would in DOS commands, that the subdirectory is directly under the root directory.

3. Type \EXAMPLES and press Enter, or point to \EXAMPLES with the mouse and click.

About 200 sample files appear, listed in alphabetical order.

4. Type MAPLE and press Enter, or point to MAPLE with the mouse and click.

Notice that you get a new set of colors when you **Load** a Template, but otherwise the picture you drew doesn't change. You could now draw with the new template to add a new fractal to the same picture. For this introduction, though, you should clear the existing picture and start a new one.

5. Select **Clear**, either by pressing the PageUp key or clicking with the left mouse button on the **Clear** menu item.

Now the *seed shape* (parent) is a rectangular trunk. The *copies of the seed* (children) are the first level of branches.

6. **Draw** again by pressing D.

Can you see why this might be handy for real-world modeling?

Trees are just the beginning. There's much more here than meets the eye. I'll leave most of the juicy stuff to the remainder of the book, but you should look at one more good one now:

7. Press Page Up or pick **Clear** with the mouse to clear the picture again. Notice that the template stays.

8. Press T. This is a shortcut for loading a sample template without looking at the list of files. You can use it to quickly load examples as I present them in the book.

9. Type VSWIRL, and press Enter.

10. Press P or select **Paint** with the mouse.

You'll learn how to make more realistic looking galaxies later, but this should make it obvious that the possibilities here go far beyond just trees.

11. The spray of dots will eventually stop and the template will return. (To stop **Paint**ing before it's done, just press the Esc key.)

But now, the lines of the template obscure the picture. To see the picture without the template or menu:

12. Press V or select **View**. When you've gazed long enough, press any key to return to the menu.

Throughout this book, I will ask you to load example templates. You've seen two ways to do this:

■ Press L for **Load**, then T for **Template**. Go to the EXAMPLES sub-directory (if you haven't already done so for a previous **Load**), and choose the file you want from the list.

  …or…

continues

■ Just press T at the main menu and enter the name of the file. You don't need to be in the EXAMPLES subdirectory to use the T shortcut—it will find the examples automatically from any nearby directory. (I recommend that you save your own creations in the main FRACTAL directory, and use the T shortcut to load sample files without switching to the EXAMPLES subdirectory. This way, your work will stay separated from the examples.)

Each figure created with FractalVision contains the name of an example template in parentheses at the end of the caption. Appendix A also features an alphabetical index to all the sample files, with a short description of each and references to the figures in the book.

Starting the Online Tutorial

I'll provide step-by-step instructions on how to use the software along with hands-on examples throughout this book. However, you should still go through the online help system tutorial to familiarize yourself with the controls of the program. This isn't absolutely necessary, but it will give you some extra freedom to explore on your own.

To start the help tutorial, just press H. When you get to the help index, press Enter for the first topic. While you are within the help system, the program is fully functional and you can try anything you like—even **Load** examples and **Save** your experiments. Each time you press H and press Enter, the help system will automatically move to the next topic.

To escape from the help system at any time, just press the Esc key. The picture and template that were on-screen when you entered help will be restored.

For Programmers Only: Compiling the C Programs

Executable files for all the C programs discussed in this book are provided and are automatically installed when you install FractalVision. To run the executable files, simply type the name of the program you want. (Type MENU for a list of program names.)

You can compile the C programs in this book with all major C (or C++) compilers, including Microsoft, Borland, Zortech, and Power C. You can also use add-on graphics libraries such as Genus GX Graphics. If your compiler or graphics library isn't supported directly, you can easily create a graphics header file that supports it, probably without changing any code in the programs themselves. See Appendix D or the GRAPHICS.TXT file for an explanation of the graphics macros and functions used in the programs.

To compile one of the C programs with your particular compiler and graphics library, simply use one of the following batch files.

Compiler/Graphics Library	Header	Batch file for compile
Microsoft/Microsoft Graphics	FVMS.H	CMS.BAT or CMS2.BAT (see note below)
Borland/Turbo C/BGI	FVTC.H	CTC.BAT
Zortech/Flash Graphics	FVZT.H	CZT.BAT
Power C/MIX Graphics	FVPC.H	CPC.BAT
Microsoft C/GX Graphics	FVGX.H	CMSGX.BAT
Borland/Turbo C/GX Graphics	FVGX.H	CTCGX.BAT

continues

Microsoft users:

If you combined GRAPHICS.LIB into your main libraries when you installed the Microsoft C compiler, use CMS2.BAT instead of CMS.BAT, because CMS.BAT assumes that you have a separate GRAPHICS.LIB. If you're not sure what all that means, just look in the LIB compiler subdirectory for GRAPHICS.LIB. If it's there, use CMS.BAT. If not, use CMS2.BAT.

Borland users:

When you run a program compiled to use the Borland Graphics Interface (the graphics library that came with your compiler), you must make sure that EGAVGA.BGI, or another valid BGI driver file, is in the subdirectory where the program resides, on your PATH.

For example, to compile changes you had made in the LAND.C program from Chapter 2 with Borland Turbo C or Borland C/C++, you would enter

```
CTC LAND
```

The .EXE files supplied on the disk have been compiled with GX graphics, which supports faster operations and higher resolution Super VGA modes than most native graphics libraries. Therefore, you should copy the originals to another directory for safekeeping before you recompile any of them.

The full C source code for FV.EXE is not included with this book, but it is available directly from Cedar Software. See the registration form in the back of the book for details.

You Can Do It: Introducing FRACTINT Software

If you don't already have a copy, I strongly recommend that you get FRACTINT from one of the sources listed earlier. It's worth more than a few bucks for the 3-D projection features alone, not to mention the fractals.

You will need Version 16 or higher to use the sample files included with this book, so you may want to get the latest even if you have an earlier version. In addition to the capability to load and save predefined parameter files, versions 16 and above have many new fractal types and 3-D capabilities.

For convenience in using FractalVision and FRACTINT together, you might want to install them in the same subdirectory. (If you obtain FRACTINT by sending in the FractalVision registration form, it installs itself in the \FRACTAL subdirectory by default.)

1. In any case, to start FRACTINT you simply type FRACTINT from the directory where it resides.

The famous opening screen lists the names of the *Stone Soup Group*, a loosely affiliated group of volunteer programmers headed by Bert Tyler, Tim Wegner, Mark Peterson, and Peiter Branderhorst. They banded together on CompuServe's electronic bulletin board (COMART section 15) to assemble FRACTINT and offer it free to the world.

For more details about FRACTINT's fascinating history—and, even more fascinating, how to use it—you can tap into over 500 pages of online documentation.

2. Just press the F1 function key. (This help key works anytime, anywhere within FRACTINT. The Esc key backs out of the help system.)

Why not browse through the online help right now? You may not need to come back to this Introduction!

Okay, for those of you who did come back, here's a quick tour:

The first thing you'll always need to do when you start FRACTINT is choose a video mode.

3. Generally, the 640x480 256 color Super VGA mode is a good compromise between speed and resolution. You can get this mode by pressing Shift-F5 (hold down Shift and press the F5 function key). If you don't have Super VGA, press the Delete key to choose from an extensive list of video modes.

The fractal that appears automatically is the Mandelbrot set, which you have probably seen in computer magazines or other books. If you've ever tried generating it on your computer, you will notice that FRACTINT does it

continues

between 10 and 100 times faster than most other Mandelbrot set programs. The INT in FRACTINT stands for *integer math*, which is the internal secret behind FRACTINT's blazing speed. (It's also the secret behind FractalVision's blazing speed, by the way.)

4. Press Esc.

The main menu appears. From here, you can access the entire menu system, and if you get lost, all that online help is just a keypress away.

5. For the purposes of this book, the most important command to know is **load parameter file**, which you can access at any time by pressing @ (Shift-2).

A list of predefined fractals appears, called *parameters*.

6. The ones you see at first are defined by the FRACTINT authors. To see the ones that go with this book, press the F6 function key, and select the file named FV.PAR. (If FRACTINT is not in the same directory as FractalVision, you will have to type C:\FRACTAL\FV.PAR and press enter because FV.PAR won't appear on the list.)

7. A brief explanation of each parameter set is listed, along with the number of the figure that illustrates it in the book. Select **APreview** now.

A magnified portion of the Mandelbrot set appears, with two miniature Mandelbrot sets hanging on an electrical filament. (In Chapter 5, you'll discover what this has to do with real-world modeling.)

I promised you a tour, and a tour you shall have. But I'll leave it to the authors of FRACTINT to guide you through its nether regions of beautiful abstraction.

8. Press Esc twice, and then press Y when you are asked if you would really like to exit FRACTINT.

9. Once you're back at the DOS prompt, type DEMO and press return.

Sit back, enjoy the show. But after you've seen the pretty lights of FRACTINT, return to FractalVision and discover how this exotic geometry of extraterrestrial vortexes ended up finding hundreds of down-to-earth applications.

Organization of This Book

The best way to read this book is the way it's printed: from chapter to chapter, cover to cover. But each chapter stands on its own, and you will find the **You Can Do It** and **For Programmers Only** boxes easy to follow even if you haven't read all the surrounding material. If you discover something intriguing in the software, use the index of sample files to locate the part of the book that explains it.

Chapter 1 introduces fractal geometry by following its history, from the caves to the supercomputing laboratories. You'll retrace the evolution of a radical new geometry and find out how "pathological" shapes, which appalled their inventors, have revitalized modern science, mathematics, and art.

In Chapter 2, you discover the deep simplicity behind nature's complex face by creating visual models of rivers, trees, mountains, and earthquakes. You'll also learn how to graph fractal curves and fit them to actual data. Then I'll discuss several current applications of fractals, from economics to chemistry and physics.

Chapter 3 presents the startling revelations of nonlinear thinking. You will see the intimate connections between chaos and fractals in an interactive movie of population dynamics and uncover profound questions beneath the enchanting shapes.

In Chapter 4, it's your turn. I'll lead you step-by-step through the creation of your own original fractal models of trees, galaxies, and more. By studying the visual vocabulary of fractal design, you will learn to control fractal templates as a painter controls his brush. At the end of the chapter, you'll get a chance to breed new species of fractals by simulating natural selection—with you playing the role of Nature herself.

Chapter 5 reveals how FractalVision and other fractal programs work, and gives you visual, intuitive explanations of all the key concepts and equations. I present a program that enables you to interact with 3-D fractal models, and a closer look at seemingly abstract fractal sets that find the "geometry of nature" in pure mathematics.

Appendix A is a manual for the FractalVision program, including detailed installation and troubleshooting instructions, information on exchanging images and data with other software, a quick reference guide, and a listing of sample files.

Appendix B helps you brush up on linear algebra and complex numbers. It includes a detailed exposition of the formulas and algorithms used in the software.

Appendix C points you toward further fractal adventures. There's advice on using FractalVision as a companion for several other books and an extensive listing of catalogs, books, articles, newsletters, and software relating to fractals and chaos.

Appendix D contains detailed compilation instructions for Microsoft C, Borland C, Power C, Zortech C, or your own custom compiler, along with listings of the graphics macros and functions used in the C programs, and a sample header file.

Finally, a glossary defines all the technical terms, so you don't have to remember where I first presented a word or phrase to remember what it means.

Conventions Used in This Book

Software commands such as **Paint** and **Draw** appear in boldface. Keystrokes are given in regular type as commands: "Press the Enter key," for example.

The first few occurrences of new terms, such as *bifurcation*, appear in italics. These terms appear in the glossary and index. Proper names of creative works such as *Sierpiński's Triangle* and Michael Barnsley's book, *Fractals Everywhere*, are also italicized. Italics is occasionally used for emphasis only.

C source code appears in a monospaced font:

```
void main(void)
{   makeafractal();
}
```

Filenames, program names, and commands to type at the DOS prompt appear in capital letters. Unless a filename includes an extension (SAMPLE.FIP or 3DFERN1.IFS), it is fractal template (LEAF1 or KOCH2) with the extension .FRT assumed. A filename in parentheses at the end of a figure caption is the name of a sample fractal template that reproduces the figure.

1

A History of Fractals and Chaos

In this chapter you take a visual tour through the history and prehistory of fractal geometry. You discover how a few obscure and contradictory shapes have generated a revival of beauty and utility in mathematics.

The history of fractals as such is not a long one. It began abruptly in 1975 with mathematician Benoit Mandelbrot's revolutionary paper *A Theory of Fractal Sets*, which later became his casebook and manifesto, *The Fractal Geometry of Nature*. Mandelbrot coined the word *fractal*, however, to bring together the work of many before him.

Mathematicians such as Wacław Sierpiński, David Hilbert, Georg Cantor, and Helge von Koch crafted the first fractals mostly as abstract entertainments, having no idea of their lasting significance. Many of them considered these shapes pathological, unwieldy, or even repulsive. How shocked they would be to learn that they are now best known for the very shapes that appalled them the most!

Some of these pioneers had good reasons for their distaste for these geometric aberrations. They sensed they had uncovered something that defied and threatened some of their most prized beliefs. Hindsight has revealed that their era (about 1875-1925) was, in fact, a period of crisis in mathematics. Over and over again, mathematicians ran into bizarre shapes that challenged their concepts of space, area, distance, and dimension.

I present the story of fractals in a roughly chronological order, from the dawn of human history to the latest advances in image processing. Be warned, however, that fractal time is no more linear than fractal space. The development of these theories and concepts has often backtracked, stumbled, and folded over itself during the years, and your journey through the history of fractals will skip around a bit, too.

This is a history of ideas. It does not attempt to present the extensive human history behind fractal geometry. Although I refer to some especially influential names and dates, many others go unmentioned. If you'd like more details on chronology and personalities, Appendix C supplies plenty of references. In particular, I recommend the appendices in Mandelbrot's book, *The Fractal Geometry of Nature*.

The Prehistory of Fractals

If you wish to advance into the infinite, explore the finite in all directions.
    —Johann Wolfang von Goethe, *Epigrams*, early nineteenth century

What was the first intentional mark made by a human being? It may have been made by a finger in the sand, a stroke of stone on stone, or a swing of the foot through mud. We can't know exactly how or when it happened, but we can be pretty sure what shape it took: it was probably a line.

That first "written" mark, the actual dawn of recorded history, differed from all previous line-like tracks and stains in one way: it had a meaning. What did the line mean? What does a line still mean in our language today? 1. Which one? I.

It's no coincidence that we still use a simple stroke to mean the self, the one experiencing all else. A line, or more mathematically, a *line segment*, is the simplest and easiest mark to make on the world. What better symbol to express one's existence, as well as the singular existence of "any-one"?

So what has all this prehistorical philosophy to do with fractals and computer graphics? Fractals are the first shapes not based on lines, or *linearity*. Because fractals are nonlinear, they cannot be constructed by smooth pen strokes, which is why we need computers to draw them. The shapes in Figure 1.1a are linear; you could trace them quite quickly with a good old fashioned pen. The fractals in Figure 1.1b, however, display a nonlinear intricacy that the human hand cannot easily follow.

This is big news, after a million years or so of linearity. To understand just how big the news really is, you need some more background on what the line has become over the last few millennia.

The Sacred Line

The ancient Hellenes were people who believed very strongly in the power of the human mind to determine what things ought to be. Plato had the nerve to define God; a mind with that kind of chutzpah has no problem telling us what stars and planets ought to be.
—D.E. Thomsen, *Science News*, 1987

Thinkers in ancient times noted that there were two fundamental shapes, the *line* and the *curve*. Drawing a curve by hand takes quite a different type of attention and effort than drawing a line. The line is traditionally associated with logical thought, which values efficiency and visits each idea in sequential order. The curve, on the other hand, was traditionally associated with a force of will, which is always turning things from their natural or logical path. Lines have always been the favored children of intellectuals, while curves have been revered by dancers and artists.

The Greeks and Romans saw the line as an embodiment of truth and virtue. In their time, however, finding a good straight line was more of a challenge than it is today. Only the most refined architecture could boast precisely level floors, smooth cuts of stone, and cleanly hewn boards. Even more precious and rare were classic linear rectangles and arcs, and any artifact approximating a perfect circle held an obvious mystical connection to the sun and moon themselves.

Humans experienced the world as an interwoven, irregular swarm of living matter, out of which one could only hope to sculpt approximations of order. Linearity was an ideal—seldom seen, but often sought. Inspired by a deeply intuitive sense that the straight line was an embodiment of truth and goodness, the ancients set out to create as many of them as possible. Our love affair with the line had begun.

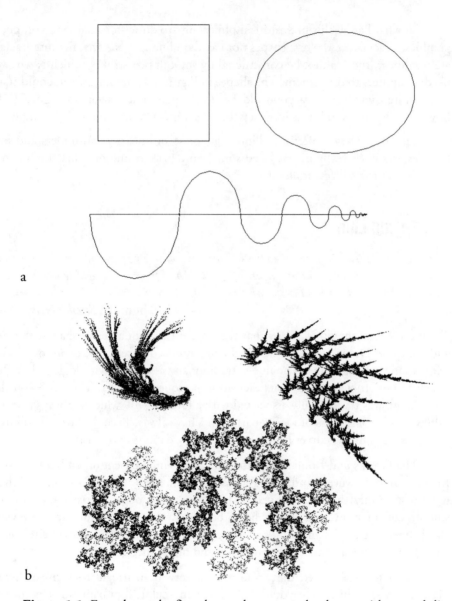

a

b

Figure 1.1. Fractals are the first shapes that cannot be drawn with smooth linear strokes.

Euclidian Cartesian Coordinates and the Calculus

The great trick of regarding small departures from the truth as the truth itself—on which is founded the entire integral calculus—is also the basis of our witty speculations, where the whole thing would often collapse if we considered the departures with philosophical rigour.
—Georg Christoph Lichtenberg, *Aphorisms*, 1764-1799

Geometry as we know it was invented circa 300 B.C. by Euclid of Alexandria, who has dominated Western thought ever since. Beginning with intuitive axioms such as, "A line is a breadthless length," Euclid developed a consistent set of logical rules to describe points, lines, and simple shapes.

Euclid's geometry was an abstract universe of its own, with no clear connection to everyday physical reality. He created his axioms from intuition and derived all his relationships and rules by applying pure logic to the axioms. No proper Greek would permit his intellect to be sullied by the mundane realm of the senses, and so observation played no part in Euclid's thought games at all.

Several centuries later, in the early 1600s, the French philosopher René Descartes scored a great victory for the linear cause by bringing Euclid down to earth. While others subjugated stone and wood to the saw blade, he dissected physical space itself. He suggested that our universe could be measured by three intersecting perpendicular poles notched in perfectly even gradations, thus giving everything in existence a precise location in three straight-line *dimensions*. All of creation, then, could be seen as a giant stack of tiny, perfectly cubic boxes. This idea formed the foundation of the modern scientific view of the world.

We have become so accustomed to the idea of straight-line dimensions that it is difficult for a twentieth century mind to appreciate how revolutionary Descartes' concepts really were. Before his time, people perceived space in terms of objects and events, rather than abstract measures. Figure 1.2 depicts the intellectualization of the senses brought by Euclid, with his idealized shapes, and Descartes, with his dimensional grid.

a

b

Figure 1.2. The Euclidian idealized world (a) versus the Cartesian world of equally sized boxes (b).

You Can Do It: Modeling Linearity

Your computer can make lines and boxes very well. To see the dreams of Euclid and Descartes come true, follow these steps. You might just discover some secrets about the origins of fractals, too.

1. Start FractalVision and **Load** the example **Template** named GRID1. (If you are not sure how to start FractalVision or how to load an example file, review the **You Can Do It: Introducing FractalVision Software** section in the introduction to this book.)

2. A large square appears on-screen, divided into four smaller squares. When you select **Draw** (type D or click **Draw**), FractalVision continues the pattern, dividing the screen into smaller and smaller squares.

3. If you let it go long enough, the subdivided squares become so small that they fill the entire region, and it appears solid. Unless you have a very fast computer, you'll probably want to press the Esc key or click the right mouse button to stop the drawing before it progresses that far.

This is Descartes' holy vision incarnate. Notice, however, that the square grid is imperfect, with a complex pattern of "errors" where the sides of the squares don't quite match up. Why? Because in the original template, the four squares were ever so slightly misaligned. The lesson here is that the Euclidian geometry and Cartesian coordinates assume perfect precision of measurement and control. Even a small error in measurement can compound itself and create strange "noise" in the appearance of the universe. Scientists try their best to maintain enough precision to minimize that noise.

What exactly is this stuff called noise? And how much precision is enough? If you're a scientist, you might not like the answers you find when this example returns in Chapter 3, "The Philosophy of Fractals."

Sir Isaac Newton and Baron Gottfried Wilhelm von Leibnitz took the Cartesian worldview to its logical conclusion a hundred years later by inventing *differential calculus*. The whole point of calculus is to turn curves into lines so that linear thought can deal with them. Leibnitz proposed that all curves are made up of infinitesimally small line segments (called *tangent lines* or *differentials*). As you magnify the edge of any squiggle or arc, it looks more and more like a line (see Figure 1.3). Calculus offers tools for finding the *limit* of this process—the line that the squiggle would resemble at infinite magnification.

Tangent lines lie at the heart of almost all modern mathematics and science. Today, everyone from architect to economist uses the techniques of *differentiation* and its inverse, *integration*, to formulate an understanding of the universe. Although they may not know it, they are all relying on the assumption that every curve is nothing more than an infinite number of line segments.

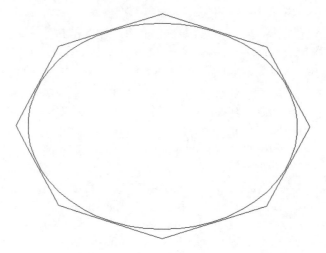

Figure 1.3. Smooth curves can be approximated with tangent lines.

Newton and Leibnitz both knew they were making dangerous assumptions. In fact, Leibnitz was forced to abandon the idea of infinitesimal line segments when it proved mathematically unsound. He could not explain why his theory worked so much of the time, yet sometimes hit strange inconsistencies. Now, mathematicians dance around the problem by distinguishing between the *limit* as the magnification "approaches" infinity and what you would actually see at infinite magnification.

Every introductory calculus student learns the notation

$$\frac{dx}{dt}$$

which Leibnitz originally meant to express the slope of an infinitesimally tiny line segment. The notation is useful because the equations for curves often behave as if a ratio between the *infinitesimals* "dx" and "dt" actually existed. Although Liebnitz himself proved the notation unreliable and meaningless when he abandoned the idea of infinitesimal line segment, it remains in use, and proves mysteriously accurate for most problems.

Curves somehow resist being entirely reduced to lines, even though most of our understanding of nature is based on the assumption that they are infinitely similar to lines. As you will soon discover, the ancient feud between lines and curves is not over, and the lines may not come out on top after all.

You Can Do It: Beyond Linearity

In some sense, fractals represent the ultimate in linearity, as the GRID1 example showed.

1. **Load** the **Template** ARCHY for a form that "out-Greeks" the Greeks themselves. The template is a table supported by two columns.

2. Select **Draw** to divide the entablature and each column into a miniature table and columns, and each subcolumn into smaller tables and columns. Although a Grecian architect might scoff at this somewhat crude implementation of base, shaft, capital, and cornice, this is the simplest and purest implementation of classical nested linear structure.

FractalVision simply takes linear shapes and repeats their linear geometry over and over on smaller and smaller scales. This is the perfect linearity machine!

3. Select **Clear** to erase this image.

4. **Load** the **Template** ARCHY2 for another example. Here, the columns have been turned on their sides, and a third thin column has been added in the middle.

5. Select **Draw** to watch the superlinearity game again, played with this slightly altered shape. As before, boxes are stacked within boxes—only

continues

9

this time, with a twist. Can you see where they are heading? Something is growing out of the linear pavement…

6. Now select **Clear** and **Paint** to see the shape that these boxy tables and columns are approaching. Somehow, the absolutely linear, perfectly repetitive motions of a computer have revealed the unruly forms of a primeval forest.

7. **Clear**, **Load**, and **Paint** the example templates PALMLEAF and LEAF1 for more examples of linearity lost in the jungle.

Welcome to fractals: linearity taken beyond its "limits." If only Newton and Leibnitz had had a PC and the right software, geometry might have taken quite a different turn in the eighteenth century. As it happened, though, art preceded science into the wilderness of nature's geometry.

The Rift Opens: Art Versus Science

Art is a lie that lets us recognize the truth.

—Pablo Picasso

Scientists and mathematicians weren't the only ones trying to imitate and understand nature with lines. Long before the origins of science as we know it, humanity used the linear pen mark and brush stroke to mimic the environment.

While scientists hailed their own achievements in comprehending and modeling the natural world, artists enjoyed considerably more success at crafting immediately recognizable representations.

Over the centuries, art and science moved further apart in their approaches to understanding the universe. Artists concentrated on the most beautiful and the most common: landscapes, portraits, and self-expression. Scientists gravitated toward the opposite extreme, focusing on artificially simplified laboratory experiments where the observer was diminished to only an emotionless "controlled variable."

Art flaunted its beauty, while the elite elegance of mathematics and science hid behind equations and test tubes. Even geometry, the most artistic of mathematical subjects, was becoming more an exercise in logic than visualization. Geometricians came to value textual proofs over constructions of compass and pencil, and analysis became more important than pattern.

Something in Leibnitz' confusion over infinitesimals was destined to reshape the relationships between art, math, and science. But let us return to our story: the glory days of mathematics had just begun…

You Can Do It: The Art of Weaving

As impressionists and realists assembled lines and brush strokes into nature's nonlinear shapes, craftspeople and artisans were also weaving lines into fractal-like abstractions.

1. **Load** the **Template** example called TARTAN. The theme is a square patch of cloth with four strips of color woven into it.

2. **Draw** to let the weaving begin. Threads combine in an intricate plaid.

3. Select **Clear**, and **Load** the **Template** LACEWORK. Here the theme is a radial web rather than a square.

4. Select **Draw** to weave webs within webs, making each part resemble the whole. *Self-similarity* is the foundation of modern fractal geometry, but it is certainly not a new idea.

5. Religious art attempts to point toward the infinite and has often used nested patterns to do so. **Load** the MANDALA example, then **Clear** and **Draw**. Is it a Buddhist sand painting or Catholic stained glass window?

Holy ones and artsy folk have always known that self-reflection is the key to higher awareness of all things. Like it or not, the math and science types would soon find this out on their own.

The Great Crisis: Multiplying Monsters

The certainties of one age are the problems of the next.
—R.H. Tawney, *Religion and the Rise of Capitalism*, 1926

By the nineteenth century, many mathematicians believed that little progress remained to be made. Centuries of refinement had left the work of Euclid, Descartes, and Newton essentially unchanged. All that remained of mathematics was playful expansion upon basic themes set up ages ago.

Geometricians adored the word *curvilinear*. In using it, they demoted curves to the status of "bent lines" and reveled in victory over all things wild and twisty. Let the artists dirty their hands with messy phenomena like clouds and forests; these would fall under the scientists' control in a only a few more years.

After all, if the position and velocity of every particle in the universe was known (as it surely was known by an omniscient God), the curvilinear paths of every particle could be predicted with absolute certainty from simple linear equations. This favorite fantasy of the French astronomer Pierre-Simon Laplace had become the gospel of all science. Scientists would henceforth spend their time hammering out those minutiae, progressing steadily toward ever more perfect prediction and control of their universe. Mathematicians would freely explore the nether regions of untethered intellect and forget the real world entirely.

The Golden Age of Mathematics had come…or had it?

Sierpiński's Triangle

Those who hear of curves without tangents, or of functions without derivatives, often think at first that Nature presents no such complications, nor even suggests them. The contrary, however, is true, and the logic of the mathematicians has kept them nearer to reality than the practical representations employed by physicists.
—Jean Perrin, *Revue de Mois*, 1906

The trouble began in 1875, when the acclaimed German mathematics genius Karl Weierstrass described a continuous curve that could not be differentiated, and so apparently had no tangent lines. With the turn of the century, a tide turned in mathematics, and an alarming number of such strange curves suddenly appeared.

Perhaps the most famous of these "prefractals" is called *Sierpiński's Triangle*. You can construct it in several ways, but I present two of the earliest. To draw the shape, Polish mathematician Wacław Sierpiński began with a triangle. He then divided the triangle into four equal pieces. Figure 1.4 shows how he divided the outside three pieces the same way as he had divided the initial triangle, continuing this process indefinitely. If you could draw infinitely small dividing lines, you would get the mathematical shape Sierpiński defined.

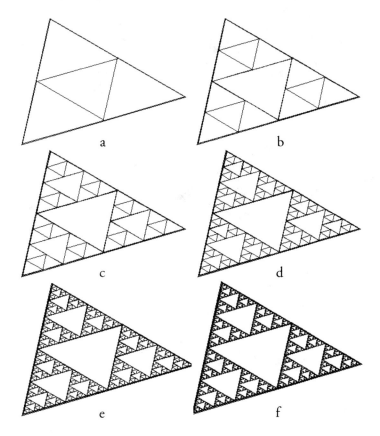

Figure 1.4. Sierpiński's Triangle is an infinitely detailed shape constructed by subdividing a triangle forever (SIERPIN).

This all seems innocent enough. It might be difficult to imagine an infinitely detailed shape, but certainly no mathematical laws have been shattered.

Now consider another method of constructing the same shape. Take a filled-in triangle and punch holes in it instead of filling it with lines. First, punch out the middle piece, then a smaller hole in each of the three corner pieces, and so on. You would end up with the same triangle, although it's sometimes called *Sierpiński's Gasket* when built this way (see Figure 1.5).

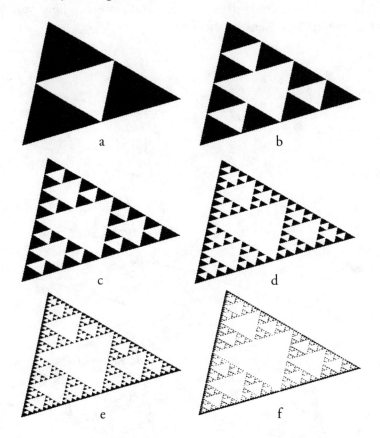

Figure 1.5. Another way to build Sierpiński's Triangle. This version is also known as Sierpiński's Gasket (SIERPIN2).

Sierpiński first encountered confusion when he tried to find the area covered by this shape. On one hand, infinitely many holes will eventually eat away every bit of the filled region, and the shape will cover an area of zero. On the other hand, at each step you take away only one-fourth of the remaining area, leaving three-fourths (most of it) still covered. No matter how long you do this, you leave more than you take every time. The area never reaches zero.

So is the area zero, or isn't it? Intuition might say it is, but a simple, rigorous proof shows us that it can't be. This sort of problem confounded Leibnitz, and even pestered the Greeks in ancient times. Until the twentieth century, mathematicians had always managed to dance around paradoxes of this sort. More sneaky numbers, however—like the area of Sierpiński's Gasket—kept falling through the cracks between finity and infinity.

Mathematicians settled on the answer of zero, mostly because they couldn't answer the question, "If it isn't zero, what is it?" Besides, the first construction method used only lines, and no filled areas at all. Because a mathematical line or line segment has no width, it covers no area. The area of the shape must always be zero, no matter how many lines you use to construct it. Sierpiński and his colleagues could not refute this argument, so they gritted their teeth and prayed that the confusing business of infinitely small but nonzero area was just a bad dream.

You Can Do It: Modifying Sierpiński's Triangle

You can watch Sierpiński's Triangle grow on-screen, and perhaps even design some mathematical oddities of your own.

1. Sierpiński's Triangle is defined in the example template called SIERPIN. **Load** this **Template**. The big red triangle is a starting shape, or *seed shape*, and the three gray copies show the first step in constructing the curve.

2. Select **Draw**, and the triangles shrink until they theoretically cover no area at all. Meanwhile, so many perimeter lines appear that they eventually add up to an infinite length.

You might wonder what this shape would look like if one of the three triangles was different from the others—perhaps a bit smaller or larger, or in a different place. Why not find out?

3. Select **Clear** to erase the finished shape (notice that the template remains unchanged).

continues

4. Now select **Next Part**. The T-shaped *handle* moves to the middle of one of the small gray triangles.

5. Select **Shrink**. The triangle does just that.

6. **Draw** again, and notice how your change is carried throughout the construction process, changing the entire curve.

7. Select **Clear** and try some other actions on the bottom of the menu, such as **Spin**, **Stretch**, and **Skew**. You can also use the arrow keys to move the triangle around.

8. If you'd like to play with the Sierpiński's Gasket rather than the Sierpiński's Triangle, **Clear** and **Load** SIERPIN2.

Poor Sierpiński had to sketch his infinitely detailed shapes by hand, so he never got to explore the intriguing variations that you can construct so easily. He did, however, have a few more tricks up his sleeve.

Magic Carpets and Space-Filling Curves

Fractals live in a nether world between conventionally dimensioned spaces…between their one-dimensional parts and their two-dimensional home.
—William McWorter, "Creating Fractals," *BYTE*, 1987

What if you could prove that even a shape made entirely of lines could end up covering some area? Before you do just that, have a look at another of Sierpiński's creations, a magic carpet. The starting shape is just a horizontal line segment. To begin the construction, replace the line with eight line segments, arranged as in Figure 1.6. Each of those eight small line segments is replaced with the whole shape, and so on ad infinitum.

Sierpiński's Carpet is very similar to Sierpiński's Triangle. You could construct an identical shape by punching holes in a filled-in square. The same debate between zero and nonzero area would ensue.

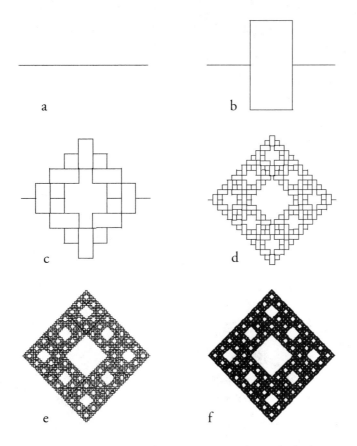

Figure 1.6. Sierpiński's Carpet. As the weave gets tighter, the holes get smaller (CARPET).

Now take a gander at Figure 1.7. This is the same as the Carpet in Figure 1.6, except that a ninth line segment has been added right in the middle. If you construct this shape with FractalVision software (the next **You Can Do It** box tells you how), a continuous curve winds its way around the screen, circling in figure eights within figure eights.

An Italian mathematician named Guiseppe Peano invented this shape in 1890, while serving in the position of "extraordinary professor of infinitesimal calculus" at the University of Turin. (He was later promoted to "ordinary professor," by the way.) With it, he demonstrated that a continuous curve with no width—and thus no area—could fill a region of space. Each successive level leaves less space between the little squares. At the infinite level defined as the *space-filling curve*, no empty space whatsoever would be left between the lines.

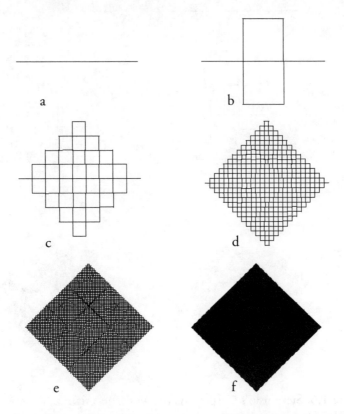

Figure 1.7. Weaving one more thread into Sierpiński's Carpet seals up all the holes to make Peano's Space-Filling Curve (PEANO).

Consequently, the curve would have an area equal to that of the square which bounds it. Yet, it must also have an area of zero because it is still made up of lines! Another way of saying this is that a one-dimensional set of line segments somehow fills part of a two-dimensional plane.

You Can Do It: Magic Carpets and Space-Filling Curves

Sierpiński and Peano's curvaceous carpets are included with FractalVision, ready for your inspection, improvement, and improvisation.

1. **Clear**, **Load**, and **Draw** the CARPET example to see Sierpiński's handiwork in action. Notice that the shapes are lines instead of triangles.

2. As with the earlier SIERPIN examples, you can use **Next Part**, the arrow keys, and the **Grow**, **Shrink**, **Spin**, and **Skew** menu choices to twiddle these shapes to suit your curiosity and creativity.

As a lesson in creative twiddling, see if you can modify Peano's Space-Filling Curve so that it doesn't *quite* fill space anymore:

3. **Load** the PEANO template and **Draw** to see it fill a two-dimensional square with one-dimensional lines. Press the Esc key if you trust that it will fill the square but don't feel like waiting to see it finish.

4. **Clear** the picture, so you can see to work with the template more easily. (Notice that whenever you **Clear**, you can select **Restore** to bring the picture back.)

What would happen if the line segments that make up Peano's Curve didn't quite touch? Would the collection of one-dimensional lines still magically become two-dimensional?

5. Find out by **Shrink**ing each part of the template a little bit. Select **Next Part** and **Shrink**, then **Next Part** and **Shrink** again for each of the remaining eight parts. The quickest way to do this is to repeatedly press Tab / (the Tab key followed by the / key) until you return to the part where you started.

6. Now **Draw** to see the result. The separation between the lines appears as smaller and smaller cracks, and the shape no longer becomes truly two-dimensional.

If the truth be known, it isn't strictly one-dimensional anymore either. What dimension does it have, then? Read on for the answer.

"A Gallery of Monsters"

Historically, the revolution was forced by the discovery of mathematical structures that did not fit the patterns of Euclid and Newton.... The mathematicians who created the monsters regarded them as important in showing that the world of pure mathematics contains a richness of possibilities going far beyond the simple structures they saw in Nature.
—Freeman Dyson, "Characterizing Irregularity," *Science*, 1978

Troublesome curves kept cropping up to form a "Gallery of Monsters," as they were called by reputable scientists and mathematicians such as Jules-Henri Poincaré near the dawn of the twentieth century. The dimensional quarrels were not just between lines and planes or even between famous and obscure personalities. The widely respected German mathematician Georg Cantor, who singlehandedly developed modern set theory, often fell under the poignant sarcasm of Poincaré, who deemed many of Cantor's creations "pathological." One such shape, constructed by Cantor in 1877, seems to somehow "jump" dimensions—it is constructed by chopping up one-dimensional line segments, but in the end it contains only zero-dimensional points, without length or width (See Figure 1.8).

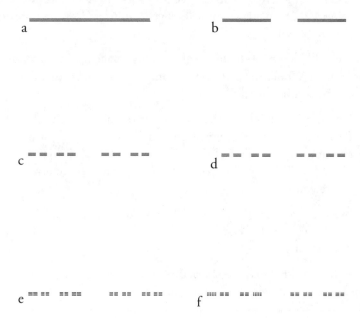

Figure 1.8. If you chop up a line segment forever, you get a set of points called Cantor's Dust (CANTOR).

Following in Cantor's footsteps, the British science journalist Edmund Edward Fournier d'Albe (hereafter, Fournier) described an infinite set of points constructed by nesting a series of octahedrons (eight-sided, three-dimensional shapes) inside one another. Fournier was no mathematician; he constructed his set in 1907 as a fanciful way to explain to his readers how the universe could contain an infinite number of stars without causing a solid white "blazing sky" effect.

Figure 1.9 shows a two-dimensional approximation of *Fournier's Multiuniverse.* Fournier's shape, like Cantor's, consists entirely of zero-dimensional points, even though it is constructed entirely from two- or three-dimensional polyhedrons. How can this be? The definition of a zero-dimensional point, going all the way back to Euclid, is that which is separate from all else without having to be cut away from it. Because Cantor's Dust and Fournier's Multiuniverse are both constructed by endlessly cutting apart a line or a solid, each part is entirely separate from all the other parts when the cutting is done. Therefore, those parts must by definition be zero-dimensional points. Of course, Cantor's Dust is still made up of two-dimensional line segments, and Fournier's Multiuniverse is still made up of 3-D solids, even though both consist of only "0-D" points.

(By the way, if you find this business of "jumping dimensions" a tad overwhelming, you're not the first: Cantor died in a psychiatric ward after spending his later years in insane asylums. Schoenfliss, a friend and colleague, was convinced that the problem of how an infinite continuum can be reduced to countable points, coupled with the sudden rejection of his work by other mathematicians, drove Cantor over the edge. The "continuum problem" plagued him constantly until his death.)

You Can Do It: Watch the Monsters Grow

With FractalVision, you can experiment with the crazy curves that turned The Golden Age into The Great Crisis. To view Cantor's Dust and Fournier's Multiuniverse at their best, you need to learn how to control the *level of detail.*

1. **Load** the **Template** FOURNIER. (Remember that you can load a template quickly without viewing the list of files by hitting the letter T or clicking **Load** with the right mouse button.)

continues

2. Select **Draw**. Like the modified PEANO curve you created previously, cracks appear between parts of the drawing at every level of detail. Well, not quite *every* level of detail, because the shape is drawn down only to the third level. You can change that to see the pattern continue further.

3. Select **Adjust** and then press the number 4 to increase the **Level** setting by one. (You could do the same thing by clicking **Level 4** with the mouse, or simply by pressing the right arrow key once.)

4. Press Enter to return to the main menu, then **Draw** again. This time, the shape is fleshed out more than before.

You can **Adjust** the **Level** of detail up to Level 15, or down to Level 0 (which would only draw the seed shape). Moreover, you can actually skip straight to the *infinite level* without bothering with the intermediate levels at all. You'll learn the mathematical magic trick behind this in Chapter 5, "The Math Behind the Magic," but here's how to make it happen:

5. **Clear** the picture and select **Paint**. The entire shape sprays onto the screen, as intricately detailed as your video card pixels will display.

6. Many shapes can be seen only by taking this shortcut to infinity. **Load** the CANTOR template, for instance.

7. It may look like a line, and even when you **Draw**, it still looks like a line because each level is drawn on top of the previous one.

8. When you **Clear** and **Paint**, however, the true nature of Cantor's Dust shines through. At the infinite level, no line segments remain at all, and the shape becomes a collection of separate points.

If you think something peculiar is going on here, you're right. No matter how high you set the **Level** of detail, you'll always be **Draw**ing tiny one-dimensional lines (with CANTOR) or two-dimensional boxes (with FOURNIER). At the infinite level, somehow magically produced by **Paint**, the tininess itself suddenly takes over, and the lines and boxes transform themselves into zero-dimensional points.

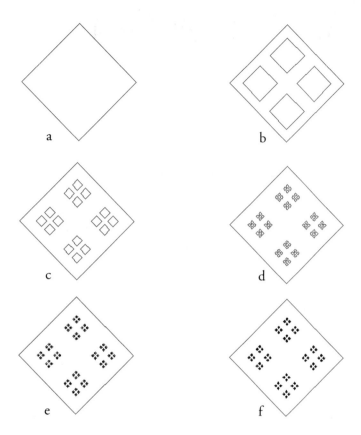

Figure 1.9. Fournier used this "Multiuniverse" to prove that there could be an infinite number of stars in the universe without making the night sky solid white (FOURNIER).

These paradoxes could not be resolved within the framework of nineteenth century mathematics. Mathematicians had to devise an entirely new conception of area and dimension. Before we attend the revolution, let's take a walk on the beach…

How Long is the Coast of Maine?

Everything in the universe goes by indirection. There are no straight lines.
—Ralph Waldo Emerson, 1870

Anyone from Maine (like me) will proudly tell you that over 6,000 miles of coast stretch between New Hampshire and New Brunswick, which are barely 300 miles apart. How are such measurements made, and how accurate are they?

If you measure the length of an irregular coastline, your results would depend on the length of your ruler. A measuring stick 50 scale miles long reports a shorter distance than a 10-mile measure. Lay 1-mile-long sticks end to end along the bays and peninsulas, and you get a longer estimate still. On the beach itself, you'd walk even further, and if you could outline the edge of the waves with toothpicks, that line would be even longer.

Precision has its limits, and the 6,000 miles were presumedly measured in Yankee strides. What if you imagined an idealized coastline that never "smoothed out" no matter how closely you examined it? Could you measure its total length? This question is closely intertwined with the dimensional confusion Sierpiński and Peano faced.

Figure 1.10 is a mathematical "coastline." This shape was invented by Swedish mathematician Helge Von Koch in 1904, during the great crisis in mathematics. (Like so many of his contemporaries, Koch was obsessed with infinity. Besides fractal coastlines, mathematics is indebted to him for the tools to solve infinite matrices of linear equations.) To construct his coastline curve, Koch began with a line and drew a triangular "bump" on it. An identical bump is raised on each line segment of that shape, and so on.

Successive approximations of the Koch Coastline possess increasingly greater lengths. If the seed line was 1,000 miles long, the first level approximation would be four-thirds of that, or 1,333 miles. (Why four-thirds? If the original line was created by lining up three toothpicks of equal length, you could make the first level approximation by tilting the middle toothpick and adding one more. Each level is four-thirds the length of the previous one.) The next approximation would be four-thirds of that (1,777 miles), the next would be 2,370 miles, and so on. These increasing approximations go on forever, so the total length would seem to be infinite.

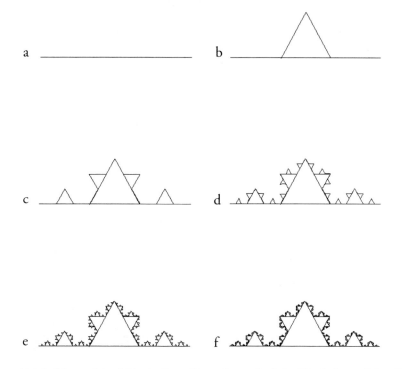

Figure 1.10. The original Koch Coastline, also called the Koch Snowflake Curve (KOCH).

That's a pretty comfortable answer (for a mathematician), but it isn't very useful. For one thing, it implies that all such coastlines would be of equal (infinite) length, no matter how much longer each successive approximation was than the last.

Figure 1.11 is another Koch Coastline, very similar to the first. You start with a line, place a bump on it, and propagate the bump to infinity.

Like the other curve, this one would seem to be infinitely long. Yet, it doesn't seem as though this curve could be the same length as the last. The first level approximation is five-thirds the length of the seed line, rather than four-thirds, and every successive approximation is longer, too. Table 1.1 summarizes the first few levels.

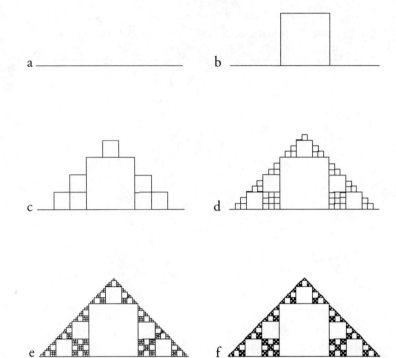

Figure 1.11. A "Square" Koch Coastline is longer than the one in Figure 1.10. But how much longer? (KOCH2).

Table 1.1. Lengths of two different Koch Coastlines as they grow.

Level	Approximate length of triangular coastline	Approximate length of square coastline
0	1,000	1,000
1	1,333	1,666
2	1,778	2,777
3	2,370	4,630
4	3,160	7,716
5	4,214	12,860

Level	Approximate length of triangular coastline	Approximate length of square coastline
6	5,619	21,433
7	7,492	35,722

Obviously, the second curve is always much longer than the first. Saying that these two curves both have the same "infinite" length seems absurd.

To complicate matters, the second Koch curve could also be constructed by "hole-punching," as with Sierpiński's Gasket. Again, we would be stuck with a curve that had a nonzero area but was identical to a curve constructed of zero-area lines. Unlike Peano's Space-Filling Curve, this curve does not even become fully two-dimensional. The whole idea of *area* is beginning to seem rather nebulous.

You Can Do It: Koch Coastlines and Islands

You may have seen the Koch Coastline before. It is one of the world's most famous fractals, and it has appeared in many books. By placing three Koch Coastlines around a triangle, you can create another shape that is even more famous, the Koch Snowflake.

1. **Load** the KOCH template. This will become the top part of the snowflake.

2. Select **Shrink** four times to reduce the size of the whole template. (Notice that when the handle is on the seed shape, commands such as **Shrink**, **Grow**, and **Spin** affect the entire template, but when the handle is on a copy of the seed—as when you were modifying Sierpiński's Triangle—the commands affect only that one part.)

3. Press the up arrow eight times. The whole template moves up to make room for the rest of the snowflake.

4. Select **Draw** to create one side of the snowflake.

continues

Now you need to add the bottom two sides. Once you get used to FractalVision, you can move and rotate templates with the mouse. For this exercise, however, I will guide you through using the keystrokes.

5. Select **Spin** (press the + key) exactly ten times to rotate the template.

6. Select **Precision** (press the End key) to change to small movements. The handle becomes smaller, and every movement or rotation from now on occurs in tiny steps.

7. Select **Spin** exactly five more times so that the template is parallel to one of the sides of the Koch curve you just drew.

8. Select **Precision** again to return to big movements.

9. Press the down arrow seven times. The top of the template should now be even with the bottom of the Koch Coastline you drew before.

10. Press the right arrow four times. The right tips of the template and the drawing should now approximately line up.

11. Select **Draw** to create the second side of your snowflake.

12. Select **Spin** (the + key) ten times, select **Precision** (the End key), and select **Spin** five times again. The template should be parallel to the top right side of the snowflake drawing.

13. Select **Precision** to return to big movements.

14. Press the left arrow key exactly eight times to move the final side of your snowflake into place.

15. **Draw** one more time.

16. You may want to save all that hard work. Select **Save Picture**, type a name for your masterpiece, and press Enter. (If you just press Enter without typing a name, the name of the last file you loaded (KOCH) is used. This creates a KOCH.PCX file and does not replace or erase the KOCH.FRT template file.)

If you'd like to see the Square Koch Coastline, it is called KOCH2. If you get lost while trying to make the Koch Snowflake, you can simply **Load** and **Draw** KOCHA, KOCHB, and KOCHC (without selecting **Clear** in between).

Fractal Dimension

There's a whole progression…an infinite number of possible dimensions…but in between, we haven't had measuring sticks that are very convenient.
— Alan Norton, quoted by Peter Sorensen in "Fractals," *BYTE*, 1984

The problems of comparing infinite lengths and infinitesimal areas are really two sides of the same coin. The twentieth century brought a desperate need for a completely new way to measure space and dimension. Two mathematicians named Felix Hausdorff and Abram S. Besicovitch answered this call. Not only did they literally unveil new dimensions, they actually redefined "dimension" itself.

Traditionally, any shape has a dimension of either 0 (a point), 1 (lines and curves), 2 (planes and surfaces), or 3 (space). These dimensions had been extended to include a theoretical 4th dimension, and higher integer dimensions had been vaguely imagined.

Besicovitch, expanding on the earlier work of Hausdorff, proposed that shapes could actually have *fractional dimensions,* such as 1.5 or 2.3. Curves like Sierpiński's and Koch's would then fall between the ordinary dimensions, and much of their odd behavior would be explained. This new fractional dimension could be computed precisely, based on measurements from simple approximations of a curve.

Specifically, the Hausdorff/Besicovitch dimension is defined as a ratio between the logarithms of the number of copies and the size of the seed relative to each copy. For the Triangular Koch Coastline, you would find $\log(4)/\log(3)$, equal to about 1.2618, because there are four copies and each is one-third the size of the seed.

Quantifying Infinity

Nature has played a joke on the mathematicians… The same pathological structures that the mathematicians invented to break loose from 19th-century naturalism turn out to be inherent in familiar objects all around us.
— Freeman Dyson, "Characterizing Irregularity," *Science*, 1978

The Triangular Koch Coastline's fractional dimension is about 1.26, and the fractional dimension of the Square Koch Coastline is about 1.46. You no longer need to say that the second curve has a "longer infinite length" than the first or that it "fills infinitesimally more area." You can now just note that it is "closer to two-dimensional," which is much easier to grasp. Furthermore, you can state exactly how much closer to "filling the plane" it is, which is a giant step forward indeed.

In fact, the idea of fractional dimension has turned out to be much more powerful that its originators imagined. Because nature abounds in self-reflective shapes such as coastlines, we can now characterize much of our environment with this new index. Mountains, clouds, trees, and flowers all have dimensions between two and three, and we can read much of something's character simply from its dimension. The rough coast of Maine has a higher fractal dimension than the smooth beaches of California, dramatic puffed storm clouds "fill space" more than a gentle fog, and richly textured Beaux Arts buildings are measurably "more three-dimensional" than featureless skyscrapers.

The *fractal dimension*, as Benoit Mandelbrot later renamed it, was even more important for mathematicians. They were suddenly able to measure an entire universe of forms that were previously immeasurable. For the first time since Descartes, a truly new meter of space itself was created. Exactly what we could measure with this meter was still unknown. Certainly, Sierpiński, Koch, and Hausdorff did not suspect that their excursions into infinity's most abstract and "unnatural" shapes would return to become the first genuine "geometry of nature."

You Can Do It: Computing Fractal Dimension Automatically

With FractalVision, you can automatically estimate the fractal dimension of any shape you create. First, you compare the dimension of the Triangular Koch Coastline and the Square Koch Coastline. Then you compare the coast of New England to the coast of Old England.

1. **Load** the KOCH template and **Clear** any picture that might be on-screen.

2. Select "infinite" **Paint** by pressing the letter I or clicking **Paint** with the right mouse button. This will paint until the end of time, or until you press the Esc key, whichever comes first. (If you pressed P rather than I, the Paint function would automatically stop after a while.)

3. Wait until the shape is very solid and well defined, with no spray paint-like appearance. When the shape looks well done, take it off the burner by pressing the Esc key.

4. Now select **Extra** and then select **Fractal Dim.** to estimate the fractal dimension. Read the short explanation that appears and press the Enter key to begin estimating. (It will take a while.)

Here's how FractalVision estimates the fractal dimension. First, it divides the screen into boxes 2 pixels wide and counts the number of boxes which contain part of the curve. Next, it divides the screen into boxes 4 pixels wide and counts again. By comparing the difference between the two counts, it estimates the roughness—or irregularity—of the image. That roughness is the fractal dimension. To obtain a more accurate estimate, the program repeats this procedure for box sizes up to 8 pixels wide and averages the results.

Because this is an estimate and not a precise calculation, the exact number you get will depend on the resolution of your video hardware. Your estimate should be somewhere between 1.16 and 1.36.

5. Now **Load** the KOCH2 template for comparison.

6. **Clear** and **Paint** (again, by pressing I, not P).

7. When the shape looks complete, press Esc to stop painting.

8. Select **Extra** and **Fractal Dim.**, then press Enter to start estimating. Watch the computer count boxes.

9. The fractal dimension of this curve is about 1.46, which is higher than the other. This confirms our visual intuition: it looks rougher and more irregular, as if it "filled more space."

The fractal dimension of these particular curves can be calculated much more precisely with the formulas $\log(4)/\log(3)$ and $\log(5)/\log(3)$, or 1.2618 and 1.4649. This technique, however, only works for curves made out of lines that are just touching, without any overlap.

The box counting method used by FractalVision, although less accurate, is much more general and can even be used for finding the fractal dimension of natural objects. For a demonstration, let's compare Britain's coast to Maine's.

10. **Load** the **Picture** (not template) named MAINE. This is the real thing, taken from a map.

continues

11. Select **Extra** and **Fractal Dim.**

12. Now **Load** the **Picture** UK and select **Extra/Fractal Dim.** again.

Which is rougher? Did the results match your visual intuition? Notice that the numbers you get (a little over 1.1) are lower than the fractal dimensions of the real coastlines (which are over 1.2, but under 1.3) because these images were taken from a linear map and not an aerial photo.

For Programmers Only: Box Counting

This short C program uses the box counting method to compute the fractal dimension of whatever is currently on-screen. As the name implies, the program draws successively larger boxes and counts the number of boxes that touch any color other than the background color. The program then scales both the counts and box sizes logarithmically and takes the ratio between them.

You can use this code to find the fractal dimension of shapes created with drawing routines of your own creation (or any routine from other **For Programmers Only** boxes in this book).

Appendix D contains complete instructions for compiling the programs in this book with various compilers, along with listings of the header files used.

Listing 1.1. BOXCOUNT.C. A program to estimate fractal dimension.

```
/* BOXCOUNT.C
 *
 * This program estimates the fractal dimension of
 * anything on-screen using the box counting method.
 */

#include <stdio.h>        /* Standard input/output libraries */
#include <stdlib.h>
#include <math.h>         /* for logarithm computation */
```

```
#define MAIN          /* See Appendix D for compile*/
#include "fv.h"       /* instructions and header info. */

#define ESC 27        /* The Escape key code */
#define drawclr 15    /* Color to make the dots */

void boxcount(void);  /* function prototype */

void main(void)
{   int vidmode, i, j;      /* video mode and counters */
    vidmode = pickmode(detectmode());   /* get video mode */
    printf("\n\nThis program will estimate the fractal "
           "dimension of a squiggle.");
    printf("\nIt will take a while, so be patient!\n\n");
    printf("Press any key to begin.");
    getch();
    if (setvidmode(vidmode, 1) != 1)
    {   printf("\nUnable to set graphics mode.\n");
        exit(0);
     }
    j = scrny / 2;              /* draw a squiggle */
    setcolor(drawclr);
    moveto(0, j);
    for (i = 0; i < scrnx; i++, j += rand() % 21 - 10)
        lineto(i, j);

/* The following line has no effect in Turbo C or Power C! */

    getscreen();       /* remember what's on-screen */
    boxcount();        /* estimate its fractal dimension */
    closedown();       /* close down the graphics and quit */
}

/* The actual function to estimate fractal dimension */

void boxcount(void)
{   int x, y, pixels, xx, yy, n;  /* a few counters */
    char a;                       /* for keyboard input */
```

continues

33

Listing 1.1. continued

```
    long count;                      /* for great big counts */

    /* arrays to store the finished logarithmic estimates */

    double logct[9], logpix[9], slope[9], temp;

    /* start with 2-pixel sized boxes, work up to 8-pixel */

    for (pixels = 2, n = 0;
         pixels <= 8;
         pixels = pixels += 2, n++)
    {   count = 0L;                  /* start the count at zero */

/* The following line has no effect in Turbo C or Power C! */

        putscreen();          /* put the image on-screen */

      /* how many boxes contain at least one lit-up pixel? */

        for (x = 0; x < scrnx - pixels; x += pixels)
            for (y = 0; y < scrny - pixels; y += pixels)
            {
                /* scan through an individual box until find a
                lit pixel or look at every pixel in the box */

                for (xx = x; xx < x + pixels; xx++)
                    for (yy = y; yy < y + pixels; yy++)
                    {   if (getpixel(xx, yy) != 0)
                        {   count++;   /* found a lit pixel */
                            xx = 9999; /* break out of loop */
                            break;
                        }
                    }
#ifndef NOGETSCREEN /* Don't display if no getscreen() */

                /* If we found a pixel in the box, xx = 9999.
                   draw a filled square over the box to
                   show the user what's going on. */

                if (xx >= 9999)
                {   fillrect(x, y, x + pixels - 1,
                            y + pixels - 1, pixels);
```

```
            }

            /* If we didn't find any pixels, just draw
               a dot to show the progress of the
               counting across the screen. */

            else putpixel(x, y, drawclr);
#endif
            /* If user presses the Esc key, stop counting */

            if (kbhit())
            {   a = getch();
                if (a == ESC) return;
            }
          }

      /* To estimate fractal dimension from the box count,
         scale the counts logarithmically and store them
         for reporting later.  Also scale and store the
         size of the box. */

      logct[n] = log((double) count);
      logpix[n] = log(1.0 / (double) pixels);

      /* Unless we're on the first count,
         use this count and the last to
         do an estimate of fractal dimension.  */

      if (n > 0)
      {   temp = logpix[n] - logpix[n - 1];

          /* divide the difference in the counts by the
             difference in box size to get the slope,
             which equals the fractal dimension */

          if (temp == 0) slope[n] = 0;
          else slope[n] = (logct[n] - logct[n - 1]) / temp;
      }
  }
  settextmode();  /* all done.  Go to text mode. */
  printf("ESTIMATED FRACTAL DIMENSION");  /* report */
  temp = 0.0;
```

continues

35

Listing 1.1. continued

```
for (x = 1; x < n; x++)
{    printf("\n\nBox size %d gave "
            "a Fractal Dimension of %f",
            x * 2, slope[x]);
     temp += slope[x];
}
printf("\n\nAverage Estimated "
       "Fractal Dimension = %f", temp / 3);
printf("\n\nPress any key to continue.");
getch(); /* wait for a keypress, then we're done. */
}
```

The Monsters Come to Life

...the computer can be a powerful friend to the imagination. Like mathematics, it doesn't only stretch the imagination. It also disciplines and controls it.
—Richard Dawkins, *The Blind Watchmaker*

Research into complex curves was stopped short in the early twentieth century by an insurmountable barrier: arduous computations. Mathematicians spent days, even months, scribbling and sketching to produce even the roughest approximations of infinitely detailed, nonlinear curves. Still, their first representations of self-reflective shapes were grossly inaccurate and woefully lacking in detail. From 1925 to 1960, the limits of hand calculation prevented any serious progress in the geometry of complexity and infinity.

Then came computers. At first, no one even thought of applying these expensive machines made for accounting or military uses to pure mathematical research. Then computers began courting the mathematicians, offering lovely gifts such as the hundredth digit of pi (π), e, or the square root of two. Mathematicians, however, remained wary of "cheating" through computational approximation. It was a biologist who first dared to base a mathematical theory on computer simulations.

Aristid Lindenmayer introduced the idea of *cellular automata* to model the growth of living organisms in 1968. In particular, he was interested in cell development and the branching patterns of plants. The theory itself, however, can be applied to any number of complex forms.

Cellular Automata

Computation offers a new means of describing and investigating scientific and mathematical systems. Simulation by computer may be the only way to predict how certain complicated systems evolve.

—Stephem Wolfram, *Scientific American*, 1984

In general, a *cellular automaton* is an artificial universe with simple natural laws. You choose the structure of that universe and the laws it obeys, and you can then leave it to follow those laws on its own. By programming those laws into a computer, you can simulate your automated universe and watch it evolve.

These automated universes are *cellular* because they usually consist of many identical "cells" that divide and multiply in a fashion similar to real cells. For example, Lindenmayer's original cellular automata were made up of written letters. A simple universe might contain two kinds of cells, F and G. This universe would also post *rules of propagation*:

Rule 1: An F cell divides into two F cells, FF.
Rule 2: A G cell becomes GFG.

To run the cellular automata, begin with an initial universe and let the rules take over. In this example, you start with only one G cell:

Beginning:	G
1st generation:	GFG
2nd generation:	GFGFFGFG
3rd generation:	GFGFFGFGFFFFGFGFFGFG

The letters are then interpreted graphically to draw a shape on a computer screen. For instance, F might translate to "draw a line one inch long," and G might mean "move one inch forward without drawing a line." The Fs and Gs in the previous example would then appear as a visual sequence resembling Morse code. By adding letters to mean "turn 30 degrees left" or "turn 60 degrees right," Lindenmayer could represent complex shapes like those in Figures 1.12 through 1.14.

Figure 1.12. A Lindemayer cellular automaton to model plant growth (LINDEN).

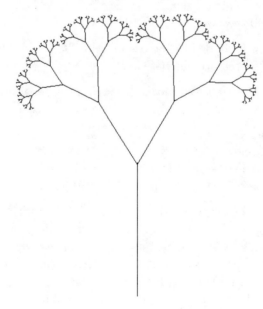

Figure 1.13. Another Lindenmayer plant model (FLOWER).

You Can Do It: L-Systems

You can reproduce almost all the shapes that Lindenmayer created using FractalVision. The "Flowers and Dragons" **You Can Do It** section later in this chapter shows you how.

If you have a copy of FRACTINT (an easily available freeware program that I highly recommend—see the introduction for specific information on how to get a copy), you can also design geometric cellular automata using the same text-based rule generation that Lindenmayer himself uses. Here's how to design your own *Lindenmayer Systems* (called *L-Systems* for short).

1. Run FRACTINT and choose a video mode. (If you're not familiar with FRACTINT, read the **You Can Do It: Introducing FRACTINT** section in the introduction to this book.)

2. Press the letter T (the hot key for fractal **Type**) and choose **lsystem** with the arrow keys, or type LS. Press Enter.

3. From the list of predefined L-systems, choose **dragon** and press Enter again.

The alphabetic definition of the dragon L-system appears on the bottom of the screen, and FRACTINT prompts you to enter the *order* near the top of the screen. Here, the word *order* means the same as *level of detail* in FractalVision—higher numbers take more time to generate and will produce more intricate patterns.

4. Type 10 and press Enter. Fast computers display Heighway's Dragon right away. Slower computers display the message "L-system thinking (higher orders take longer)" for a while and will eventually draw the dragon.

For complete information on creating your own L-systems within FRACTINT, press T and select **lsystem** again, then press F2 rather than Enter. Extensive online help explains how to write and run original L-systems.

Conway's Game of Life (or simply, Life), where points on a grid live and die according to the status of nearby points, has probably stolen more total hours of computing time than any other graphical cellular automata. It was designed in 1970 by British mathematician John Conway and became an obsession of John Von Neumann, who also designed the digital computer as we know it.

Many interesting multicellular lifeforms arise in the Life universe. Some are stable, some glide along by switching among two or three configurations, and some disappear quickly. Eventually, you always end up with either a few unchanging lifeforms or a lifeless desert. It isn't easy to gauge how long a particular scenario might take to stabilize; however, one extra cell in the right place may mean long-term survival or instant death for the entire group.

In other words, the stability of this artificial universe is extremely sensitive to initial conditions. As you will discover in the next two chapters, this kind of quirky behavior often pops up in the real universe, too.

Each rectangular cell in Life's universe grid can light up (live) or go dark (die). The rules are:

- If a dead cell has three live neighbors (out of the eight cells touching it), it comes to life.

- If a live cell has two or three neighbors, it survives. Otherwise, *it dies.*

That's it. But wait till you see the complex lifeforms that can evolve out of these simple rules!

You Can Do It: The Good Life

As this book went to press, I discovered the fastest, easiest-to-use, and most fulfilling Life yet. I've been dealing with Life for over a decade, and I discovered things with this implementation that I had never even imagined could happen in Life. Of course, I immediately called the creator, Al Hensel, and asked him to share his Life with you by putting it on the FractalVision disk. He agreed, so now you can experience the good Life, too. Al deserves a medal for this one, but all he asks is that you support his efforts by sending him the $10 shareware registration fee if you find yourself enjoying Life. (Make it $20, and he'll send you the source code, too.) His address is:

Al Hensel, RD 4 Box 87, Cranbury, NJ 08512

Are you ready to start your new Life? Here's how:

1. Change to the LIFE subdirectory (where Life was automatically installed when you installed FractalVision) by going to the directory where FV lives, and typing:

   `CD LIFE`

2. Begin Life by typing `LIFE`. (If only it was always this easy!)

Notice the pull-down menus at the top of the screen. You can use these by pressing Esc, or you can simply use the shortcut keys listed on the menus. I'll teach you the shortcut keys as we go through Life together.

3. Make a row of three dots on the screen by pressing the Spacebar and left arrow key each three times.

4. Press the letter O to make **One step**, or generation, of Life go by. By referring to the rules above, can you see why the horizontal line of dots became a vertical line of dots? What will happen when you press O again? Go ahead and find out. This arrangement is called a "blinker."

5. Now for your first real Life form: Press C and then Enter to **Clear** the universe, then use the Spacebar and arrow keys to make the following shape:

6. This shape is called a "glider." Why? Hold down the O key to find out. Up, up, and away!

Gliders are the key to Life. By assembling various patterns that shoot off gliders, you can create any number of pulsing, interacting critters. Fortunately, Al has given you a head start on populating your new pet universe by providing a hundred predesigned Life forms with the program. The most important things in Life are glider guns.

7. Press L to **Load** a predefined pattern, type GUN, and press Enter. Hold down the O key to step through a few generations and see the gun go off.

continues

Life gets interesting when you start shooting guns off at whatever tickles your fancy. To stage a shooting match, however, you'll need a bit more elbow room than the text screen provides.

8. Press the - key to zoom out into high resolution mode and hold down the O key again.

9. Guns are no fun with nothing to shoot at. Press C and Enter to **Clear**, and then press L for **Load and Enter** RABBIT.

10. It looks like an innocent little critter (press + to see it up close, and - to go back to hi-res), but it's actually a living time bomb. Stand back and press Enter to set Life in action. Remember, the rabbit started with just six cells!

11. Once the fires die down, you might like to start them up again (heh heh). Make sure the NumLock light is lit on your keyboard (if it isn't, press the NumLock key) and press 7 on the numeric keypad to move your viewport up and to the left. (The other number keys move in their respective directions, too, but just go up and to the left for now.)

12. Keep pressing 7 until the tiny blinking cursor is out of the rubble and then **Load** the GUN again. Enter starts the show. Will you shoot through the rubble, or will the gun be consumed in the explosions?

Enough of this mayhem. Life should be orderly and meaningful. How about a Life form that actually does something purposeful?

13. Press C and Enter to clean up the mess and then **Load** PUSHER. Press Enter and watch the dot on lower right. Keep watching, and you'll see why this is called PUSHER. Again, recall that you're looking at a grid of boxes that are lighting up and darkening according to exceedingly simple, completely local rules.

14. If you just can't help yourself, use the arrow keys to move the cursor up to the middle one of the glider guns that make up this Life form and press the Spacebar to change just one cell. Press Enter again. Did I ever tell you about something called "sensitive dependence on initial conditions?" Some people just call it "chaos."

15. Speaking of chaos, **Clear** and **Load** RANDGUN, and set it in action. I'll let you figure that one out.

Be sure to **Load** and run more of the hundred varieties of wildLife included on the disk. (You might like to print a directory listing of the .LIF files for reference.) Also, don't miss all the helpful hints on the better parts of Life in Al's good-humored LIFE105D.DOC text file. Remember, if you think Life is a worthwhile experience, don't forget to pay the benevolent creator for his good work.

For Programmers Only: Life Itself

Life is fun for everyone. Programmers just get the extra fun of modifying it to make an artificial universe which obeys their own rules. This text-mode implementation will not set any speed records for the most generations per second, but it is short and sweet, and much easier to understand than super-turbo-charged versions like Al's.

The universe in Life is round. The cells on the far left are neighbors to those on the far right, and cells on the top of the screen are neighbors to those on the bottom.

Blank spaces represent dead cells, and living cells appear as asterisks (*). Whether a cell lives or dies in the next generation depends upon how many living neighbors reside in the eight locations surrounding it. The rules are:

■ If a live cell has two or three neighbors, it continues to live.

■ If a live cell has less than two or more than three neighbors, it dies.

■ If a dead cell has exactly three neighbors, it comes back to life.

■ If a dead cell has more or less than three neighbors, it remains dead.

With this program, you can place cells wherever you like, or generate a random array of cells at the start. Here are the controls:

■ The arrow keys move the cursor (one solid square).

continues

- The 0 (zero) changes the state of the cell under the cursor. (It brings a dead cell to life, or kills a living cell.)

- The Delete key kills all living cells, so you can start a new arrangement from scratch.

- The Insert key fills the entire grid with a random array of 20 percent dead and 80 percent living cells.

- The Spacebar steps forward one generation.

- The Enter key calculates generation after generation until you press any other key.

- The Q key quits the program.

Listing 1.2. TEXTLIFE.C. Conway's Game of Life.

```
/* TEXTLIFE.C
 *
 * This program plays Conway's game of life, a famous cellular
 * automaton, using text characters to represent cells.
 */

#include <stdio.h>  /* Standard input/output */

#define NUMROWS 24  /* Size of the grid of cells */
#define NUMCOLS 80
#define GRIDSIZE 80*24

#define DEAD ' '    /* What dead cells look like */
#define ALIVE '*'   /* What live cells look like */
#define CSR 219     /* What the cursor looks like */

#define ESC 27      /* Key codes */
#define DEL 'S'
#define INS 'R'
#define UP 'H'
#define DN 'P'
#define LT 'K'
#define RT 'M'
```

```c
/* Create two grids in an array, one for the last generation,
   and one for the next generation.  c is temporary storage */

unsigned char grid[2][GRIDSIZE + 1], c;

/* gen is the number of generations so far
 * n is a counter
 * cc is the horizontal cursor position
 * cp is the current cursor position within the array
 * done tells us if we're done yet
 * t and t1 are the last grid number and next grid number
 *           (they toggle between 0 and 1)
 * step is 1 when doing one gen. at a time, -1 for continuous
 */

int gen, n, cc, cp, done, t, t1, step;

void displaygrid(int t);  /* function prototype */
void live(void);

void main(void)
{   for (n = 0; n < GRIDSIZE; n++)
        grid[0][n] = DEAD;      /* initialize the grids */
    grid[0][GRIDSIZE] = '\0';  /* put terminators on arrays */
    grid[1][GRIDSIZE] = '\0';  /* so they print as strings */
    cc = NUMCOLS / 2;           /* put cursor in the middle */
        cp = ((int) (NUMROWS / 2)) * NUMCOLS + cc;

    /* main loop enables user to edit the array of cells */

    while(1)
    {   step = -1;          /* unless Spacebar, go forever */
        c = grid[t][cp];    /* remember the current cell */
        grid[t][cp] = CSR;  /* replace it with the cursor */
        displaygrid(t);     /* display the grid */
        grid[t][cp] = c;    /* put cell back the way it was */
        switch(getch())     /* get a keystroke */
        {   case '0':       /* change the value of this cell */
```

continues

Listing 1.2. continued

```
            if (c == DEAD) grid[t][cp] = ALIVE;
            else grid[t][cp] = DEAD;
            gen = 1;    /* start count over */
                break;
        case ' ':
            step = 1;   /* do one generation only */
        case '\r':
            live();     /* go continually until step = 0 */
            cc = NUMCOLS / 2;  /* put cursor in middle */
                cp = ((int) (NUMROWS / 2)) * NUMCOLS + cc;
                break;
    case 'Q':
    case 'q':            /* quit the program */
        exit(0);
                break;
    case '\0':           /* user presses a special key */
            switch(getch())
            {   case UP:        /* move cursor up */
                    if ((cp -= NUMCOLS) < 0)
                        cp += GRIDSIZE;
                    break;
                case DN:         /* move cursor down */
                    if ((cp += NUMCOLS) >= GRIDSIZE)
                        cp -= GRIDSIZE;
                    break;
                case LT:         /* move cursor left */
                    if (--cc < 0)
                        cc = NUMCOLS - 1, cp += cc;
                    else --cp;
                    break;
                case RT:         /* move cursor right */
                    if (++cc == NUMCOLS)
                        cp -= cc - 1, cc = 0;
                    else ++cp;
                    break;
                case DEL:        /* clear the grid */
                    for (n = 0; n < GRIDSIZE; n++)
```

```
                              grid[t][n] = DEAD;
                                gen = 1;
                                break;
                    case INS:          /* fill grid randomly */
                        for (n = 0; n < GRIDSIZE; n++)
                        {   if (rand() < 8000)
                                grid[t][n] = ALIVE;
                            else grid[t][n] = DEAD;
                        }
                        gen = 1;
                        break;
                }
                break;
            }
        }
}

/* This routine decides who lives and who dies */

void live(void)
{   int dl, dr, du, dd,          /* left, right, up, down */
        changed;                 /* flag for any change */
    for (; step-- != 0; gen++)   /* go until step hits 0 */
    {   displaygrid(t);          /* display a generation */
        if (kbhit()) getch(), step = 0;  /* stop if keypress */
        t1 = t;                  /* switch generations */
        t = -(--t);
        changed = 0;             /* no change yet! */
        for (cc = cp = 0;
            cp < GRIDSIZE;
            ++cc, ++cp)          /* step through the grid */
        {   n = 0;               /* neighbor count */
            dd = NUMCOLS;  /* assume that neighbors are */
            du = -dd;      /* in normal positions, then see */
            dr = 1;        /* if on an edge of the grid. */
            dl = -dr;      /* If so, look over edge */
            if (cp < NUMCOLS)
                du += GRIDSIZE;
```

continues

Listing 1.2. continued

```
            else
                if (cp >= GRIDSIZE - NUMCOLS)
                    dd -= GRIDSIZE;
            if (cc == 0)
                dl += NUMCOLS;
            else
                if (cc == NUMCOLS - 1)
                    dr -= NUMCOLS, cc = -1;

            /* count neighbors */

                if (grid[t1][cp + dd + dl] == ALIVE) n++;
                if (grid[t1][cp + dd + dr] == ALIVE) n++;
                if (grid[t1][cp + du + dl] == ALIVE) n++;
                if (grid[t1][cp + du + dr] == ALIVE) n++;
                if (grid[t1][cp + du] == ALIVE) n++;
                if (grid[t1][cp + dd] == ALIVE) n++;
                if (grid[t1][cp + dl] == ALIVE) n++;
                if (grid[t1][cp + dr] == ALIVE) n++;

            /* If I'm alive and I have 2 or 3 neighbors,
               I live.  Otherwise, I die. */

            if (grid[t1][cp] == ALIVE)
            {   if ((n == 2) || (n == 3))
                    grid[t][cp] = ALIVE;
                else
                    grid[t][cp] = DEAD, changed = 1;
            }

            /* If I'm dead and I have exactly 3 neighbors,
               I am born.  Otherwise, I stay dead. */

                else
            {   if (n == 3)
                    grid[t][cp] = ALIVE, changed = 1;
                else
```

```
                    grid[t][cp] = DEAD;
              }
         }
      if (!changed) step = 0;      /* If no changes, stop. */
    }
}

/* display the current generation on the text screen */

void displaygrid(int t)
{   system("cls");                 /* clear the screen */
    printf("%s", grid[t]);         /* print the grid */
    if (step != -1)
        printf("%d      ", gen);
    else
        printf("0=place cell  arrows=move cursor  "
              "DEL=clear  INS=random  Enter=go!  Q=quit");
}
```

Heighway's Dragon

Seeing a completed dragon can't compare to the thrill of watching it being drawn. And it's hard to resist the temptation to see what "this one little change" will do as you explore these fascinating creatures.

—William McWorter, "Creating Fractals," *BYTE*, 1987

Figure 1.14 shows the development of another famous graphical cellular automaton. Here, the "universe" is made of geometric "cells" that appear as lines. Only one rule of propagation exists: each line divides into two half-length *child* lines—the first begins at the same point as its *parent* and goes off at a 45 degree angle, and the second continues back to the ending point of its parent. The first two parts of Figure 1.14 represent the geometric model of this rule. The horizontal line is the parent, and the two angled lines are children.

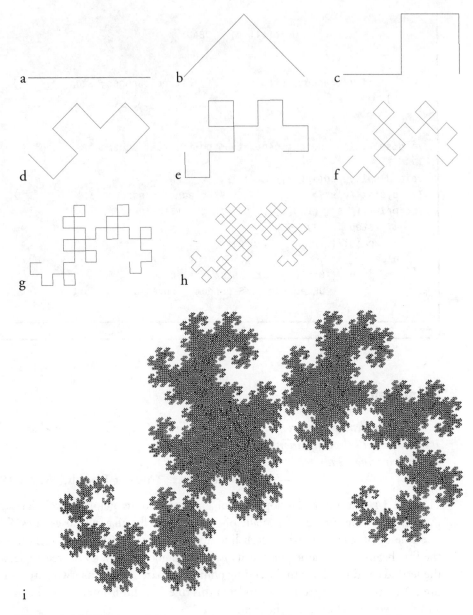

Figure 1.14. Heighway's Dragon grows from a skinny worm to a mighty monster with a thousand spiral talons (HEIGHWAY).

Physicist John Heighway originally imagined constructing this dragon in 1960 by repeatedly folding a long strip of paper, then opening the creases to right angles. Lindenmayer later recognized this and other geometric construction procedures as special types of cellular automata. At that time, computer displays were barely sufficient to represent complex geometric shapes, but computerized cellular automata have since been used to create many spectacular fractal designs. Figures 1.12 through 1.15 are classic geometric cellular automata. In the early 1970s, Martin Gardner and Donald Knuth popularized these and many other shapes designed by Lindenmayer, Heighway, and their colleagues.

You Can Do It: Flowers and Dragons

Heighway and Lindenmayer were fascinated by the lifelike, complex shapes that arose from quite simple rules. At heart, FractalVision is a visual language for creating cellular automata: the seed defines a *cell*, and the arrangement of the copies defines the *rules of propagation*.

Look at some of the geometric cellular automata Lindenmayer and his contemporaries explored. For starters, you can create a fractal flower garden:

1. **Load** and **Draw** the LINDEN sample template. Lindenmayer used simple automata such as this to model *monopodial branching*, where a central stalk continues along its path while shoots grow out of its side. Monopodial branching is most common in trees and shrubs.

2. Now **Load**, **Clear**, and **Draw** the FLOWER template, an example of *polychotomous branching*. Many flowers and some trees show this type of branching, where the central stalk splits off in two or more directions at once.

3. By pressing the right arrow a few times and selecting **Draw** again, you can add another flower beside this one.

4. To add more flowers to your online garden, try **Load**ing and **Draw**ing the templates FLOWER1, FLOWER2, FLOWER3, FLOWER4, and FLOWER5. You can use **Grow** and **Shrink** to make flowers of different sizes. Use the arrow keys to arrange their placement.

continues

5. You may wish to **Save** your **Picture** once the flowers are arranged to your satisfaction.

Now, if you dare, I'll let you sneak a peek at a battle between two fractal dragons:

6. **Clear** the garden picture, unless you want the dragons to trample your flower beds.

7. **Load** the **Template** HEIGHWAY. The seed shape for the *cells* is defined as a horizontal line, and the *rules of propagation* are defined: at each step in the life of the dragon, every line will become two lines forming a V shape from its ends.

8. **Draw** and behold Heighway's Dragon, feared throughout the linear land.

9. Now **Load** the next dragon template, named HORTER after its original designer. The cells look the same as Heighway's, a simple line segment. The rules of propagation are different, though: instead of splitting into two lines, each cell splits into four, arranged as a box with the lid open.

10. **Draw** and behold once more. Horter's dragon is an identical twin to Heighway's, and they are locked in mortal combat!

In fact, you could use these dragon skins as tiles, and they would lock together perfectly to cover an area as large as you had dragons to fill. I leave this infinite fractal snake pit as an exercise (or nightmare?) for you to consider.

A Geometry is Born

Every revolution was first a thought in one man's mind.

—Ralph Waldo Emerson, 1870

By the 1970s, the stage was set for a revolution in geometry. The scenery included Koch and Peano's tempting glimpses at infinity, Hausdorff's new dimensions, Heighway's intriguing swirls, and Lindenmayer's models of self-replication. The props consisted of new technology capable of breaking through the computation and visualization barriers that everyone had run up against. Enter the stars of the show: an adventurous mathematician named Benoit B. Mandelbrot and the latest devices made by his employer, IBM.

Troublesome Noise

Nature's great book is written in mathematical symbols.

—Galileo

Mandelbrot became a staff mathematician at IBM's Thomas J. Watson research center in 1958. His first accomplishment on the job was halting a multimillion dollar research project to eliminate the troublesome "noise" that plagued signal transmission.

When he examined this noise, Mandelbrot discovered an intricate but familiar structure that told him the technology IBM was trying to build couldn't possibly control it. He knew it simply wasn't controllable or predictable. It was *chaos*.

How did Mandelbrot grasp the deep structure of line noise so quickly? He had never worked with telecommunications or even any kind of electrical signals. Strangely enough, he recognized it because it looked so much like the price of cotton.

Since the early 1950s, Mandelbrot had been studying the unpredictable yet nearly cyclic rise and fall of the commodities market. Cotton prices had been a pet subject of his because reliable data was available for hundreds of years of trading. The cost of cotton behaves with an odd sort of constancy: it varies no more over a period of centuries than a period of decades, or a period of years. In fact, if you magnify a graph of cotton prices over time, each part has almost exactly the same visual roughness as the whole. Mandelbrot called this statistical resemblance of the part to the whole *scale invariance*.

The records of other unpredictable phenomena, such as river discharges and stock market prices, show the same deeply cyclic structure. Cyclic is not quite the right word, though. Mandelbrot's favorite curves do possess cycles with cycles within cycles, but none of the cycles ever actually repeat exactly. Although the *amount* of variation within the curves remains constant, variations within variations make them stubbornly unpredictable at every point in time and every level of scale.

Mandelbrot knew this and was beginning to understand this mathematically, but could not convince anyone else. His equations were too abstract, and his conclusions too disturbing. Who wants a theory that says things are complex, uncontrollable, and chaotic? Doesn't that just mean there is no real theory at all? For more than a decade, Mandelbrot's strange ideas remained his own private obsession.

A Picture is Worth....

It seems that nobody is indifferent to fractals. In fact, many view their first encounter with fractal geometry as a totally new experience from the viewpoints of aesthetics as well as science.

—Benoit Mandelbrot, *The Beauty of Fractals*, 1986

In 1968, Mandelbrot teamed up with a hydrologist to study persistent patterns in the levels of the Nile, like the "seven years of fat and seven lean years" of the Bible. They plotted real fluctuations and then produced deliberate forgeries using Mandelbrot's formulas. When these graphs were shown to experienced hydrologists, not one could tell them apart, although graphs made from traditional models were immediately recognized as fakes.

The realism of Mandelbrot's graphs unquestionably demonstrated that he was on to something significant. He went on to produce forgeries of other chaotic phenomena: stock market and commodity prices, coastlines, and mountains. In each case, the visual character of his images was compelling. As he put it, "Before, people would run a mile from my papers, but they could not run from my pictures."

What was the secret factor in Mandelbrot's graphs that made them unmistakably realistic? What principle lay behind their visual texture? It was none other than Hausdorff's fractional dimension. Mandelbrot intentionally explored the land between dimensions that Cantor and Fournier had stumbled into 50 years earlier. He transformed their bizarre snapshots of infinity into startlingly realistic portraits of complex natural and social phenomena.

You can see how Mandelbrot created his forgeries in Figure 1.15. All the phenomena he studied fluctuate up and down in cycles, like the sine wave shape approximated here. What makes the fluctuations so complex is that they contain cycles within larger cycles within even greater cycles. To simulate this, Mandelbrot used repetitive techniques, such as those that Sierpiński and Koch had employed to construct their infinitely detailed curves. Figure 1.15 is a curve reflected back into itself this way. To create the curve on the right, each small box on the left becomes a set of smaller boxes in the same arrangement. Each of those smaller boxes in turn becomes a sine wave-shaped set of tinier boxes, until each box is too small to distinguish.

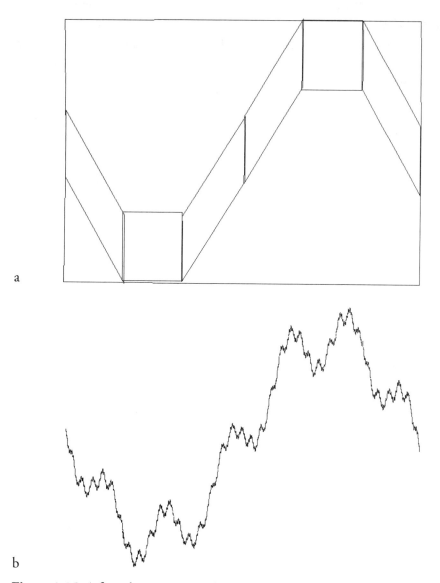

a

b

Figure 1.15. A fractal sine wave: cycles within cycles within cycles… (SINE).

Mandelbrot completed his forgeries by introducing a random factor at every step, so the curve would not be periodic and unnaturally regular. Figure 1.16 achieves a similar effect without using randomness. By making each small box different—stretching, flipping, and skewing each one in a unique way—a complexity arises that looks almost indistinguishable from true random variation. Chapter 2, "Fractals in the Real World," introduces many more techniques for making realistic fractal forgeries.

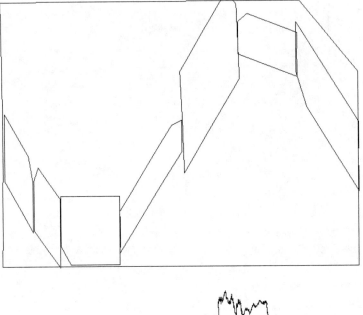

a

b

Figure 1.16. A variation on Figure 1.15 resembles the graphs of a wide variety of economic and scientific data (RANDY).

You Can Do It: Creating a Fractal Forgery

Because your computer is more sophisticated than the best equipment of 1970, you should at least be able to fool your stockbroker.

1. **Load** the SINE template. Copies of the large box have been arranged to roughly approximate a sine wave shape.

2. Select **Paint** to see sine waves within sine waves within sine waves. Mandelbrot discovered cycles within cycles of this sort in all sorts of natural, social, and technical data.

Of course, real market phenomena usually have complex local variations. With FractalVision, you can achieve a similar effect by making each part of the template unique.

3. **Clear** the picture, **Load** the RANDY example, and notice how each copy of the seed has been **Skew**ed, **Squish**ed or **Stretch**ed differently.

4. When you **Paint** the curve, it has a convincingly random visual texture. This could be an approximation of line noise, a mountain, or a stock market graph.

For Programmers Only: Cycles Within Cycles

The program Mandelbrot used to fool climatologists and commodities brokers was as simple as this.

Listing 1.3. FORGERY.C. A program to mimic natural, irregular cycles within cycles.

```
/* FORGERY.C
 *
 * This program draws a one-dimensional "random walk",
 * which could be a forgery of a market data graph
```

continues

57

Listing 1.3. continued

```c
 * or a mountain silhouette.
 */

#include <stdio.h>        /* Standard input/output libraries */
#include <stdlib.h>

#define MAIN              /* See Appendix D for compile */
#include "FV.H"           /* instructions and header info. */

#define ESC 27            /* The Escape key code */
#define drawclr 15        /* Color to make the everything */

#define NPOINTS 640       /* Maximum number of data points */
#define SCALE 1024        /* Maximum vertical scaling factor */

/* points is the array of data points
 * npoints is the actual number of points to compute
 * scale is the actual vertical scaling factor
 */

int points[NPOINTS], npoints, scale;

void cutup(int start, int end, int scale);     /* prototype */

void main(void)
{   int vidmode, i;               /* video mode and counter */
    vidmode = pickmode(detectmode());    /* get video mode */
    if (setvidmode(vidmode, 1) != 1)
    {   printf("\nUnable to set graphics mode.\n");
        exit(0);
    }
    while(1)            /* keep going until user enters zero */
    {   settextmode();
        printf("This program will make a forgery of "
               "naturally cyclic data.\n");
        printf("Enter the number 0 to quit the program.\n");
```

```
            printf("\nEnter the number of "
                    "data points (maximum %d): ", NPOINTS);
            scanf("%d", &npoints);
            if (npoints == 0) break;
            if (npoints > NPOINTS) npoints = NPOINTS;
            printf("\nEnter a scaling factor (maximum %d): ",
                    SCALE);
            scanf("%d", &scale);
            if (scale == 0) break;
            if (scale > SCALE) scale = SCALE;
            points[0] = 0;          /* first and last points zero */
            points[npoints - 1] = 0;
            cutup(0, npoints - 1, scale);   /* compute the rest */
            setvidmode(0, 0);               /* reset graphics mode */
            clearscreen();
            setcolor(drawclr);
            moveto(0, points[0] + scrny / 2);      /* get ready */
            for (i = 0; i < npoints; i++)       /* draw the data */
                lineto(i * (float)
                        ((float) scrnx / (float) npoints),
                        points[i] + scrny / 2);
            getch();                             /* wait for keypress */
        }
    settextmode();
    closedown();            /* close down the graphics and quit */
}

/* This function chops the data set in two pieces,
   displaces the midpoint by a random amount,
   and chops each of the two pieces into two smaller
   intervals by calling itself recursively */

void cutup(int start, int end, int scale)
{   int value;                      /* the current data point */
    if (end - start <= 1) return;   /* interval too small? */

    /* average the start and end, then add a random offset */
```

continues

59

```
Listing 1.3. continued

    value = (points[end] + points[start]) / 2;
    if (scale > 1) value += rand() % scale - scale / 2;
    points[(end + start) / 2] = value;

    /* chop the interval in two and do it all again twice */

    cutup(start, (end + start) / 2, scale / 2);
    cutup((end + start) / 2, end, scale / 2);
}
```

The Fractal Geometry of Nature

Why is geometry often described as "cold" and "dry"? One reason lies in its inability to describe the shape of a cloud, a mountain, a coastline, or a tree. Clouds are not spheres, mountains are not cones, coastlines are not circles, and bark is not smooth, nor does lightning travel in a straight line.

—Opening words of Benoit Mandelbrot's *Fractal Geometry of Nature*, 1982

In 1982, Mandelbrot expanded two previous essays into his seminal work, *The Fractal Geometry of Nature*. He coined the word fractal (from the Latin *frangere*, meaning 'to break into irregular fragments') so that his diverse shapes could be unified under a single name. To officially qualify as a fractal, a shape must have a Hausdorff/Besicovitch dimension greater than its traditional topological dimension. In short, fractals are all those space-filling oddities that mathematicians had abandoned as hopelessly complex. Mandelbrot also notes parenthetically, "Since 'algebra' derives from the Arabic 'jabara: to bind together,' 'fractal' and 'algebra' are etymological opposites!"

By the 1980s, computer graphics had progressed to the point where shapes such as Koch's Coastline and Sierpiński's Carpet could be represented in explicit detail. *The Fractal Geometry of Nature* was a gallery of these and other geometric forms, many of which had never been seen before. Most of them were simple cellular automata where each line in a shape was repeatedly transformed into a series of smaller lines. Figures 1.18 through 1.25 are imitations of a few of Mandelbrot's curiosities.

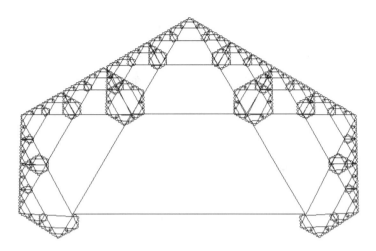

Figure 1.17. This arrowhead, and all the following curves, are borrowed from Mandelbrot's *Fractal Geometry of Nature* (ARROW).

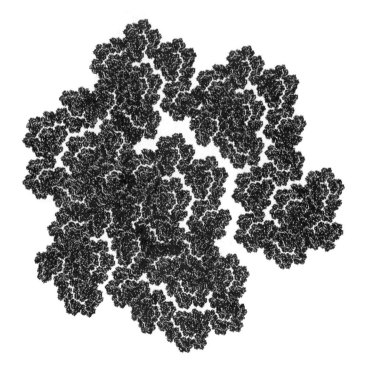

Figure 1.18. Many of Mandelbrot's "Cascades" resemble river watersheds (CASCADE).

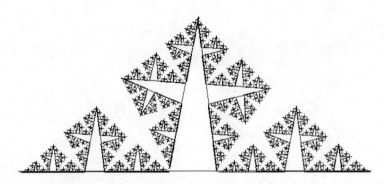

Figure 1.19. If the 85 degree angles in Cesaro's coastline curve were changed to 90 degrees, the curve would fill a solid square (CESARO).

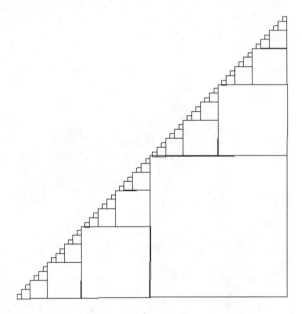

Figure 1.20. The "Devil's Staircase." Every time you go up a step, the Devil doubles the number of stairs (STAIRS).

Figure 1.21. Mandelbrot calls curves like this seven-sided sweep "good first-order models of rivers, watersheds, botanical trees, and human vascular systems" (SEVEN).

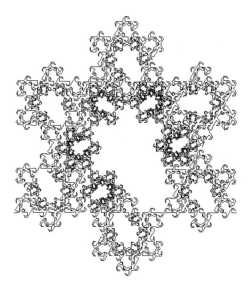

Figure 1.22. Monkey curve, also called "Split Snowflake Halls." If this were a maze, could you devise a reliable way to find your way out from anywhere inside? (MONKEY).

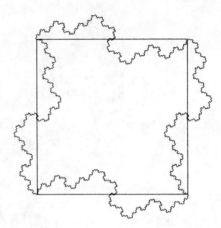

Figure 1.23. The area of Gosper's Island remains constant at every level of construction (GOSPER).

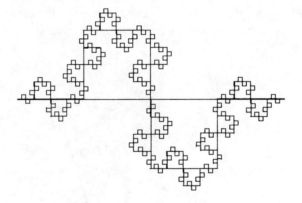

Figure 1.24. The Quadratic Coastline Curve has the same structure as ink or air dispersing through water (QUADRAT).

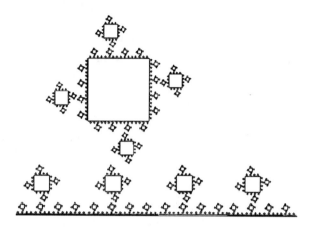

Figure 1.25. The fractal dimension of the main coastline is half that of the small islands. The fractal dimension of the whole Earth is also half that of real coastlines (ISLAND).

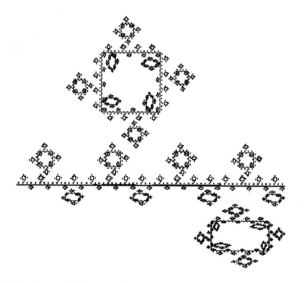

Figure 1.26. Islands with lakes and trees: is there any point on any island that is actually bare dry land? (ISLANDS).

YOU CAN DO IT!

You Can Do It: Highlights from *The Fractal Geometry of Nature*

You can reproduce and modify almost all Mandelbrot's shapes with FractalVision software.

1. The templates ARROW, CASCADE, CESARO, STAIRS, SEVEN, and TWINSKIN are a few examples. To see each of them, just **Clear**, **Load**, **Draw**, and **View**.

2. When you **Load** and **Draw** the example MONKEY, you might want to try solving one of Mandelbrot's favorite puzzles: if it were a maze, how would you get out?

3. Here's a hint: try it on a **Level 2** version by selecting **Adjust** and then pressing the following keys in order: 2 B \ A Enter PageUp D V.

4. You can also make the famous geometric coastline curves featured in Mandelbrot's book. **Load** the following templates in order, **Draw**ing each one without clearing the last: GOSPER1, GOSPER2, GOSPER3, and GOSPER4. This is called "Gosper's Island."

5. More abstract coastlines are QUADRAT, ISLAND, and ISLANDS. You can either **Draw** or **Paint** each of these.

The Mandelbrot Set

…the most complicated object in mathematics…
—John Hubbard, describing the Mandelbrot set, 1985

After doing time with self-reflective "natural" fractals, Mandelbrot discovered that similar iterative processes can produce abstract mathematical constructs such as the famous *Mandelbrot set* and *Julia set* (Figures 1.27 and 1.28). Like other fractals, these sets were discovered long before Mandelbrot's time, but were so complex that it took powerful computers to explore and visualize them. You'll learn more about these sets in Chapter 4, "The Art of Fractal Modeling."

Figure 1.27. The Mandelbrot set, often called the "granddaddy of all fractals."

Figure 1.28. A Julia set. Each point on the Mandelbrot set contains an entire Julia set.

Art Meets Science

Science and art…. We have become accustomed to seeing them as opposite poles, yet don't they depend on one another? The thinker, trying to penetrate natural phenomena with his understanding, seeking to reduce all complexity to a few fundamental laws—isn't he also the dreamer plunging himself into the richness of forms and seeing himself as part of the eternal play of natural events? This experience of oneness which the individual may feel finds no counterpart in the intellectual history of the last two hundred years.
—H.O. Peitgen, *The Beauty of Fractals*, 1986

Even before fractals were widely accepted as valid mathematics, the images they produced became immensely popular. Mathematician/artists such as Richard Voss, Greg Turk, and Alan Norton refined Mandelbrot's basic procedures to create stunning landscapes, both realistic and abstract.

This sudden revival of mathematics as art was long overdue. Science and mathematics of the nineteenth and twentieth centuries had lost touch with the visual and intuitive. Modern theories such as relativity and quantum mechanics are beautiful and elegant, but you have to be an Albert Einstein or Erwin Schrödinger to appreciate that beauty. On the other hand, laymen and mathematicians alike can appreciate even the most abstract fractal image.

Beautiful Science

That is part of the excitement surrounding these pictures: they demonstrate that out of research an inner connection, a bridge can be made between rational scientific insight and emotional aesthetic appeal; these two modes of cognition of the human species are beginning to concur in their estimation of what constitutes nature.
—Gert Eilenberger, Physicist, *The Beauty of Fractals*, 1986

While fractals were winning all the prizes at computer graphics shows, nearly every scientific discipline uncovered their beautiful, chaotic patterns. Physicists graphing particle states found deeply moving artwork emerging from their plotters. Strange *attractors* with fractal turbulence appeared in celestial mechanics. Biologists and physiologists diagnosed *dynamical diseases*, which arise when fractal rhythms fall out of sync. Seismologists even discovered fractal waves moving through solid earth. Meteorologists, economists, chemists, hydrologists, and almost every brand of engineer were all confronted with forms that were more pretty than predictable.

Don't forget the mathematicians! The 1980s saw fractals popping up in every well-understood equation and procedure from Newton's method to the simple cosine function. In university after university, blackboards filled with lines, and arcs gave way to computer screens filled with breathtaking abstract landscapes. Pure mathematicians such as Stephen Smale, John Hubbard, Harold Benzinger, Yuval Fisher, and many others started spending more time producing and examining colorful graphical representations than solving equations. Some, such as Heinz-Otto Peitgen and Robert Dcvaney, began touring with slide shows and videos of their research! The hard lines between art and science have begun to blur and squiggle. Figure 1.29 is one example of the gray area between them; it is a modern computer portrait of a timeworn mathematical tool called *Newton's method*. For centuries, scientists and mathematicians used Newton's method to solve equations, but knew nothing of the magnificent intricacy hidden behind the technique.

Figure 1.29. Chaotic symmetry hidden in a well-worn mathematical technique called Newton's method.

You Can Do It: Newton's Method

Chapters 2 and 4 explore realistic and abstract fractal art in depth. If you have a copy of FRACTINT freeware (see the Introduction for how to get one), you can take a sneak peek at the beauty of fractals by zooming into a formula from your high school algebra class. *Newton's method*, a technique for solving polynomial equations, has been used by PhDs and high school students alike for centuries.

1. Start the FRACTINT software and choose a 256-color video mode. (If you have standard VGA, press F3 for 320x200x256. If you have Super VGA, press Shift-F5 for 640x480x256. EGA, CGA, and Hercules adapters work fine, too; you just have to settle for fewer colors.)

2. Press T to select a fractal **Type**, select **newton**, and press Enter.

3. Press Enter again to accept the default parameters.

4. If you have a slow computer, take a break while the image appears and skip the next couple steps.

When the computer beeps, the image is done. The three separate areas of the screen represent three possible solutions to the cube root of 1, where 1 is really the complex number $1+0i$. (If you didn't excel in high school algebra, don't worry about it. Your math teacher didn't know it looked like this, by the way.)

5. If you have a fast computer, you may want to *zoom in* and see part of the image up close: hold down the Page Up key (or hold the left mouse button and move the mouse up) until the *zoom box* is about a quarter the size of the screen.

6. Use the arrow keys (or release the left button and use the mouse) to place the box over an interesting part of the image.

7. Press Enter or double-click the left button to zoom. Unless you have a very fast computer, the picture may take a little while to appear.

If you're surprised by the intricacy of the image that appears on your screen, you are not alone. When mathematician John Hubbard and his colleagues in Orsay, France, first graphically simulated Newton's method in the early 1980s, they were flabbergasted that an old math standby could hide so much visual richness.

8. Press the + (plus) key on the numeric keypad and look out!

9. Press the Enter key a few times to create random color palettes.

Math is beautiful.

Every Image Is a Fractal

Fractal geometry will make you see everything differently.... You risk the loss of your childhood vision of clouds, forests, galaxies, leaves, feathers, rocks, mountains, torrents of water, carpets, bricks, and much else besides.
—Michael Barnsley, *Fractals Everywhere*, 1988

In the early 1980s, mathematician Michael Barnsley joined the growing ranks of the "fractaliers." As a child, Michael was especially fascinated with certain ferns. He didn't pinpoint what gave the ferns their magical beauty until many years later. Noticing how each frond resembled the whole plant, he wrote a simple computer program to model this characteristic. The resulting image was far more realistic than expected and soon became one of the most famous fractals of all.

Barnsley went on to develop a unique new way of drawing fractals: the *Chaos Game* (described in Chapter 4 and used for the **Paint** command in FractalVision software). Even more importantly, Barnsley and John Elton proved in 1985 that any image at all could be represented with a well-known class of fractals. This was a giant step for an intellectual community inundated with fractals, but lacking a comprehensive system for representing them. One technique created fractal mountains, another ran cellular automata, and another simulated earthquake graphs. Still another was needed to produce beautiful swirls and zooms. Barnsley and Elton provided a single simple procedure for making almost any self-reflective image, including all the images that no one had thought of as self-reflective before.

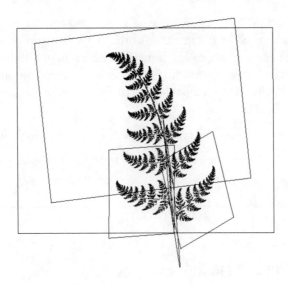

Figure 1.30. Barnsley's famous black spleenwort fern.

The first major application of their work was image compression. Barnsley was able to compress complex pictures into very small codes by translating them into fractals, achieving compression ratios of over 10,000 to one. Fractal image compression creates exciting new possibilities such as sending real-time video animation over normal telephone lines.

You Can Do It: An Image Compressed with Fractals

With FractalVision software, you can use similar techniques (described in Chapter 3) to store images as fractals. Theoretically, any image at all can be approximated with fractals, even one that doesn't seem particularly fractal-like.

1. For example, **Load** the CARTOON1 template.

2. Select **Paint**. Two round shapes… Hmmm…

3. **Load** the CARTOON2 template.

This template was created by tracing the outline of a scanned image by hand, and tiling that image with copies of itself. By coloring the tiled copies, you can squeeze a full-color approximation of the original image into two fractal templates.

4. **Paint** once more and say hello to a linear friend who decided to pay a visit to Fractal Land.

The reproduction is a bit rough around the edges (literally). You're probably more accustomed to seeing the irregularities of nature smoothed over by linear curves!

A compressed color bitmap of this image at VGA resolution would take up around 15K of memory. This fractal template takes up only about 2K of storage and could easily be squeezed down to about 200 bytes if you discard the extra information that FractalVision tacks on for "housekeeping" purposes.

I chose this image specifically to demonstrate that fractals can store linear-looking pictures, so this image could be stored as linear *vectors* in even less space. When pictures include both smooth and rough shapes, however, fractal image storage can require a tiny fraction of the space needed by linear vector data.

Fractals Today

In the quest for understanding, natural science has progressed by concentrating primarily on the simplest of systems. In this process, it has moved away from the direct experience of nature to the electronically instrumented laboratory. After all, who could describe, let alone understand, the profile of a mountain or the shape of a cloud? With fractal geometry, the quest for scientific understanding and realistic computer graphic imagery can return to the everyday natural world.

—Richard Voss, *The Science of Fractal Images*, 1988

In the 1990s, fractals are joining the mainstream. Major motion pictures use them for special effects, computer graphics rendering systems use them to create natural textures, and scientists and mathematicians have made them an indispensable tool of their trades. As the potential of this new geometry is more widely recognized and faster computers make interaction easier, fractal drawing tools will become part of most computer graphics systems.

In the following chapters, you will learn the tricks and techniques behind the most current applications of fractals and chaos theory. You will also acquire hands-on experience with real-world fractal modeling and a behind the scenes look at the cutting edge of chaos research. In the process, you will produce some stunning artwork.

Science, mathematics, and technology are no longer the flat and aesthetically deadening fields that the previous century saw them become. We can look forward to a future where intellectual works will be as beautiful and moving as the finest art of ages past.

Fractals in the Real World

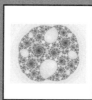

Fractals are beginning to play a vital role in almost every branch of modern science. In the following pages, you will discover why. You'll learn the scientific principles behind fractals and acquire some hands-on training, too.

This guide is not for scientists only, however. I skip the formulae and experimental procedures and delve right to the heart of science: discovering and understanding nature. Your computer becomes a graphics laboratory as you investigate the basic structure of the world.

The training is intuitive, not rigorous, so leave your lab coat and beakers behind (and be prepared to leave some of your old conceptions along with them). As you take a new look at rivers, clouds, trees, and earthquakes, you may find that other things start to look a bit different as well. You'll start seeing fractals in everything around you, from the stars in the sky to the vegetables on your table.

In short, this chapter teaches you to see the world with FractalVision. Then, you'll be ready for an in-depth look at fractal philosophy and modeling techniques in Chapter 3, "The Philosophy of Fractals," and Chapter 4, "The Art of Fractal Models."

Basic Principles

To see a world in a grain of sand,
And a heaven in a wild flower,
To hold infinity in the palm of your hand,
And eternity in an hour.

—William Blake, *Auguries of Innocence*, 1803

Each part of a fractal resembles the larger whole in which it resides. It isn't hard to think of natural objects that follow this principle: branches resemble trees, mountain tops have the same shape as mountain ranges, and small waves and clouds mirror larger ones. Many science fiction writers have noted the similarities between atoms and the solar system.

Benoit Mandelbrot presented *The Fractal Geometry of Nature* for those who, in his words, "celebrate nature by trying to imitate it." Even before you delve into whys and wherefores, you can use the observed self-similarity of Nature to imitate her.

A Fractal River

Why is it that nature is self-similar is the mystery. That nature is fractal is no mystery. Nature is fractal because nothing is perfectly smooth; a perfectly smooth surface is a mental abstraction. On the other hand not everything is self-similar, but the fact that it turns out to be so useful is the surprising thing that comes out of what Mandelbrot has been doing.
—Alan Norton, quoted by Peter Sorensen in "Fractals: Exploring the Rough Edges Between Dimensions," *BYTE*, 1984

Take a winding river, for instance. You don't need to know why the river turns to notice little bends within bigger bends within even bigger bends. Figure 2.1 is a simple fractal model of a twisting stream. The large arrow (the *seed shape*) is how the river appears if you're hanging over it in a tree—just a wide, straight channel. Looking from a little farther up, you might notice a bend that looks something like the next set of arrows. At the next level, you get the view from a helicopter. The fourth level might be the river as seen from a jet plane. Take this sequence to its logical geometric conclusion and you obtain the "infinite" satellite view.

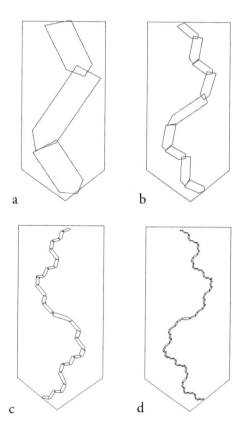

a b

c d

Figure 2.1. Views of a simplified river model as you climb higher and higher above it (RIVER).

You Can Do It: A Fractal River

To fly above the fractal river with FractalVision, you'll need to learn how to draw just one level of detail at a time.

1. **Load** the template named RIVER. (See the introduction of this book for explicit instructions for starting the FractalVision software and loading example templates.) The template defines the first level of detail—the river as seen from just above the banks.

2. Select **Draw**. Successive levels of detail appear, one on top of the other.

The results don't look quite like Figure 2.1, which shows only one level at a time. You can tell FractalVision to draw only a single level with the **Adjust** panel.

3. Select **Adjust**. This is the master control panel for setting the level of detail as well as the coloring and shading.

This control panel may seem complex, but in Chapter 4 you learn how to use it to design your own realistic fractal models. For now, however, just press the following keys in order and don't worry about understanding what you're doing.

4. Choose the background color by pressing the letter A.

5. Select **Color All Levels** by pressing the = key.

6. Select **Color** C by pressing the letter C.

7. Select **Color All Parts** by pressing the \ (backslash) key. (Not the / key!)

8. Finally, select **Color** H by pressing the letter H.

Again, don't be concerned if you didn't follow any of that. For now, just observe the results:

9. Press Enter to return to the main menu, select **Clear**, and **Draw**. The level 5 representation of the river appears, and levels 1 through 4 are not drawn.

You have managed to draw a whole river that appears much as a real one does from orbit. Yet, the only observation you needed could be made from a small hill by the banks. To draw all subsequent levels, the computer extrapolated by "reflecting" that single bend back into itself. The basic structure of the whole river was hidden in the shape of just a tiny part of it.

Already, you've uncovered the most important principle of fractal science:

In natural systems, the structure of the whole system is often reflected in every part.

As you explore a host of natural phenomena, the computer will be your fractal-scope, enabling you to see the "world in a grain of sand." Some systems are almost perfectly self-reflective, while others might seem downright un-fractal.

Why does this theorem work at all? Does some secret code exist that hides information about the whole river in every twist? Do little bends look up to their parents as role models?

There is a more plausible explanation: the forces that shape the whole resemble the forces that shape a single bend. You don't need to delve too deeply into hydrology to see that once a flow of water bends one way, changes in water velocity tend to make it bend the other way just downstream. This is true on every scale, from a 100-mile slough to a 50-foot jog.

So, the second principle of fractal science helps explain the first:

A system will appear self-reflective when similar forces act at many levels of scale.

It isn't mere coincidence that many fractals remind us of flowing or spraying water. Water often forms extremely self-reflective shapes simply because it behaves similarly over a large range of scales. Five ounces of water respond to a small force in much the same way as five tons respond to a large force, so they often end up looking the same, too.

The key to modeling a fractal system is to discover the forces that are working on many levels at once. With the river, it was sinuosity (winding).

A Cloud Study

Fractal geometry is a new language. Once you speak it, you can describe a cloud as precisely as an architect can describe a house.

—Michael Barnsley, *Fractals Everywhere*, 1988

Take another watery example: clouds. What forces affect crystallizing water vapor at many levels of scale? The most important ones are air currents. Three common types of air currents form three basic kinds of cloud shapes.

The classic puffy-white *cumulus* cloud forms from rising air moving over a warm surface. I've modeled this in Figure 2.2. First, I drew a simple polygon to represent a puff of water vapor (a) for my seed shape. Next, I added six smaller puffs to show the motion of the vapor as it crystallizes—the top parts move upward and outward, while the bottom is squeezed flat between rising air from below and the mass of vapor above (b). These forces are applied at smaller and smaller levels of scale (c), resulting in a typical cumulus on a sunny day (d).

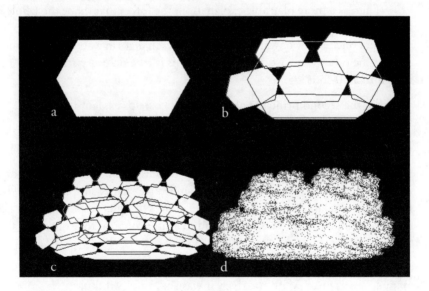

Figure 2.2. Progression of drawing a cumulus cloud by modeling the movement of air currents (CUMULUS).

By modeling different types of air currents, you can approximate the shape of the clouds those air currents create. Figure 2.3 shows two other types of clouds, along with the templates used to create them.

Figure 2.3. (a, b) Strong winds spread a cirrus cloud across the sky (CIRRUS). (c, d) Slow horizontal air movement creates stratus clouds (STRATUS).

Another common cloud type is *cirrus*: a high, wispy cloud formed by widespread, slowly ascending air. The parts of the template in Figure 2.3 (a and b) are thinly distributed and separated from one another. As with the cumulus, the template features a flat bottom and a puffy top. Low pressure and high winds often create an elongated tail—the part to the right. Notice how this tail is reflected throughout the finished cloud.

When a cold surface stirs the air in a generally stable atmosphere, *stratus* clouds can form. These are the long layers that make up an overcast sky. Parts of the template in Figure 2.3(c and d) don't protrude upward or downward from the seed, but they do drift sideways. The small difference in size between the seed and its copies induces a gradual transition between sizes of cloud mass. The completed shape is typical of a misty, drizzly day.

You Can Do It: Cloudy Skies

By graphically modeling the air currents under varying weather conditions, you can create convincing visual representations of several types of clouds.

1. **Load** the **Template** CUMULUS. This is the cumulus cloud in Figure 2.2.

2. **Draw** to watch the cloud form. The movements described in the template are applied at successively smaller levels of scale.

In real life, cloud formation takes place on a molecular level. You can skip to this level using the **Paint** command.

3. **Clear** the picture, then **Paint**. Even though each "puff" of air is as tiny as a pixel on-screen, the cloud still shows pufflike shapes at every level of scale.

4. You can view the other cloud models by **Load**ing and **Paint**ing THUNDER, CIRRUS, and STRATUS.

In each case, you've reconstructed a cloud by looking at the dynamics of cloud formation. Of course, there are many more cloud types out there (or up there, as the case may be). If you've completed the FractalVision online tutorial, you may want to try designing your own clouds by modifying these templates. Can you guess how to make a blotchy *altocumulus*, or a dramatic "mackerel sky" (*cirrocumulus*)? You're likely to learn something about them if you try.

Nature Has Her Limits

…most fractals in this Essay are invariant under certain transformations of scale. They are called scaling*…. Here, as in standard geometry of nature, no one believes that the world is strictly homogeneous or scaling…. One should not be surprised that scaling fractals should be limited to providing first approximations of the natural shapes to be tackled. One must rather marvel that these first approximations are so strikingly reasonable.*
—Benoit Mandelbrot, *The Fractal Geometry of Nature,* 1982

To review, the two basic principles I've covered so far are

In natural systems, the structure of the whole system is often reflected in every part.

A system will appear self-reflective when similar forces act at many levels of scale.

Notice that "many levels of scale" does not mean "every level of scale." If you move closer and closer to a river, you eventually reach a point where the bending stops and the river appears to be a straight channel. As you move even further away, you eventually reach a point high enough to see the whole river. You can imagine an abstract mathematical river with bends within bends down to the microscopic scale and upward until the largest bends would be the size of the whole planet. Nature, however, has her limits.

From a distance, clouds seem to have puffs within puffs within puffs down to infinity. If you get very close, however, you'll reach a scale where the action of air currents is less important than other forces. Clouds are not made up of infinitesimal clouds, but of ice crystals. Yet these crystals have a fractal structure of their own. As with clouds and rivers, these crystals show a special symmetry that applies to both the whole and the parts. If you take a closer look at the crystals, though, you'll see that a new principle comes into play as well.

Unlike clouds and rivers, where all levels of scale are formed at once, crystals grow step by step. Their symmetry does not come from similar forces acting simultaneously on many levels, but from the same force acting repeatedly. In Figure 2.4, I've started with a six-sided seed shape. If an ice particle forms on each corner of that seed, and another on each corner of those, you'll end up with a snowflake.

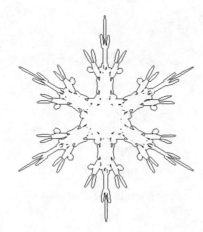

Figure 2.4. A six-sided snowflake (FLAKE1).

Figure 2.5 shows two variations on the same idea. The shape of the seed and number of spikes differ for each real snowflake because atmospheric conditions are different at every point. The crystallization does not continue forever, but stops when the edges become too thin and unstable to support more spikes (about the fourth level).

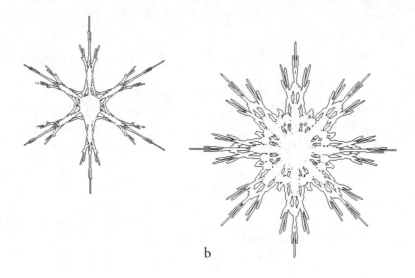

a   b

Figure 2.5. Each snowflake is unique (FLAKE2 and FLAKE3).

What would happen if the process didn't stop, but continued adding tinier and tinier spikes down to the atomic level of scale? Figure 2.6 is just such an "infinite" (and not very realistic) snowflake. A crucial aspect of modeling Nature is knowing when she stops.

Figure 2.6. The snowflake from Figure 2.4, continued to a near-infinite level of detail (FLAKE1).

A natural fractal can arise in two ways: similar forces can act on many levels at once (as in a river or cloud) or on one level after another over time (as with a snowflake). You can model both ways with FractalVision software: **Paint** forms all levels simultaneously, and **Draw** builds them one on top of another. The computer's procedures and Nature's are different, however: **Paint** creates infinite detail down to the resolution of your screen, while Nature has more realistic limits. **Draw** finishes one part before starting the next, while Nature forms all parts at once.

You Can Do It: Fractal Snowflakes

Here's your chance to make your own unique snowflake, different from every other one in the universe:

1. Choose your favorite flake from Figure 2.4 or 2.5 and **Load** it (either FLAKE1, FLAKE2, or FLAKE3). Use this as a starting point for creating your own.

2. Select **New** to replace parts of the template with new ones.

3. Decide how many spikes you want for your snowflake. Type a number between 4 and 12. That many parts automatically arrange themselves in a circle around the seed.

4. Select **NextPoint** to change the corner points of the seed shape.

5. Select **Grow** until the seed touches the spikes. If you want to be a little different, you could stop **Grow**ing before it touches them.

6. Select **Draw** to look at what you've got so far. As crystals form on the spikes, they overlap and mess up each other. Select **Clear** and we'll fix that.

7. You need to **Squish** the copies so they don't spread so far to the sides: select **Next Part** twice (the first time, you are on the seed, which doesn't need to be squished), and then choose **Squish** at least twice—it's your snowflake, so exactly how many times you **Squish** it is up to you.

8. Select **Next Part** and **Squish** the same number of times as before. Repeat this until you've **Squish**ed every spike on your flake.

9. **Draw** again. Do you like it? If not, go back and **Squish** or **Stretch** the parts until you do.

Congratulations! If you've been following this book from the start, this is your first unique fractal model. You might want to **Save** your **Template** for posterity.

The Geometry of Genetics

What else, when chaos draws all forces inward to shape a single leaf.
—Conrad Aiken, "The Room," *Collected Poems,* 1953

When you create a fractal model of a river or a snowflake, you are trying to decode the essential formative forces at work. If you can capture that "code" in your model, the resulting fractal will be realistic. Still, real rivers and snowflakes don't contain any secret code, other than the laws of nature. You are just trying to express the relevant laws visually.

In many natural systems, a "secret code" actually exists that governs formation—the *genetic code,* for example. You can model geometrically the part of that code that determines the direction of growth and branching. For example, the information necessary to draw a tree is inherent in the geometric relationships between the trunk and the first few branches.

Fractal Trees

Fractals know some of nature's algorithms…. The advantages are compelling:

Greater naturalness. The controlled randomness of fractal techniques gives a more natural image than does building from conventional geometric forms.

Deep naturalness. Fractal geometry apparently accurately models the process of growth and the underlying grammar of the natural forms it simulates.

Greater efficiency. Fractal images have absurdly modest storage requirements, if stored in the form of the generator function and generated at need.

Greater power. Fractal techniques use recursive image generation to allow any level of detail to be produced from a single stored generator function.
—Michael Swaine, *Dr. Dobb's Journal,* 1990

To draw the tree in Figure 2.7b, I simply sketched the *fractal template* from Figure 2.7a. The rest grew automatically, based on the geometry of my template.

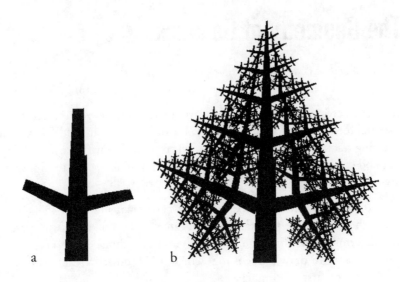

Figure 2.7. A simple model of a tree (TREE).

Each species of tree has its own characteristic branching pattern, as does each leaf on a tree. In Figure 2.8, you can see how a few geometric genetic codes (d-f) correspond to the fleshed-out tree models (a-c). Notice that the template pattern used to create the maple leaf is very similar to the one used to build a whole maple tree. The pine tree template is quite different, however.

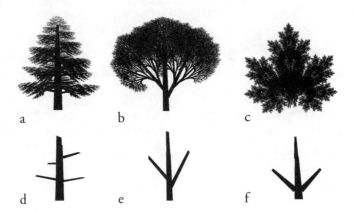

Figure 2.8. Fractal trees and the templates used to create them (PINE, MAPLE, and LEAF1).

You Can Do It: Modeling Trees

You can think of FractalVision templates as visual genetic codes. Each template that follows defines the trunk and first level of branches for a particular species of tree. The **Draw** command grows the rest of the tree from that code.

1. **Load** the MAPLE template, which defines the first level of branches on a maple tree.

2. **Draw** to generate the rest.

3. If you're willing to wait, **Adjust** the **Level** to 7 and **Draw** to get full foliage. (From the main menu, press A, 7, Enter, D.)

4. Without **Clear**ing your picture of a maple tree, **Load** LEAF1—a template "genetic code" for a maple leaf. Notice, it is very similar to that of the whole maple tree.

5. **Paint** to see the finished leaf. Why **Paint** instead of **Draw**? Because leaves form all at once; they do not branch out step by step from the central vein. You might want to try **Draw** to see the difference.

6. By contrast, the PINE template is quite different from MAPLE. **Load** and **Draw** the PINE (it will take a few minutes unless you're using a 486 or fast 386).

7. Even with all that waiting for FractalVision to draw the intricate detail of the pine tree, it still looks a bit sparse. Use **Paint** to flesh out the last few fuzzy needles.

You can often use the **Draw** and **Paint** commands together in this way: **Draw** the first few steps toward infinity and then **Paint** to jump straight to forever without having to wait forever to get there.

Modeling Real Plants

Now, Black Spleenwort Ferns have been around for a rather long time, and they sure are pretty, but nobody ever accused them of being very bright. Could the exact same process [used in computer simulation] be used by the real fern to teach itself how to grow?

To me, the odds are overwhelming that that does seem to be the case. We thus appear to be tampering with some heavy-duty stuff here.

—Don Lancaster, "Hardware Hacker," *Radio Electronics,* 1990

Can you "extract the genetic code" from a real plant to create a fractal mimic? You can, in two ways. You'll see an example of each, and then you'll investigate the relationship between them.

The first technique is to sculpt a *seed shape* that resembles the stem or trunk and then try to arrange copies of it as the first level of branches. Continuing the pattern reveals how close you came to the real thing. This works well when your subject has clearly defined branching, like the tree examples in Figure 2.8.

When the branching pattern isn't as obvious, you can take a more sneaky approach. Here's another way to model a maple leaf: trace the general outline of the whole leaf for your seed shape, and then try to cover that shape with copies of itself. Figure 2.9 shows a template and the resulting leaf which were created this way. Where the copies hang over the edge of the seed shape, they should add some details that appear in the real leaf—in this case, they add the extra tips in between the main three. Those details will appear on all the successively smaller levels as well. The *infinite level* looks like the original leaf.

Look at another, slightly trickier example: a fern. To create Figure 2.10, I went into the woods in Hardwick, Vermont, and found a real fern. I held it up to the computer screen and traced its outline in FractalVision to make a seed shape. To place the copies of the seed shape, I asked myself, "Can I see this real fern as being made up of copies of itself?" In fact, each small frond does look like the whole fern. I placed the bottom two copies right under the first two fronds on the real fern. Then I noticed that if those two fronds were chopped off, the remaining piece of fern would look almost exactly the same as it did before—just a little smaller. I could therefore call all the rest a copy of the whole. I placed a corresponding copy of the seed shape under it. The only part of the fern that wasn't included in those three parts was the stem. With a little imagination, I could see the stem as a squished copy of a whole fern; so I placed a squished copy of the seed under it.

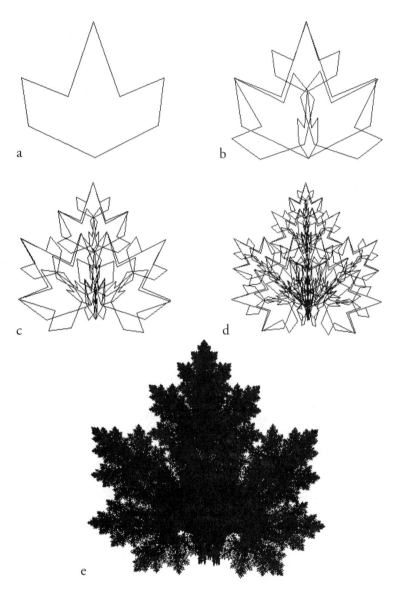

Figure 2.9. Modeling a leaf by tracing the whole (a) and tiling it with copies of itself (b-d) (LEAF2).

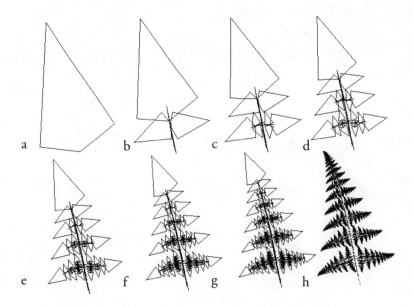

Figure 2.10. A fern created with the trace-and-tile technique (FERN2).

The trace-and-tile process is really the same one I just used for the maple leaf: I covered the fern with copies of itself. With the leaf, the copies added tips that I left out in my initial rough sketch for the seed. With the fern, the gaps between the four copies reflect open spaces in the real fern that I didn't put in the seed shape. In both examples, continuing the pattern will move closer to the real thing with each level, and the infinite level will be a detailed reproduction.

I've shown you two templates that create the same fern as in Figures 2.10 and 2.11. In Figure 2.10, I copied the stem pattern in the leaf. In Figure 2.11, I traced the leaf and tiled it with copies of itself. As you uncover the relationship between them, you'll learn something new and important about both fractals and genetics.

You may think that I created Figure 2.11 by tracing the stem of the fern for my seed and then placing copies where the fern branched out from that step. That approach would have worked, but it is not how I produced the illustration. Instead, I changed the shape of the seed to look like a stem instead of a whole fern, without altering the placement or geometric relationships between the copies.

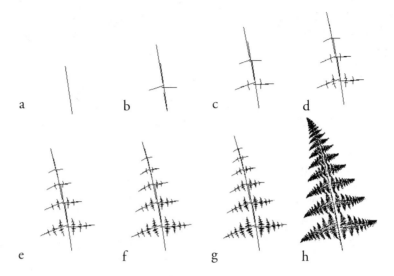

Figure 2.11. The same fern created with the stem-and-branches technique, for comparison (FERN1).

This implies an important lesson about plant geometry:

The relationship between the whole plant and its parts is the same as the relationship between the stem and its branches.

You Can Do It: Secret Life of a Fern

You can verify the preceding statement for yourself in your FractalVision graphics laboratory. In the process, you'll learn an equally important lesson about fractal modeling techniques.

1. With the FERN1 template **Load**ed, **Clear** the picture.

2. Select **NextPoint** from the menu, and use the mouse or arrow keys to move a point on the seed shape far from its current location.

3. Select **NextPoint** again, and move another. You should have something that doesn't look much like a fern.

continues

Notice that you have only changed the shape of the seed; you have not changed the placement of the copies or their relationship to one another.

4. Now select **Draw**. The first few levels don't look like much, but at each smaller level of detail, the shape more closely resembles a fern.

5. **Clear** and **Paint**, and you still get exactly the same fern as before.

Now for the proof of my little theorem about plant geometry:

6. **Load** the FERN1 template again to reset the seed to its original shape.

7. Using **NextPoint** to grab the points on the seed and the arrow keys to move them, put the points on the seed down where the "stem" copy is. (Be careful—the stem changes shape as you do this, so you remember where it was when you started.)

Remember, changing the seed this way doesn't alter the relationship between the parts, only their shape. Instead of a whole fern tiled with copies of itself, you now have a stem and three branches.

8. **Draw**, and a fern grows like the trees did. Of course, **Paint** still makes the same fern as before. (If you have trouble with this, look at the FERN2 example.)

Again, you haven't changed the relationship between the copies. The relationship between the whole and its parts is the same as that between the stem and its branches. (You may have noticed one small difference: when you define a whole tiled with copies of itself, you must add a stem part as a copy of the seed. This isn't necessary when you define a stem as the seed shape.)

The important lesson about fractals modeling:

> **Changing the shape of the seed does not change the resulting** Painting **at all.**

Why? The *copies* are always smaller than the *seed*. Therefore, each successive level of detail consists of smaller and smaller shapes. At the *infinite level* created by the Paint command, those shapes are always vanishingly small points, so you can't make out their shape anyway. All that matters is the *relationship* between them.

You've seen two different, though equivalent, approaches to modeling plants: stem-and-branches and trace-and-tile (which also could be called "whole-and-parts"—the official term is *collage*). In one case, the finished plant grows outward from a thin beginning. In the other, it is differentiated from a less detailed approximation. Which way does Nature do it? Both ways. Trees and bushes branch out step-by-step, while many leaves and succulent plants unfurl partially formed and then differentiate as they mature. Most plants, like ferns, use a combination of elaboration and differentiation. Why not, because both can be expressed in the same genetic code?

Nature's Image Compression

There's only so much information in the spore that encodes one fern. So there's a limit to the elaborateness with which a fern could grow. It's not surprising that we can find equivalent succinct information to describe ferns. It would be surprising if it were otherwise.

—Micheal Barnsley, quoted by James Gleick in *Chaos*, 1987

A couple more principles are operating in our fractal plants. First, it's obvious that the templates used to generate trees are much simpler than the finished tree drawings. This is true of all fractals—the information needed to define a fractal is generally much less than that needed to describe the picture it produces by any other means. It takes much more space on your disk to store the finished tree picture (even in a "compressed" format) than the template that completely defines it. If your computer is fast enough, you can save disk space by storing only the template and regenerating the picture each time you want to see it. Therefore:

A fractal template condenses a complex image into a simple code.

A genetic code works the same way. It lets a magnificently detailed 700-foot redwood communicate its entire structure to its offspring in a seed the size of your fingernail. As with your computer images, the price for this incredible data compression is time. It takes a few hundred years to decode the hereditary message into another fully elaborated tree.

Fractal image compression is by no means limited to plants. You learn a technique for approximating literally any image with fractal templates in Chapter 4.

Randomness

The most useful fractals involve chance.... Their regularities and irregularities are statistical.

—Benoit Mandelbrot, *The Fractal Geometry of Nature*, 1987

The next principle deals with what our fractal models lack. Each real tree is unique, for two reasons: genetic mutation and environmental influence. You can simulate genetic variation by slightly altering your template. Nature, though, has many more subtle transformations to work with than FractalVision's simple **Spin**, **Skew**, and **Shrink** commands. Environmental influences are harder to mimic. In the real world, plants are subjected to complex forces at every level of scale as they develop. Thus, the pure form defined by the genetic code is corrupted, and seemingly random variations appear. Our fractal plants, being raised in the sheltered environment of the computer, lack this random quality and look too perfect to be real.

A fractal models the essence of a species or type, not the appearance of a particular individual.

Using a random number generator, you can hint at Nature's boundless variety. Figure 2.12 shows several maple trees drawn from the same geometric model, with random variation added to make each one unique.

Some natural objects are more random looking than others. The plant models you're working with are quite realistic without adding any randomness at all. Galaxies, however, contain so much local variation in their geometry that randomness is essential in creating a recognizable representation.

Figure 2.13 shows a fractal template for a spiral galaxy, and the result without any randomness. While aesthetically pleasing, this is obviously much too self-similar to be a real galaxy. Figure 2.14, on the other hand, could easily be mistaken for a telescope photo. What's the difference? I added 40 percent random variation to the placement of each star.

Figure 2.12. Maple trees with 21 percent random variation added at every level of detail (MAPLE).

Figure 2.13. A fractal galaxy with no randomness (GALAXY1).

Figure 2.14. The same galaxy with 40 percent randomness (GALAXY2).

You Can Do It: Realistic Randomness

First, you'll see how to add randomness to a fractal tree so that each time you draw it, you get a unique individual. Next, you'll randomize a fractal galaxy.

1. **Load** the **Template** named MAPLE.

2. **Draw** a maple tree. Press the left arrow a few times and **Draw** again. This is the exact same maple tree.

3. Select **Extra** and then select **More Random** several times until the randomness setting (just below the **More Random** and **Less Random** menu choices) reads 21 percent.

4. Press Esc to return to the main menu. Then **Clear** the picture and **Draw**. This time, the maple tree is much less regular.

Unfortunately, it is also a bit disconnected. This happens because each successive level of detail uses different random numbers to compute the location of the branches. Consequently, the third level of branches does not necessarily match the second level, and each successive level is further off.

5. You can prevent this disconnection by pressing R instead of D to **Draw**. Try it: press Page Up to **Clear** the picture and then press R. This time, the tree is still irregular, but much more cohesive. (Why the letter R? It stands for **Rapid Draw**, because this method of drawing actually is faster than finishing each level before starting the next.)

6. Press the right arrow a few times and **Draw** again (remember to use the R key or the right mouse button for **Rapid Draw** instead of normal **Draw**). Each maple is now unique.

Now you'll see randomness at work on a galactic scale:

7. **Load** the GALAXY1 template and select **Paint**. It's pretty, but not right.

8. Select **Extra** and then repeatedly select **More Random** until the setting is around 40 percent.

9. Press Esc, Page Up, and P to return to the main menu, **Clear**, and **Paint**. The main spirals and dense galactic center remain, but the galaxies within galaxies are lost in the haze.

Play around with randomness a bit. How little randomness is noticeable in a tree? How much is ridiculous? What does a 100 percent random galaxy look like?

General Rules for Fractal Modeling

To him who in the love of Nature holds
Communion with her visible forms, she speaks
A various language.

—William Cullen Bryant, "Thanatopsis"

Now it's time to pull all these principles and lessons together into a general guide for finding and describing real-world fractals. The following steps describe the process used to create each of the fractal models you've seen so far.

1. **Look for self-reflection and find its limits.** Do some of the small details resemble larger parts or the whole thing? How closely can you look before the self-similarity breaks down?

2. **Find the relationship between one level of scale and the next.** Usually, you can see this best at either the smallest or largest level.

3. **Create a *seed shape* to resemble either the largest or smallest level of scale.** For example, to model a plant, you would shape the seed to look like either a rough outline of the whole plant (the largest level) or the stem (the smallest level).

4. **Place transformed *copies of the seed* to resemble the next level of scale.** For a plant, you would place either copies of the whole where they seem to occur in the real plant or copies of the stem for first-level branches.

5. **Select a *level of detail* to match your observations.** Trees, for example, usually have about five levels of branches from trunk to twig.

6. **Continue the pattern to see your results.** You can do this by hand, but it's a lot more fun if you use a computer.

7. **Fine-tune your shape to match your observations.** Add an appropriate degree of random variation if necessary.

To see this process in action, apply these rules to model the profile of a mountain and a lake.

1. **Look for self-reflection and find its limits.** On the largest scale, the mountain ascends from the earth, whereas the lake descends toward it. This is reflected in foothills and islands. On a smaller scale, you see jagged peaks, boulders, and mounds of earth. At a scale of a few inches or feet, things smooth out.

2. **Find the relationship between one level of scale and the next.** The essence of a "mountainous relationship" seems to be the change from a flat surface to an uneven contour.

3. **Create a *seed shape* to resemble either the largest or smallest level of scale.** Create a flat surface that can represent either the horizon from a great distance or a few inches of sand somewhere within your landscape.

4. **Place transformed *copies of the seed* to resemble the next level of scale.** In the template in Figure 2.15 (shown below the finished fractal curve), I've placed six copies of our flat seed shape to make an up-and-down contour. With a rectangle for the seed instead of a line, you can see the transformed copies better. I've used FractalVision's **Skew** command instead of **Spin** to tilt the copies so that the edges stay vertical and match up. The lake is less deep than the mountain is tall because a hollow or valley on any scale tends to fill with debris that erodes off nearby slopes.

5. **Select a *level of detail* to match your observations.** I figured **Level** 4 would be about right by counting like this: (1) mountain, (2) foothill, (3) hillock, (4) boulder.

6. **Continue the pattern to view your results.** In Figure 2.15, I've used FractalVision's **Paint** command to show the curve of the mountain horizon above the template. I did not actually need to limit the drawing to the fourth level of detail, because anything smaller than boulders won't show up at this magnification anyway.

7. **Fine-tune your shape to match your observations.** You might want to make many alterations. The **You Can Do It** box that follows presents some suggestions, along with a new approach for creating random variation. The result looks like Figure 2.16.

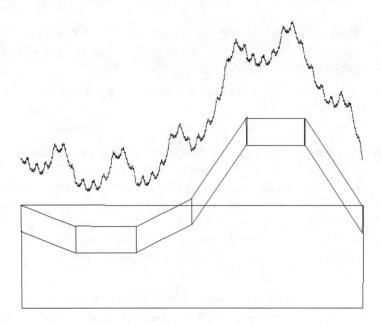

Figure 2.15. Horizon line of an artificially regular fractal mountain (MOUNTAIN).

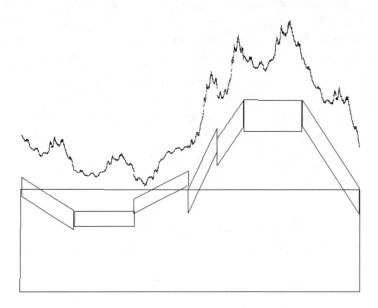

Figure 2.16. Horizon line of a mountain with complex irregularity added (MOUNT2).

You Can Do It: Modifying Mountains

You can add greater realism to the mountain model in several ways.

1. **Load** the MOUNTAIN template. **Paint** to see the horizon.

The height of the hillocks in low areas should be less than in high places because low areas tend to fill in. You can allow for this by making the lowest copy flatter.

2. **Clear** the picture and grab the part under the "lake" using **Next Part**. (Keep pressing the Tab key until the T-shaped *handle* is on the small blue rectangle on the lower left.)

3. **Shrink** and **Stretch** three times each.

4. **Draw**. Your change effects depressions at every level.

As with plants, you can vary the details of your model so that they are reminiscent of different types of mountains. You might make steeper Himalayan slopes or rounded Appalachian tops, capturing the essential form of these landscapes.

It would be especially nice to add some random variation. Try it:

5. Select **Extra** and press the exclamation point key (!) a few times to make the shape **More Random**.

6. Press Esc to exit the Extras menu, **Clear**, and **Paint**. Each point on the horizon is displaced by a random amount. This is not really what we had in mind.

7. Try **Draw**. Press Page Up and D to **Clear** and **Draw**. Again, each segment is transformed randomly. This looks more random, but makes the mountain all fuzzy looking.

Is it possible to add complex local variation while still keeping the horizon line continuous? Yes. You can introduce more variety by flipping certain sections around and adding more small copies. These variations will continue down through the levels and add a more irregular look without any genuine randomness at all.

continues

103

8. **Load** the **Template** MOUNT2 to see a more realistic mountain outline produced with these techniques.

9. **Clear** and **Paint** or **Draw**. The mountain now looks like Figure 2.16.

Always, though, you are creating an idealized, archetypal mountain rather than a realistic copy of any particular peak. To accurately reproduce Everest, for instance, your model would need to include not only the fundamental forms that characterize the Himalayas, but endless unique environmental idiosyncrasies at every level of scale.

The best mountain and landscape models come from specialized techniques that apply random variation at every level but retain surface continuity. The FORGERY.C program (See the **For Programmers Only: Cycles within Cycles** box in Chapter 1, "A History of Fractals and Chaos") produces more realistic mountain horizon lines than the self-reflective templates of FractalVision can manage (Figure 2.17).

Figure 2.17. A mountain horizon produced with the FORGERY.C program from Chapter 1.

The same procedure applied to two dimensions can also create fractal continents and coastlines like those in Figure 2.18, constructed with the LAND.C program listed in the following **For Programmers Only** box. Taken to a third dimension, a similar procedure forms fractal landscapes like those in Figures 2.19 and 2.20. The **You Can Do It** box (which follows the program listing) shows you how to make mountains like these yourself.

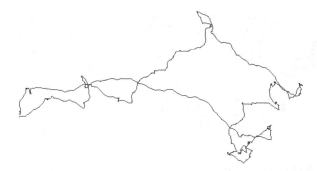

Figure 2.18. Random continental coastlines made with the LAND.C program.

Figure 2.19. Three-dimensional mountains created and rendered in FRACTINT.

Figure 2.20. The same mountains, transformed into continents on a planet.

For Programmers Only: Land Ho!

This program uses exactly the same cutup() procedure as FORGERY.C from Chapter 1, but applies it in two dimensions to create the coastlines of random continents.

This is also a good model of Brownian motion, the random wandering of microscopic critters and stuff due to molecular motion.

Listing 2.1. LAND.C. A program to forge coastlines or paths of Brownian motion.

```
/* LAND.C
 *
 * This program draws a two-dimensional "random walk",
 * which could be a forgery of a continental coastline
```

```
 * or the path of Brownian motion.
 */

#include <stdio.h>       /* Standard input/output libraries */
#include <stdlib.h>

#define MAIN             /* See Appendix D for compile */
#include "fv.h"          /* instructions and header files. */

#define ESC 27           /* The Escape key code */
#define drawclr 15       /* Color to make the coastline */
#define NPOINTS 2000     /* Maximum number of data points */
#define SCALE 2000       /* Maximum vertical scaling factor */

/* x and y are data points
 * npoints is the actual number of points to compute
 * scale is the actual vertical scaling factor
 * points is a pointer to the x or y array
 * xmax, ymax, xmin, and ymin
 *          are used to find the maximum and minimum values
 *          so we can center the continents on the screen
 */

int x[NPOINTS], y[NPOINTS], npoints, scale,
    *points, xmax, ymax, xmin, ymin;

void cutup(int start, int end, int scale); /* prototype */

void main(void)
{   int vidmode, i;      /* video mode and a counter */
    vidmode = pickmode(detectmode());  /* get video mode */
    if (setvidmode(vidmode, 1) != 1)
    {   printf("\nUnable to set graphics mode.\n");
        exit(0);
    }
    while(1)        /* Make curves until user enters zero */
    {   settextmode();
        printf(
```

continues

Listing 2.1. continued

```
        "This program will draw a fractal coastline.\n");
printf(
        "Enter the number 0 to quit the program.\n");
printf(
        "\nEnter the number of data points (max %d): ",
        NPOINTS);
scanf("%d", &npoints);
if (npoints == 0) break;
if (npoints > NPOINTS) npoints = NPOINTS;
printf("\nEnter a scaling factor (max %d): ",
            SCALE);
scanf("%d", &scale);
if (scale == 0) break;
if (scale > SCALE) scale = SCALE;
x[0] = 0; y[0] = 0;                   /* start at origin */
x[npoints - 1] = 0;          /* end where we started */
y[npoints - 1] = 0;
points = x;
cutup(0, npoints - 1, scale);  /* compute the rest */
points = y;
cutup(0, npoints - 1, scale);
xmax = x[0]; xmin = x[0]; ymax = y[0]; ymin = y[0];
for (i = 0; i < npoints; i++) /* find max & min x,y */
{   if (xmax > x[i]) xmax = x[i];
    if (ymax > y[i]) ymax = y[i];
    if (xmin < x[i]) xmin = x[i];
    if (ymin < y[i]) ymin = y[i];
}
xmax = (xmax + xmin) / 2;      /* make xmax and ymax */
ymax = (ymax + ymin) / 2;   /* offsets to center it */
for (i = 0; i < npoints; i++)  /* center all points */
    x[i] += scrnx / 2 - xmax, y[i] += scrny / 2 - ymax;
setvidmode(0, 0);              /* go into graphics mode */
clearscreen();
setcolor(drawclr);
moveto(x[0], y[0]);   /* get ready to start drawing */
for (i = 0; i < npoints; i++)     /* draw on screen */
    lineto(x[i], y[i]);
getch();               /* wait for user to press a key */
```

```
    }
    settextmode();
    closedown();              /* close down the graphics and quit */
}

/* This function chops the data set in two pieces,
 * displaces the midpoint by a random amount,
 * and chops each of the two pieces into two smaller
 * intervals by calling itself recursively
 */
void cutup(int start, int end, int scale)
{   int value;                    /* the current data point */
  if (end - start <= 1) return;    /* interval too small? */
  value = (points[end] + points[start]) / 2;   /* average */
  if (scale > 1) value += rand() % scale - scale / 2;
  points[(end + start) / 2] = value;   /* offset midpoint */
  cutup(start, (end + start) / 2, scale / 2);  /* chop it */
  cutup((end + start) / 2, end, scale / 2);  /* and again */
}
```

You Can Do It: 3-D Mountains

You can make random three-dimensional mountains with FRACTINT, a free program available all over the place. (See the Introduction for details on where and how to snag a copy.)

1. Start FRACTINT and choose a video mode with as many colors and as much resolution as your graphics adapter will support (see the Introduction for explicit instructions).

2. Press T to choose a fractal Type.

3. Select the **plasma** type by typing pl and pressing Enter.

4. Press Enter again to accept the graininess factor of two. You might want to play around with different values for this parameter later.

continues

The plasma that appears has the structure of a topographical map: the colors represent elevation, and they gradually change from peak to valley and back.

5. When the plasma is fully formed, press the letter S to save this picture. Notice the filename that FRACTINT reports when it's done saving. (The name will be something like FRACT002.GIF or FRACT003.GIF. FRACTINT increments the number at the end of the filename by one each time it saves a picture.)

Before you turn the plasma into mountains, you need to see why it's called plasma in the first place:

6. Press the + (plus) key on the numeric keypad. I said you had to see it.

7. Press Enter a few times to change the palette before you return to the mountains.

8. Press the Esc key to halt the plasmatic hypnosis machine before you succumb completely to its mesmerization rays.

9. Press the number 3 to do a 3-D transformation. This command tells FRACTINT to project a picture into three dimensions by using color values for vertical height.

10. Select the filename you just noted when you saved that plasma picture. It will be the last numbered one on the list. Use the arrow keys to point to it, and press Enter.

11. Press Enter again to verify that you want to use the same video mode as before.

12. You'll see a list of parameters, headed with the words **3D Mode Selection**. You'll have a chance to fool around with those in a minute, but for now just press Enter.

13. You'll see more choices; **Select 3D Fill Type**. Use the down arrow to select **surface fill (colors interpolated)** and press Enter.

14. Press Enter again to use the palette from the image to be loaded.

15. Even more choices appear: **Planar 3D Parameters**. For now, just press Enter again, and experiment later.

If you have a slow (or even not-so-fast-as-you'd-like) computer, the mountains may take a few minutes to appear.

16. Press the letter C and then the function key Shift+F7. Everything turns green. Try Control+F7 and Shift+F10 to see if you like them better. You might also like to press an arrow key to color cycle a little bit, for entirely pragmatic purposes.

17. Press Esc to escape the color cycling mode and press S to save your mountain picture.

To create a planet, follow the same steps, but choose **Spherical projection** under **3D Mode Selection**. I'll step through it with you:

18. Press 3 and choose the same filename as you did before. (It's no longer the last on the list if you saved your mountain picture.)

19. Press Enter to accept the video mode.

20. You should see the **3D Mode Selection** parameters. Use the down arrow key to access **Spherical Projection** and press the letter Y for Yes. Press Enter.

21. Press Enter three more times to accept all the default parameters.

22. Once the planet is finished, press C and L to load a palette map. Try landscap.map, topo.map, or volcano.map, depending on whether you want Earth, Venus, or Mars.

23. To view the mountains or planet with the 3-D red/blue glasses, repeat the above instructions, setting the **Stereo** parameter on the **3D Mode Selection** menu to 2 for **superimpose**.

Whatever you do, don't press + to color cycle. This book is about real-world modeling and real worlds just don't do that. (Okaaay, go ahead…)

Fractal Graphs

Computer graphics methods have provided crucial assistance in many mathematics problems…and the visual displays of iterative maps make visible patterns that would never have been noticed by analytic means alone.

—Lynn Steen, *The Science of Pattern*

You've learned how to model the fractal forms we can see around us. But what about all the interesting things we can't see? Scientists, economists, and sociologists use graphs to visualize phenomena that are outside our normal senses or that occur over a very long or very short span of time.

As you are about to discover, you can use fractal graphs to represent cyclic irregular behaviors. These graphs are especially well suited for complex time series data from natural and economic phenomena. You can even use software included with this book to automatically turn numerical data into fractal curves.

Seismic Activity

Come-and-go pervades everything of which we have knowledge, and though great things go more slowly, they are built up of small ones and must fare as that which makes them.

—Samuel Butler, *Notebooks,* 1912

The "shape" of an earthquake is self-reflective. Warning tremors and aftershocks are like miniquakes. The main quake is a period of intense activity comprised of similar intense periods with short lapses in between. This sort of behavior is difficult to model with traditional curves but seems well suited for fractals.

To model a fractal earthquake, set up and label a graph of seismic activity. In an imaginary (but typical) example, a quake might last for seven hours from the first tremor to the last measurable aftershock. The most intense activity might start an hour after the first tremor and last for two hours, peaking around 0.7 on the Richter scale. Activity would continue intermittently with decreasing intensity for the remaining four hours.

To model this seismic data in Figures 2.21 and 2.22, I first sketched an outline as a seed shape. Then, I tiled that shape with miniquakes, periods of activity which resembled the whole quake. Notice that I flipped the two leftmost parts horizontally to make them peak toward the end rather than the beginning. As with the preceding mountain example, I used **Skew** instead of **Spin** to tilt the parts so the vertical axis would stay straight.

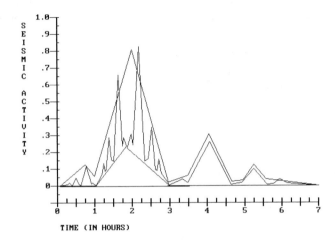

Figure 2.21. Rough sketch of a fractal earthquake (QUAKE).

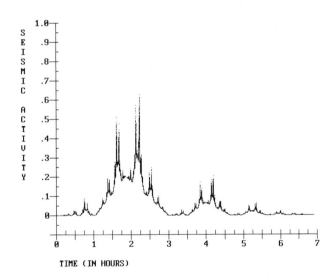

Figure 2.22. The completed fractal earthquake graph (QUAKE).

Obviously, Figure 2.21 could never pass for the graph of a real earthquake—it is much too simple and self-similar. The point here is that the figure has many advantages over more traditional methods. Like a real earthquake, but unlike any "ordinary" linear mathematical model, complex vibration occurs within even the smallest time interval. Unlike models based on random numbers, the fractal follows the overall shape of a real earthquake, from warning tremors to aftershocks. Our four-part fractal is very easy to define and work with, yet it shows the minute detail characteristic of natural systems.

You Can Do It: Earthquake!

Although it might not shake your house, a good close look at our idealized seismic graph might shake your confidence in linear models.

1. **Load** the **Template** named QUAKE. I've used the **Caption** feature of FractalVision to label the graph. This layer of text is saved along with the template and is completely independent from the picture.

2. **Paint** to reproduce Figure 2.22.

Before you zoom in to see the minute vibrations, eliminate that caption text, which will no longer be accurate at the higher magnification.

3. Select **Extra** and then **Captions**.

A blinking cursor appears, and you can now edit the caption text by typing as if you were in a word processor. Try this out, if you haven't used captions before. You're about to erase all the captions anyway, so type anything you like.

4. Select **ClearText**—the same Page Up key that clears the picture when you're on the main menu. All the text disappears, but the picture underneath remains unchanged.

5. Press the Enter key to stop editing the captions. You don't need to back out through the Extras menu; you just pop right back to the main menu automatically.

Here's what this earthquake looks like up close:

6. **Clear** the picture and select **Grow** a few times.

7. **Paint**, and a magnified view of the graph sprays onto the screen.

The picture contains just as much detail as before, representing momentary vibration within the larger upheavals. The ability to account for behavior on many scales at once with simple models makes fractal geometry the mathematics of choice for simulating complex natural phenomena.

Climate Data

It is desirable at times for ideas to possess a certain roughness, like drawings on heavy-grain paper. Thoughts having this quality are most likely to match the texture of actual experience.

—Harold Rosenberg, *Discovering the Present*, 1973

The earthquake model was an off-the-cuff estimation. For the next graph, I'll take some actual data and see if we can find a fractal curve that approximates it. The subject this time is atmospheric temperature variation in Middlesex, Vermont. (Many thanks to our local weather hero and National Weather Service monitor, Roger Hill, for sharing his personal store of data.)

Long-term climate records often show self-reflective cycling. There are heat waves that last several years, longer warm spells of a decade or so, and even longer ones that last a century or more. Records for the Nile reveal millenia-long dry spells and evidence from deep sea isotope counts indicate cyclic temperature variations on the scale of hundreds of thousands of years.

Day-to-day life suggests that irregular temperature cycling continues on a monthly and weekly basis. Figure 2.23 confirms this intuition. The yearly temperature swing shows up most prominently, but the astute observer will discern gentle temperature cycles on the order of months and weeks as well. Hourly temperature variations are not apparent because the data are daily averages.

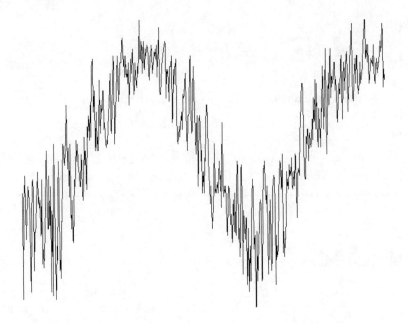

Figure 2.23. Six hundred days of daily average temperature readings from Middlesex, Vermont (AVGTEMP.PCX).

Traditional linear techniques offer no easy way to characterize this type of data. A simple yearlong sine wave with pseudorandom variation might appear similar to the graph at first glance, but this model would lose all hints of nested cyclic structure—the exact structure that would be most interesting to model.

If you could approximate this data with a fractal curve, on the other hand, you could more easily model the nested cyclic behavior than avoid it. I created Figure 2.24 by hand-sculpting an approximation of Figure 2.23 with FractalVision software. (The template appears as polygons around the curve.)

Figure 2.24 is by no means the only possible fractal that could model this data. A little more twiddling and fiddling led me to the somewhat better approximation in Figure 2.25.

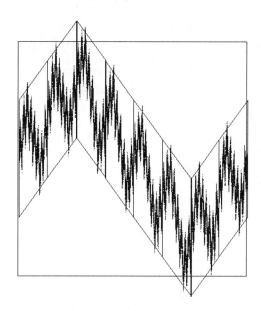

Figure 2.24. A simple fractal approximation of Figure 2.23. (AVGTEMP1).

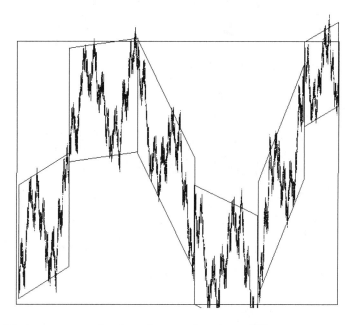

Figure 2.25. A more complex fractal approximation of Figure 2.23. (AVGTEMP2).

Though no less accurate on a point-by-point basis than a linear-plus-random model, this figure evokes the essential character of the curve much more successfully.

This is not a predictive model. If you use it to forecast the daily temperature next July 12, your prediction would be statistically less accurate than a prediction based on simple yearly averages. What good is it then? It models several hypotheses about *temperature variation* that can be tested:

■ The amount of variation on average remains constant over time.

■ The amount of variation on average remains consistent over a large range of scales.

■ The amount of variation, expressed as fractal dimension, is between 1.4 and 1.5.

All three statements hold true for both the fractal model and the real data over a longer period of time. None hold true for a linear or linear-plus-random model. (The first statement can be true for a linear-plus-random model if you discount yearly fluctuation. In the fractal model, yearly fluctuation is simply part of the general case and you don't need to filter it out at all.)

You Can Do It: Building a Fractal Graph

How did I derive Figure 2.24 from Figure 2.23? Start FractalVision and see for yourself.

1. If you have been working in FractalVision, **Load** the STARTUP template because some of the following steps will give different results depending on which template you started with.

2. **Load** the **Picture** named AVGTEMP. If you have a VGA screen, the picture should look just like Figure 2.24. If you're using a monochrome graphics adapter, you won't be able to load this picture, but you can follow along anyway.

I started by framing the part of the curve I wished to model with a rectangular seed shape. If you want to try this on your own, go on to step two. If you need some help, **Load** the AVGTEMP1 **Template.**

3. Select **NextPoint** to grab a corner of the seed shape.

4. Now create a new seed with four corners: select **New**, press the number 4, and then press the Enter key.

5. Select **Spin** (the + key) four times to make the square parallel to the sides of the screen. Because your handle is on a corner point of the seed shape and not a part, only the seed shape spins.

6. The vertical size of the seed square should be approximately the same as the high-to-low vertical size of the curve. If it isn't, **Grow** or **Shrink** until it is.

At this point, you should know that pressing the Esc key makes the menu disappear so you can see underneath it. When you need the menu, press Esc again to bring it back. While it's gone, all the menu action keys still work, so you may not need to return to it very often.

You have a seed shape. Now position the template over the curve.

7. Select **NextPart** (the Tab key) to grab the whole template.

8. Use the arrow keys to line up the top and bottom of the box with the curve and position the left side near the middle of the first climbing portion of the curve.

9. Select **Stretch** once to widen the box just a little so that its right-side width is also in the middle of a climbing portion of the curve. You may need to press the right arrow once to line it up again.

The next step is to construct the model geometry by placing copies of the seed over parts of the curve which represent subcycles within the large cycle. If you get lost or want a guide, just **Load** the AVGTEMP1 template.

10. Select **New** again (the 0 key), press 1, and then Enter. Because your handle is on a *part* and not a *point*, you get one new copy of the seed instead of a new seed shape.

11. Select **Next Part** (Tab) to grab the new copy of the seed and use the arrow keys to move it down to the middle of the left side of the square seed shape.

continues

119

12. Use **Skew** (the ' key), **Squish** (the [key), and the arrow keys to transform and place the part so that it covers a region of the curve.

To place and skew the part just right, you will probably want to use the **Precision** command (the End key). This toggles back and forth between large jumps and small jumps when transforming and moving.

13. Press Insert to make another copy of the seed.

14. Using the arrow keys, place this copy so that its left edge lines up with the right edge of the previous copy.

15. **Insert** another copy.

16. Select **Skew** (the ; key, to skew counterclockwise) eight times to make the angle of this part match the down-slope of the curve.

17. Place this copy next to the previous one.

18. Continue **Insert**ing and placing copies until your template resembles the one in Figure 2.25. If you get the idea but don't want all that practice right now, just **Load** the AVGTEMP1 **Template**.

You might like to check your model's fractal dimension to see if it matches that of the original data.

19. **Clear** the picture, and press I to **Paint** "Infinitely long." When the curve looks very solid and full, press Esc.

20. Select **Extras** and **Fractal Dim.** to check the fractal dimension.

The fractal dimension of the data (which you can check by **Load**ing the AVGTEMP picture and repeating step 19) is a bit higher than 1.4. Yours is probably higher than that, around 1.6. How can you change the fractal dimension without reconstructing the whole curve?

21. Select **NextPart** until you're on the first copy of the seed—the one on the far right.

22. Select **Shrink** (the / key) twice, and then **Stretch** (the] key) twice. This squashes the vertical size of the part, making it smoother. Consequently, the fractal dimension is lower.

23. Select **Next Part** and repeat step 21. Squash down every part and go back to step 18 to see how the fractal dimension changed.

(I've done all the squashing for you in the AVGTEMP2 template, if you prefer to **Load** it.)

By tweaking placements, varying orientations, and turning some parts upside down, you can craft a more complex and more accurate model, like that in Figure 2.25.

24. **Load** the AVGTEMP3 template to poke around with my improved model and see some of the flips and flops I did to create it.

Automatic Fractal Interpolation

Fractal interpolation functions also provide a new means for fitting experimental data. Clearly it does not suffice to make a polynomial "least-squares" fit to the wild experimental data of Strahle for the temperature in a jet exhaust as a function of time.... Nor would classical geometry be a good tool for the analysis of voltages at a point in the human brain as read by an electroencephalograph. However, fractal interpolation functions can be used to "fit" such experimental data.... Moreover, one can ensure that the fractal dimension of the graph of the fractal interpolation function agrees with that of the data, over an appropriate range of scales.

—Michael Barnsley, *Fractals Everywhere*, 1988

Hand-crafting fractal curves can be rewarding, but it is an exacting and difficult task. Isn't there any way to automatically find a fractal to fit a data set, as is commonly done with linear curves?

Fortunately, *fractal interpolation*—finding a fractal curve that passes through given points—is at least as easy as linear interpolation. Even more fortunately, you got a program to do it when you bought this book. I present the source code for INTERPO.C in the **For Programmers Only** box appearing toward the end of this section, but you don't need to have written any programs to use the INTERPO.EXE program itself.

INTERPO reads a regular text (ASCII) file of x,y data points, prints their values for you to see, and plots them graphically on-screen. It then constructs a fractal curve that passes through those data points and displays that curve, along with the numerical definition of the curve.

You can give INTERPO any number of data points (though you'll need to change the source code if you give it more than 100). I recommend limiting the data, however, to only a few select points that characterize the largest fluctuations in the curve. INTERPO creates a transformation (equivalent to a copy of the seed in FractalVision software) for each interval between two successive points. Therefore, if you give it 100 points, you'll get a curve defined by 99 transformations. You would almost certainly get a better model by supplying INTERPO with five key points, providing you select the right five.

Which points should you choose? Ideally, they should be endpoints to portions of the curve that resemble the whole. If you can't recognize any self-similarity, try a regular sample of every 10th or 50th or 500th data point, depending on how many points you have.

The next few paragraphs describe the data format that INTERPO needs to understand your data. If you aren't ready to try INTERPO with your own data right now, I recommend that you skip ahead to the **You Can Do It** box to try working with the sample data supplied on your program disk.

Once you have your data points, you'll need to put them in a text file and add some extra information. How you do this depends on the software that generates or gathers the data. Consult the appropriate documentation for generating a plain ASCII file. Once you convert the data to ASCII (text) format, you can use any text editor (the EDIT program that comes with DOS 5.0, for example) to add a few necessary finishing touches.

For each interval between two data points, you can specify a vertical scaling factor for the fractal interpolation curve. What does this scaling factor do? It determines the relative roughness of that particular part of the curve as compared to the rest. For example, if the first interval has a scaling factor of .5 and all the other intervals have a scaling factor of .2, the leftmost part of the curve is taller and rougher than the rest. A negative scaling factor such as −.3 turns the corresponding part of the curve upside down. If you aren't sure what to use for scaling factors, just make them all .5 and experiment later to see the results. Scaling factors should always be between −1 and 1.

Finally, you need to add two extra pieces of information at the top of your data file. Place the total number of data points in the file on the first line. On the second line, tell INTERPO what size to make the background "graph-paper" guidelines, which the program draws behind the data. If you enter 1 1 on this line, for example, then a graph line appears on-screen at intervals that correspond to 1 unit in both the x and y directions. If the x data is on the order of 300 to 500 and the y data varies between 0.01 and 0.02, you might specify the graph line intervals as 50 0.001. The x and y data themselves are automatically scaled to fit on-screen. You only need to specify where to put the graph lines.

One last requirement: you must place x values in numerical order. Each y value should be on the line with its corresponding x value, with the vertical scaling factor for the next interval on the same line. So an INTERPO data file should look like this (without the parenthetical remarks):

```
5                       (the total number of data points)
1      0.3              (the grid line increments)
2      0.3    .5        (x, y, vertical scaling factor)
4      1.2    .2
6      0.1    .5
9      0.8   -.3
10     0.3    0
```

The final scaling factor is meaningless because no interval exists after the last point. You should put a number there anyway, just because the program input reads three numbers on each data line.

INTERPO doesn't care what you call your data files, so long as you tell it the full name with the extension when it asks. The sample data files on the disk have the extension .FIP (for fractal interpolation), so you might want to use that extension also.

Figure 2.26 shows the output of INTERPO, given the data file listed previously.

Can you use INTERPO to automatically construct a fractal model of the Middlesex temperature data? You bet. To create Figure 2.27, I selected every 50th day for a year and fed it to INTERPO. When the program runs, it asks what fractal dimension you want the curve to have and adjusts the vertical roughness accordingly. I gave the curve a dimension of 1.42, to match the estimate of fractal dimension that FractalVision gave me for the original data graph.

```
sample.fip  5 points, graph scale =   1.00 x   0.30  Dimension = 1.300000
x =   2.00   4.00   6.00   9.00  10.00
y =   0.30   1.20   0.10   0.80   0.30
s =   0.51   0.20   0.51  -0.30
a =   0.25   0.25   0.38   0.13
c =   0.11  -0.14   0.09  -0.06
e =   1.50   3.50   5.25   8.75
f =  -0.08   1.41  -0.23   1.02
```

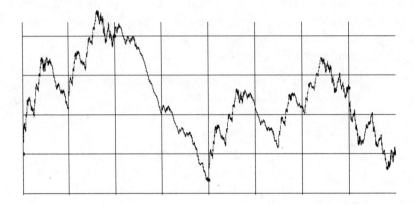

Figure 2.26. A fractal curve generated automatically with the INTERPO program (SAMPLE.FIP).

```
avg50.fip  8 points, graph scale =   50.00 x  10.00  Dimension = 1.500000
x = 100.00 150.00 200.00 250.00 300.00 350.00 400.00 450.00
y =  61.00  77.00  79.00  62.00  41.00  30.00  36.00  59.00
s =   0.38  -0.38   0.38   0.38   0.38   0.38  -0.38
a =   0.14   0.14   0.14   0.14   0.14   0.14   0.14
c =   0.05   0.00  -0.05  -0.06  -0.03   0.02   0.06
e =  85.71 135.71 185.71 235.71 285.71 335.71 385.71
f =  33.16  99.70  60.59  44.73  20.87   5.01  52.70
```

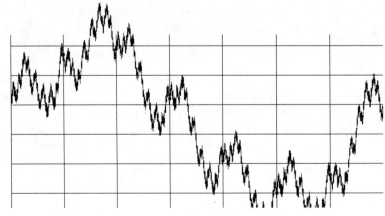

Figure 2.27. Every 50th day of the Middlesex temperature data, automatically interpolated with INTERPO (AVG50.FIP).

Notice that the selection of every 50th data point was not arbitrary. Figure 2.28 is one example of what happened when I tried every 100th data point. Every 50th seemed to contain a good general outline of the curve and seemed to match the largest self-similarities I could see in the data.

```
avg100.fip  8 points, graph scale = 100.00 x  20.00  Dimension = 1.420000
x =    0.00 100.00 200.00 300.00 400.00 500.00 600.00 700.00
y =   10.00  68.00  77.00  37.00  71.00  61.00  11.00  68.00
s =    0.32   0.32   0.32   0.32   0.32   0.32   0.32
a =    0.14   0.14   0.14   0.14   0.14   0.14   0.14
c =    0.06  -0.01  -0.08   0.02  -0.04  -0.10   0.05
e =    0.00 100.00 200.00 300.00 400.00 500.00 600.00
f =    6.77  64.77  73.77  33.77  67.77  57.77   7.77
```

Figure 2.28. Every 100th day produces a less satisfactory model (AVG100.FIP).

You Can Do It: Fractal INTERPOlation

Once you create an INTERPO-compatible data file (described previously), viewing a fractal approximation of your data is a one-step process:

At the DOS prompt, type:

```
INTERPO AVG50.FIP 1.42
```

continues

125

Alternatively, you can just type INTERPO, and the program prompts you for the name of the data file and the desired fractal dimension. When you're done viewing the graph, press any key to return to DOS.

You might wonder how the fractal dimension input changes the curve. For a demonstration:

Type FRACDIM SAMPLE.FIP at the DOS prompt. This runs a batch file that equips INTERPO with successively greater fractal dimensions for the same curve.

For Programmers Only: The INTERPO Source Code

INTERPO uses the same *Iterated Function System* (IFS) *codes* that FractalVision uses. Chapter 5, "The Math Behind the Magic," explains the mathematics and algorithms for IFS Codes as well as the algorithm used to control the fractal dimension of fractal interpolation curves.

Listing 2.2. INTERPO.C. A program to approximate a fractal curve from data.

```
/* INTERPO.C
 *
 * This program finds a fractal curve which fits a
 * set of data read from an ASCII file.
 * See chapter 2 and the file SAMPLE.FIP for
 * information about the data format for input files.
 */

#include <stdio.h>        /* Standard input/output */
#include <stdlib.h>
#include <string.h>       /* for strcpy */
#include <math.h>         /* for float math functions */


#define MAIN             /* See Appendix D for compile */
```

```
#include "fv.h"          /* instructions for header files. */

#define drawclr 13       /* Color to make the curve */
#define pointclr 15      /* Color to make the data points */
#define gridclr 1        /* Color to make the graph lines */

#define NPOINTS 100      /* Maximum number of data points */

float   x[NPOINTS], y[NPOINTS],       /* data from input file */
        scale[NPOINTS],               /* y scaling factors */
        a[NPOINTS - 1], b, c[NPOINTS - 1],     /* IFS codes */
        e[NPOINTS - 1], f[NPOINTS - 1];

void main(int nargs, char **arg)     /* accept command line */
{   int vidmode, i, j;               /* video mode and counters */

    float x1, y1, x2, y2,              /* used to display curve */
          xscale, yscale,        /* scaling for screen display */
          maxx, maxy, minx, miny,      /* max and min x and y */
          dim, sum, ratio,       /* used to compute dimension */
          xgrid, ygrid;     /* graph scaling from input file */

    int xoffset, yoffset, yadjust,    /* screen positioning */
        npoints;                /* number of data points in file */
    FILE *diskfile;                /* file handle and file name */
    char filename[20];

    vidmode = pickmode(detectmode()); /* confirm video mode */
    if (nargs > 1) strcpy(filename, arg[1]);
    else     /* if filename not on command line, ask for it */
    {   printf("\n\n");
        printf("This program will find a fractal"
                " curve to fit data from\n");
        printf("a text file of x,y points.  Try "
                "SAMPLE.FIP for sample input.");
        printf("\n\nEnter the name of the file to use: ");
        scanf("%s", filename);
    }
```

continues

Listing 2.2. continued

```
    if (nargs > 2) dim = atof(arg[2]);
    else    /* if dimension not on command line, ask for it */
    {   printf("\n\nEnter the desired fractal "
                "dimension (between 1 and 2): ");
        scanf("%f", &dim);
    }
    if ((dim > 2.0) || (dim < 1.0))   /* is dimension okay? */
    {   printf("Fractal dimension must be "
                "between 1 and 2 (i.e. 1.2).");
        exit(0);
    }
    if ((diskfile = fopen(filename, "r")) == NULL)
    {   printf("Can't find a file named %s.", filename);
        exit(0);
    }
    fscanf(diskfile, "%d", &npoints);            /* read data */
    fscanf(diskfile, "%f %f", &xgrid, &ygrid);
    for (i = 0; (i < npoints) && (i < NPOINTS); i++)
        fscanf(diskfile, "%f %f %f", x + i, y + i, scale + i);
    fclose(diskfile);             /* with no error checking!! */
    if (setvidmode(vidmode, 1) != 1)
    {   printf("\nUnable to set graphics mode.\n");
        exit(0);
    }

    /* Scale the data to fit on the screen */

    yadjust = scrny / 20;           /* distance from bottom */
    maxx = x[0]; minx = x[0];
    maxy = y[0]; miny = y[0];
    for (i = 1; i < npoints; i++)  /* find largest/smallest */
    {   if (x[i] > maxx) maxx = x[i];
        if (y[i] > maxy) maxy = y[i];
        if (x[i] < minx) minx = x[i];
        if (y[i] < miny) miny = y[i];
    }
    xscale = scrnx / (maxx - minx);     /* scale x,y to fit */
    yscale = (scrny / (maxy - miny)) / 2;
    xoffset = - (int) (minx * xscale);   /* move origin to corner */
```

```
yoffset = scrny - yadjust + (int) (miny * yscale);

/* Compute the skew transformations
   and sum the scaling factors */

b = x[npoints - 1] - x[0]; /* b is used only to compute */
sum = 0.0;                      /* sum up the scale factors */
for (i =   0; i < npoints - 1; i++) sum += fabs(scale[i]);
ratio = pow(npoints - 1, dim - 1) / sum;
for (i = 0; i < npoints - 1; i++)  /* compute IFS codes */
{   scale[i] *= ratio;
    a[i] = (x[i + 1] - x[i]) / b;
    e[i] = (x[npoints - 1] * x[i] - x[0] * x[i + 1]) / b;
    c[i] = (y[i + 1] - y[i] - scale[i] *
            (y[npoints - 1] - y[0])) / b;
    f[i] = (x[npoints - 1] * y[i] -
            x[0] * y[i + 1] -
            scale[i] *
            (x[npoints - 1] * y[0] -
            x[0] * y[npoints - 1])) / b;
}

/* Print the raw data and the codes
   for the resulting curve */

printf("%s  %d points, "
       "graph scale = %6.2f x %6.2f  Dimension = %f",
       filename, npoints, xgrid, ygrid, dim);
printf("\nx =");
for (i = 0; i < npoints; i++) printf(" %6.2f", x[i]);
printf("\ny =");
for (i = 0; i < npoints; i++) printf(" %6.2f", y[i]);
printf("\ns =");
for (i = 0; i < npoints - 1; i++) printf(" %6.2f",
                                          scale[i]);
printf("\na =");
for (i = 0; i < npoints - 1; i++) printf(" %6.2f", a[i]);
printf("\nc =");
```

continues

Listing 2.2. continued

```c
for (i = 0; i < npoints - 1; i++) printf(" %6.2f", c[i]);
printf("\ne =");
for (i = 0; i < npoints - 1; i++) printf(" %6.2f", e[i]);
printf("\nf =");
for (i = 0; i < npoints - 1; i++) printf(" %6.2f", f[i]);

/* display a reference grid */
setcolor(gridclr);
xgrid = xgrid * xscale;  ygrid *= yscale;
for (x1 = (float) xoffset; x1 < scrnx; x1 += xgrid)
    drawline((int) x1, scrny / 2 - yadjust * 2,
             (int) x1, scrny - 1);
for (y1 = (float) yoffset;
     y1 >= (float) scrny / 2 - yadjust * 2;
     y1 -= ygrid)
    drawline(0, (int) y1, scrnx - 1, (int) y1);

/* plot the points themselves as small squares */

for (i = 0; i < npoints; i++)
{   x1 = x[i] * xscale + xoffset;
    y1 = yoffset - y[i] * yscale;
    fillrect((int) x1 - 2, (int) y1 - 2,
             (int) x1 + 2, (int) y1 + 2, pointclr);
}

/* put the curve on the screen */

x1 = (float) xoffset;                    /* start at origin */
y1 = (float) yoffset;
while(!kbhit())               /* keep going until key hit */
{   j = rand() % (npoints - 1);         /* use chaos game */
    x2 = a[j] * x1 + e[j];         /* to display attractor */
    y2 = c[j] * x1 + scale[j] * y1 + f[j];
    x1 = x2, y1 = y2;
    putpixel((int) (x1 * xscale + xoffset),
             (int) (yoffset - y1 * yscale), drawclr);
}
```

```
      /* clear the keypress, go back to text mode, and quit */
      getch();
      settextmode();
      closedown();
}
```

Current Applications of Fractals and Chaos

…there have always been large tracts of science where…simple analytic methods hardly applied. The natural phenomena were just too complex. Over them people waved their hands in frustration and made qualitative theories, or grossly approximate theories or no theories at all. It is in these realms that fractals are finding application after application.
— D.E. Thomsen, *Science News*, 1987

You've seen some of the advantages of using fractal geometry to model both the appearance and behavior of real world systems:

- Fractals can easily represent similar forces acting on many levels of scale, whereas linear geometry cannot.

- Fractals often provide a more compact method of recording complex images and data than linear vectors.

- You can automatically find a fractal curve that fits any set of data.

- With fractals, roughness or irregularity are an essential part of the model rather than noise to be discarded.

- You can use fractals to construct useful models of inherently unpredictable and chaotic systems, whereas linear equations fail entirely.

Because of these advantages, people are using fractals extensively in diverse disciplines, from ornithology to cardiology. Unfortunately, a detailed discussion of nearly every subject known to man is beyond the scope of this book. I can, however, highlight a few of the areas where fractals have proved particularly valuable.

You'll probably find at least one book listed in Appendix C that specifically discusses applying fractals, nonlinear dynamics, and chaos theory to your particular field. Whatever your specialty, you may soon join the increasing number of people who are finding that lines don't quite work in their line of work.

Economics

Ultimately, to reliably predict the market, one needs to not only detect the building blocks or patterns of the nonlinear system but also to untangle the nonlinear meaning of the multiple interactions between successive patterns. The task is a difficult one, but the potential rewards are equally enormous.
—Victor Krynicki, "Market Prediction Through Fractal Geometry," *Technical Analysis of Stocks and Commodities,* 1992

Benoit Mandelbrot founded fractal geometry based largely on his successful simulations of commodities price trends, and market analysis remains one of the most exciting applications of fractal geometry.

The Holy Grail of all market analysts is, of course, to predict the behavior of prices with enough accuracy to get filthy rich very quickly. If anyone has captured this Grail, they're spending some of their billions guarding their secrets. In the marketplace, as in other places where fractals and chaos crop up, they seldom prove as useful for *prediction* as for *simulation*.

What's the difference? Fractal simulations (such as those made with the FORGERY program in Chapter 1 and the INTERPO program earlier in this chapter) can model and predict the general statistical nature of a system without predicting its specific behavior at any given moment in time. For example, Mandelbrot's 1953 simulations of cotton pricing continue to accurately predict the amount of variation in the price of cotton, both monthly and yearly. They do not, however, even pretend to tell us the cost of cotton in July, 1995.

One of the major revelations of fractal market analysis is *memory* or *persistence* in the market. Traditional economic models usually assume a consumer or investor who lives totally in the moment, like a Zen monk of the marketplace. This idealized person makes purchasing and selling decisions based completely on the current market prices and a perfectly rational desire to maximize his profits at every given moment. When the price is low, our ultra-intellectual Bhudda broker buys big. When prices rise, he sells exactly as much as probability theory dictates. He has no recollection of how he lost his house and car when PanAm went bankrupt after he bought a million shares. He forgot all about the time when he bought Microsoft at a high price and made enough to retire on in two months. This model man has no memory, and neither does his model market. When attempting to predict tomorrow's pricing, the model only uses today's data.

Fractal analysis has shown conclusively that any model based on such assumptions will be grossly inaccurate. Not only does the market show both long term and short term memory, it shows persistence on every possible scale, from hours to centuries. The real participant in the economy apparently remembers not only the time when he lost his shirt, but the time when Grandad lost the farm.

If you decide to try modeling the stock market with the INTERPO program presented earlier, you won't be alone. Several cutting-edge investment analysts are using *iterated function systems* to develop a language of patterns so that they can understand the movements of economic indices. They are finding that certain fractal patterns often appear just before changes in the marketplace. By modeling these patterns and learning how to interpret them, they are polishing a new mathematical lens for viewing market data (see Figure 2.29).

Bowing humbly to those who venture bravely into the arena of economic forecasting, I won't guarantee that "you can do it" on this one. (In a crowd, I'll pass for a scientist or mathematician; investment advisor I ain't.) When you take your newfound knowledge of fractals to the exchange and hit it big, just remember your good buddy Dick who taught you everything you know.

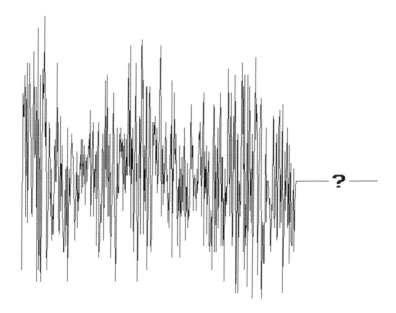

Figure 2.29. You can search for patterns in economic data using the techniques described earlier for climate data.

Astronomy

The old problem of the stability of the solar system is still unsolved. Around 1800 stability was thought to be proven…. Today we have to admit that a prognosis about the long-time behavior of the solar system (even when we restrict the problem to gravitational interactions) is not possible: the equations are "not integrable," as the expert says. A very small imprecision in the initial conditions can grow to an enormous effect in the later motion. Both the expert and the layman are confused by the complexity in what we thought to be simple equations.

—H.O. Peitgen, *The Beauty of Fractals*, 1986

One of the first and most famous mathematical fractals was invented by an astronomer. In the early 1960s, Michel Henon of the Nice Observatory in France noticed disturbing behavior in a simple model of stars orbiting within a galaxy. Some of the orbits were smooth and stable, while others seemed nearly random. At first, he and his colleagues simply ignored anomalous orbits, assuming they occurred due to some unexplained error in the computations.

Henon eventually discovered that this sort of *chaotic* behavior was an essential part of the dynamics of stellar orbits. After studying models developed to explain the turbulent behavior of earthly phenomena, he developed a similar model to explain planetary orbits.

Though the term was not in use at the time, we now call the type of models that Henon used *strange attractors.* (You'll learn more about strange attractors in the following section on climatology.)

The shapes of Henon's orbits are not the classical Newtonian ellipses that astronomers have used for centuries. If one planet did orbit one star in an otherwise empty universe, the linear curves of Newton and Kepler would accurately model its path through space. In the real universe, though, gravitational attractions from other planets and stars make a planet's orbit much less predictable.

Henon's models (see Figure 2.30) suggested that stellar and planetary orbits might be nonperiodic and extremely sensitive to even the smallest gravitational influences. Unlike classical linear models, which seemed capable of predicting the exact paths of heavenly bodies for all eternity, strange attractors offer a bizarre mix of uncertain behaviors. Orbits may remain essentially stable for eons and then suddenly change course or even break off into a new region of space.

While the old models retain their predictive power for the relatively near future, recent research has confirmed that the long-term behavior of our solar system is uncertain at best. Astronomers are no longer even sure how long our own planet's orbit will remain stable. (Don't pack your bags and call NASA just yet. They *are* reasonably sure Earth's orbit isn't going to fall apart for at least a few million years.)

Figure 2.30. Close-up of Henon's attractor.

You Can Do It: The Henon Attractor

What's so *strange* about Henon's *attractor*? With FRACTINT software, you can see for yourself. (FRACTINT may not be a free lunch, but it is a nearly free buffet smorgasboard of fractal goodies—see the Introduction for an invitation to the feast.)

continues

1. Start FRACTINT and choose a high-resolution video mode. The number of colors is not important for viewing this fractal.

2. Press T to choose a fractal **Type**.

3. Select **henon** by typing he and pressing Enter.

The formula for the Henon attractor is displayed on the bottom part of the screen, and you are given the chance to specify values for a and b to plug into the equations.

4. Just press Enter to accept the default values for a and b.

The image that appears is not a realistic visual representation of a planetary orbit, but it does capture many characteristics of real orbits. Zoom in for a closer look:

5. Hold down the left mouse button and move the mouse up until the **zoom box** is about one-third the size of the screen. (You can use the Page Up key to zoom if you don't have a mouse.)

6. Release the left button and move the mouse so that the zoom box is over the top center part of the curve. If you don't do mice, use the arrow keys.

7. Double-click the left mouse button or press Enter to zoom.

As you move in closer, the image takes longer to appear. The dots don't move along the orbits; they jump in seemingly random order all over the *attractor* until they eventually reveal its shape. Visually, this resembles the random spray of FractalVision's **Paint** command. Here, however, no randomness is involved. The deterministic equations are hopping around in their own strange rhythm over the fractal. No one has found a way to predict how close together successive points will fall.

8. Zoom in again on the upper set of lines.

Notice how orbital paths are clumped: any particular path always has other paths close to it, sort of close to it, far away from it, and very far away from it. What looks like a single orbit becomes many clumped orbits at a higher magnification. Even if you zoomed in a thousand times, you'd always see distinct and separate paths. These nearby orbital paths may travel in different directions later. Because the paths are so close together, only an impossibly precise measurement of a celestial body's position could predict its long term course.

Meteorology

Everybody talks about the weather, but nobody does anything about it.
—Charles D. Warner, 1890

Meteorologists and economists have a lot in common. Both have spent mind-boggling amounts of effort, money, and energy trying to predict what will happen tomorrow and next week. Both have installed worldwide computer networks to gather and process up-to-the-second information. Both groups make hundreds of thousands of predictions daily, employing well-accepted theories based on centuries of thought and research.

Both have fallen flat on their faces. Weather forecasting, like economic forecasting, is notorious for its inaccuracy. Every day, billions of dollars worth of human labor and computer equipment conspire to predict the weather at every point on the globe for the upcoming week. Statistically, their predictions for six days from now will probably be no more accurate than your best guess made by holding up a wet finger and squinting at the sky.

Fractals have helped a little in the weather prediction game. They have helped a lot in explaining why it isn't working.

Edward Lorenz, a meteorologist at MIT, made it into the history books by discovering the *Butterfly Effect* in 1961. He was simulating weather on his computer when he decided to try an interesting sequence over again from the middle. His model used only a few variables, the values of which completely determined how the artificial weather would evolve. So, he typed the numbers from midway through a previous printout to watch the same weather play itself out again. As expected, the same pattern began to unfold on the printouts. But then the pattern began to change. Before long, the simulated weather was completely different than before (see Figure 2.31).

Lorenz assumed there had been some error, either when he had typed the numbers or when the (somewhat unreliable) computer had carried out the calculations. When he checked all the work, however, he found only one possible source of the "errors." Internally, the computer's calculations were accurate to the sixth decimal place, but the printouts only included four digits after the decimal point. By typing his data at only four-digit accuracy, Lorenz had introduced a tiny difference between the first and second run.

He concluded that excruciatingly tiny perturbations in the data quickly compounded into a huge difference in the weather. If Lorenz' model resembled the real world at all, a miniscule influence such as a butterfly flapping its wings in the Amazon could drastically alter next week's weather in Massachusetts. So, if you hope to predict the weather at MIT, you'd better measure every butterfly in Brazil.

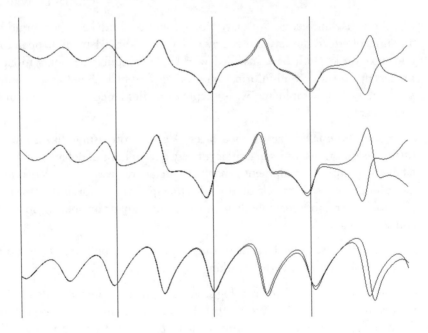

Figure 2.31. Two three-variable systems begin nearly identical paths, but quickly fall out of sync. Each of the three curves splits into two paths: one path had the initial starting value of 1.0000, and the other had the initial value of 1.0001.

As it turns out, Lorenz' model resembled not only real-world weather, but a host of other real-world phenomena, too. The Butterfly Effect, properly known as *sensitive dependence on initial conditions*, is a common property of complex natural and social systems.

Lorenz went on to develop both simpler and more complex models that displayed sensitive dependence on initial conditions. His most well-known set of equations is the *Lorenz attractor*, a three-variable system that models turbulence in a fluid flow. You'll explore these equations in the **You Can Do It** and **For Programmers Only** boxes that follow.

You Can Do It: The Butterfly Effect

You can look over Lorenz' shoulder as his weather patterns defy prediction, using the LORENZ program listed in the **For Programmers Only** box that follows. The LORENZ.EXE file is included, so you don't need to be a programmer to see the action.

1. From the DOS prompt (or using your favorite DOS shell, if you like), run the LORENZ program. A short note about it appears.

2. Press any key to start the display.

The three wavy curves that flow across the screen could represent environmental variables, such as wind speed, cloud cover, or humidity. They could also represent the internal workings of a layer of fluid having constant depth and a constant temperature difference between the top and bottom of the layer.

You are actually seeing two nearly identical systems evolve beside one another. The green curve starts with an initial value of 1.0001 for each of the variables, whereas the red curve (almost completely hidden behind the green curve) starts with values of exactly 1.0000.

So far, so good: the curves deviate only a tiny bit from one another by the end of the first screen, representing a few minutes of system time.

3. Now press any key again to see the system continue where it left off. This time, the red curves deviate wildly from the green, reaching opposite values by the end of the screen.

continues

If this were a weather prediction program, our barometer and wind meters would need to be accurate to one part in ten thousand to differentiate between the green curve (which reads 100 percent humidity around the end of the screen) and the red (which reads near 0 percent humidity at the same time). As it turns out, even with accuracy to one part in ten million, the curves would still diverge fairly rapidly.

4. As long as you keep pressing a key, this complex dance continues. From then on, if the two systems coincide, it's a coincidence.

Our atmosphere harbors considerably more complexity than this three-variable system. The moral of the story is: If your weatherman is wrong 40 percent of the time, praise him for the great job he's doing. If he's right 90 percent of the time, he is talking to God and not the National Weather Bureau's central computer.

5. Press the Esc key to quit.

For Programmers Only: The Lorenz Attractor

Complex, chaotic behavior and sensitive dependence on initial conditions arise in very simple nonlinear systems. The Butterfly Effect comes from just three equations:

$$\frac{dx}{dt} = a(y - x)$$

$$\frac{dy}{dt} = bx - y - zx$$

$$\frac{dz}{dt} = xy - cz$$

Where x, y, and z are the variables to be observed, and a, b, and c are constants.

The values used for a, b, and c in this program are 5, 15, and 1, but you can experiment with different values. To compare the behavior of different constants, start x1, y1, and z1 exactly equal to x3, y3, and z3, but make a1, b1, and c1 different from a2, b2, and c2. (Hint: The systems behave very differently if c1=3.5 and c2=3.6, when a1=a2=5 and b1=b2=15. What happens if c1=3.54 and c2=3.56?)

Listing 2.3. LORENZ.C A program that simulates changes in weather.

```
/* LORENZ.C
 *
 * This program simulates a vastly oversimplified model
 * of weather changes, based on turbulent fluid flow
 * in a single convection cell. It runs two nearly identical
 * simulations next to each other. Three variables start out
 * almost exactly the same, yet diverge quickly.
 */

#include <stdio.h>        /* Standard input/output libraries */
#include <stdlib.h>

#define MAIN              /* See Appendix D for compile */
#include "fv.h"           /* instructions and header files */

#define ESC 27            /* The Escape key code */
#define xclr1 4           /* Colors to draw x, y, and z */
#define yclr1 4
#define zclr1 4
#define xclr2 2
#define yclr2 2
#define zclr2 2
#define gridclr 1         /* Color for the guide lines */

void main(void)
{   int vidmode, i;       /* video mode and a counter */
    float a1 = 5, b1 = 15, c1 = 1,  /* constants  for first */
          a2 = 5, b2 = 15, c2 = 1,  /* and second model */
```

continues

Listing 2.3. continued

```
        dt = 0.02,                  /* time step */
        x1 = 1.0000, y1 = 1.0000, z1 = 1.0000, /* model 1 */
        x2, y2, z2,
        x3 = 1.0001, y3 = 1.0001, z3 = 1.0001, /* model 2 */
        x4, y4, z4,
        scale;      /* vertical scaling factor for display */
int xoffset, yoffset, zoffset;   /* placement on screen */
vidmode = pickmode(detectmode()); /* confirm video mode */

printf("\n\nThis program demonstrates the "
       "Butterfly Effect, sensitive dependance\n");
printf("on initial conditions.  We will run "
       "two simultaneaous dynamical models,\n");
printf("identical except that one starts with "
       "initial values of 1.0000 and the\n");
printf("other starts with initial values of 1.0001.  "
       "When each screen is done,\n");
printf("press any key to continue watching the "
       "system evolve.  Hit Esc to quit.\n");
if (getch() == ESC) exit(0);

if (setvidmode(vidmode, 1) != 1)
{   printf("\nUnable to set graphics mode.\n");
    exit(0);
}

scale = scrny / 80;         /* scale and place on screen */
xoffset = scrny / 4 - 40;
yoffset = scrny / 2;
zoffset = scrny * .75 - 40;

do                          /* loop until user hits escape */
{   clearscreen();    /* clear screen, draw guide lines */
    setcolor(gridclr);
    for (i = 0; i < scrnx; i += 80)
        drawline(i, 0, i, scrny - 1);
    for (i = 0; i < scrnx; i++)  /* sweep across screen */
    {   x2 = x1 - (a1 * x1 * dt) + (a1 * y1 * dt);
        y2 = y1 + (b1 * x1 * dt) -
```

```
                        (y1 * dt) - (z1 * x1 * dt);
            z2 = z1 - (c1 * z1 * dt) + (x1 * y1 * dt);
            setcolor(xclr1);            /* display model 1 */
            drawline(i - 1, x1 * scale + xoffset,
                    i, x2 * scale + xoffset);
            setcolor(yclr1);
            drawline(i - 1, y1 * scale + yoffset,
                    i, y2 * scale + yoffset);
            setcolor(zclr1);
            drawline(i - 1, z1 * scale + zoffset,
                    i, z2 * scale + zoffset);
            x1 = x2; y1 = y2; z1 = z2;

            x4 = x3 - (a2 * x3 * dt) + (a2 * y3 * dt);
            y4 = y3 + (b2 * x3 * dt) -
                    (y3 * dt) - (z3 * x3 * dt);
            z4 = z3 - (c2 * z3 * dt) + (x3 * y3 * dt);
            setcolor(xclr2);            /* display model 2 */
            drawline(i - 1, x3 * scale + xoffset,
                    i, x4 * scale + xoffset);
            setcolor(yclr2);
            drawline(i - 1, y3 * scale + yoffset,
                    i, y4 * scale + yoffset);
            setcolor(zclr2);
            drawline(i - 1, z3 * scale + zoffset,
                    i, z4 * scale + zoffset);
            x3 = x4; y3 = y4; z3 = z4;
        }
    } while(getch() != ESC);   /* key press between screens */
    settextmode();
    closedown();          /* close down the graphics and quit */
}
```

Unlike the other phenomena I've examined in this book, Lorenz' dynamical systems look like smooth curves. Is the *Lorenz attractor* really a fractal? Mathematicians debate the issue, but all agree that it does display the hallmark of fractal geometry: complex detail under infinite magnification.

To show this complex detail, Lorenz plotted the three variables of his attractor as if they were x, y, z coordinates in physical space. Even though that isn't what they represent, the resulting abstract motion picture offers a compelling image of chaotic dynamics in action (Figure 2.32).

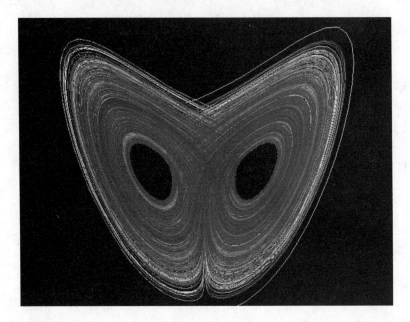

Figure 2.32. The Lorenz attractor, plotted as a shape in 3-D space. The orbiting lines represent the motion of a 3-D point over time.

Set in motion, the Lorenz attractor streaks through space, orbiting two invisible "black holes." It jumps from one orbit to the other in an unpredictable dance, now zipping in close to the left, now swinging wide around the right.

A closer look (Figure 2.33) seems to reveal paths on which the two orbits coincide for a while, and then take off in separate directions again. In truth, the orbit never follows precisely the same path twice. It will pass immeasurably close to a previous path, just as Lorenz brought his second run immeasurably close to his first. Soon, however, the tiny difference in trajectory will compound into a major difference. Consequently, two trajectories that look identical at one moment will be orbiting different centers a few moments later.

So, no matter how much you magnify the curve, it will always reveal complex (read: fractal) detail as infinitely many orbit lines narrowly avoid one another. The very quality that makes the curve chaotic, sensitive dependence on initial conditions, also makes it a fractal.

Figure 2.33. At any magnification, the orbital paths will still appear to touch. They actually miss one another by an imperceptible margin.

You Can Do It: The Lorenz Attractor Revisited

The LORENZ program presented earlier in this chapter is a realistic model of turbulence. If you have FRACTINT (which the introduction tells you how to get), you can see the Lorenz attractor projected into 3-D space.

1. Start FRACTINT and choose a high resolution video mode. The number of colors doesn't much matter.

continues

2. Press T and choose the fractal type **lorenz**. Press Enter to accept the default parameters.

3. Use the zoom box (Page Up or mouse) to dive in close. Notice how the lines are no further apart than they were before.

4. If you want to make this a real multimedia experience, press X, go down to **Sound**, and choose either x, y, or z. This will make a squeaky noise that varies in tone as the point orbits.

With the pair of red/blue 3-D glasses included with this book, you can see the attractor in true 3-D stereo vision:

5. Press I, go to the last parameter (Stereo), and enter 2 (**superimpose**). Then press Enter, press T, and choose the **lorenz3D** type.

Finally, for you programmers who tried changing the c constant in the LORENZ program, you might like to see what those changes would look like in space-time:

6. Press T and choose the **lorenz** type again. This time, enter 3.5 for the c parameter, leaving a and b unchanged. Try 3.6, 3.54, and 3.55 for c. How about 3.541229 vs. 3.541230?

Fluid Dynamics and Chemistry

Big whorls have little whorls
Which feed on their velocity
And little whorls have lesser whorls
And so on to viscosity
        —Lewis F. Richardson, *Weather Prediction by Numerical Process*, 1922

Turbulence, a scourge to scientists for decades, is that marvelous complex waviness that makes marbled paper so pretty. From an analytical perspective, it isn't pretty at all. It stubbornly resists all linear approximation and sucks down supercomputer time like Kool-Aid. You can look at the behavior of Lorenz' weather systems as an attempt to answer a question about turbulence: If a leaf floats into a turbulent cascade (or flies into a turbulent storm), can we predict where it will come out? As you may have guessed, we can't (but at least we know why we can't!).

More accurately, the Lorenz attractor is a realistic model of the turbulent "weather" in a tiny closed cylinder of fluid as heat is continually applied to the bottom of the cylinder. The three variables actually correspond to the velocity of the fluid, the temperature, and the rate of temperature change.

Lorenz pioneered the exploration of nonlinear analysis of fluids, but his attractor was only the tip of the fractal iceberg. From the turbulent realm of fluid dynamics to the rigid order of crystals, fractal modeling is the rule rather than the exception in many branches of materials science and chemistry.

One powerful technique for simulating many different physical, chemical, and electrical phenomena is *diffusion limited aggregation*. At the beginning of the computer simulation, one small bit of artificial matter is placed in the center of a circle. The computer then launches thousands of particles one by one from random points around the circle. These particles wander from their launching points at random until they either stumble outside the circle or encounter another bit of matter, where they stick. Gradually, fractal dendrites crystallize outward as virtual particles accumulate (Figure 2.34).

Figure 2.34. Fractal dendrites formed through diffusion limited aggregation.

The physical processes that form shapes nearly identical to Figure 2.34 include soot aggregation in chimneys, zinc deposition in electrolytic cells, diffusion of gas bubbles through viscous liquids, and electrical discharge in air. Why do these diverse phenomena all look the same, and why are they fractals? Is their actual mechanism of formation similar to the procedure used in the computer simulation? Why do loops rarely form? In the words of Leonard Sander of Exxon Research and Engineering, "Answers to these questions remain at large, and they pose a remarkable problem to the theoretical physicist because none of the ordinary mathematical tools seems to work when applied to them."

We do know that all these systems are far from *equilibrium*, meaning that they are receiving and dissipating significant amounts of energy. In most cases, the dendritic structure forms rapidly from the inside out, in contrast to the slow inward wander of the computer's artificial particles. Like the inflow of simulated particles, however, the outgoing stream of matter or energy is attracted to the tips of each branch as it forms. The computer simulation apparently turns the real-world phenomena inside out.

Because diffusion limited aggregation shapes are fractal, they possess unique scaling properties. Unlike amorphous blobs or regular crystals, they become less dense as they increase in size. Because of this, the speed of chemical reactions that occur on a fractal cluster vary over time, whereas similar reactions in free space occur at a constant rate.

Creeping aggregations and turbulent motion are not the only strange behaviors that appear when systems are far from equilibrium. In the next section, you'll find that even more exotic forms of geometric order can arise.

You Can Do It: Diffusion Limited Aggregation

Even if you're short on zinc electrolytic cells or high voltage electrical discharge apparatus, you can still explore the intricate branching patterns they produce.

1. Start up FRACTINT (see the introduction for how to bring FRACTINT into your life cheaply and easily) and choose a low resolution video mode. Diffusion limited aggregation takes a long time, and fewer pixels on-screen will speed it up significantly.

2. Press T and select the **diffusion** fractal type.

FRACTINT will prompt you for the **Border size**. This parameter controls the size of the circle around which particles wander. Larger numbers produce more intricate patterns, but also run much slower. I recommend dividing the speed of your computer (in Mhz) by two and Entering the result as a border size. If you have a 10 Mhz 286, enter 5. If you have a 33 Mhz 486, enter 16. You get the idea.

3. Sit back and watch it grow. You can watch the individual particles wander around by pressing O to turn on the visible Orbits option.

Physics

Our physical world is no longer symbolized by the stable and periodic planetary motions that are at the heart of classical mechanics. It is a world of instabilities and fluctuations, which are ultimately responsible for the amazing variety and richness of the forms and structures we see in nature around us. New concepts and new tools are clearly necessary to describe nature, in which evolution and pluralism become the key words.

—Grégoire Nicolis, *Exploring Complexity*, 1989

Can time flow backwards? According to the linear equations that have ruled physics for the last 200 years, the answer is usually yes. According to the new science of complexity, the answer is usually no.

Imagine that you are ten years old again, swinging on a swingset. If you get one big push and then just enjoy the ride without moving your legs, your path can be described by a simple set of linear equations. Furthermore, any physicist who happened by to measure your position and velocity with some handy lab equipment could easily compute your position and velocity at any earlier or later time. You wouldn't mind if he neglected air resistance would you? I didn't think so.

A simple pendulum (like a lazy kid on a swing) is a *time reversible* system: the state of the system at any given moment will tell you the state of the system in the past as easily as the future. If time flowed backward, it wouldn't make any difference to the physicist (at 10, you might be anxious to grow up, but the physicist would probably enjoy getting a little younger). He could still predict both past and future.

Now imagine that you start swinging your feet to make yourself go higher. Being somewhat uncoordinated, your pushes proceed according to your own inner rhythm and don't quite match that of the swinging. All of a sudden, the physicist turns grey. Despite his fancy lab equipment, he can no longer find a linear set of equations to describe your path. Instead of swaying rhythmically, you wobble back and forth through periods of stability and instability, occasionally flying upward like a rocket when your push coincides with some complex combination of velocity and inertia in the rope and swing.

Your path could be modeled with a chaotic fractal attractor, but the physicist is rather old-fashioned. He says you're wasting his time and threatens to go measure the parabolic trajectories of the kids playing baseball if you don't start playing fair.

So, you concede to stop pushing, but insist on principle that he stop neglecting air resistance. Fine, he says, and graphs a lovely damped sine wave, tapering off to a line as you coast to rest. Can time still flow backwards? No.

You're sitting at rest on the swing, chewing your bubble gum, and you ask the physicist to tell you your position at t=−1 minute. He can't do it, because any number of possible paths would all result in you being at rest due to air resistance. He can now predict your future, but not your past. Time has suddenly taken on a favorite direction.

Finally, you challenge the physicist to account for air resistance while you push yourself on the swing. He just gets mad and stomps off.

You and your physicist friend have seen four fundamental classes of physical systems: *conservative linear systems* (a frictionless pendulum swinging free, Figure 2.36), *conservative nonlinear systems* (a frictionless pushed pendulum), *dissipative linear systems*, (a free swinging pendulum in a resistive atmosphere), and *dissipative nonlinear systems* (a pushed pendulum in a resistive atmosphere, Figure 2.35).

Like most physicists of the old school, your chum loved working with conservative linear systems, where everything is predictable both forward and backward in time. Dissipative linear systems are considered a degraded special case—who cares about predicting the past anyway? Nonlinear systems are weird and, therefore, shouldn't matter. Nonlinear dissipative systems are just plain hopeless.

These attitudes of the old school are quickly giving way to a new school that recognizes that the real world consists of dissipative nonlinear systems. Real kids push their swings with less than perfect rhythm, and both their atmosphere and swingsets produce friction.

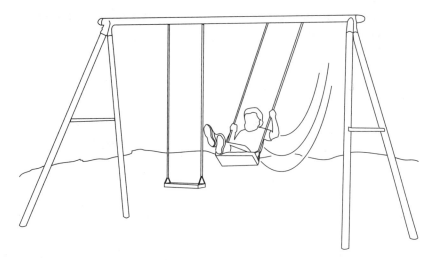

Figure 2.35. A dissipative nonlinear system (a pushed pendulum in a resistive atmosphere).

The archetypal dissipative system is a cold tank full of water in a warm room: the water gets warmer and the room gets colder until they reach equilibrium. This process is in gracious accord with the good old second law of thermodynamics: entropy, or disorder, increases as the system becomes less organized and more homogeneous.

We are now finding, however, that the second law of thermodynamics has a flip side: many natural systems are *self-organizing* and create order spontaneously where no order previously existed. As with the aggregating chemical reactions and electrical discharges discussed previously, we can create spontaneous complex order by pumping in energy and holding the system far from equilibrium.

If you applied increasing heat to the bottom of the fish tank, the temperature in the tank would at first vary smoothly from hot at the bottom to cool at the top. As you turned up the heater, however, the system would reach a *critical* point where regular cells of rotating water, called Bénard cells, would form (Figure 2.37). These cells represent organization on a macroscopic scale, suddenly popping up in a system where only microscopic variations existed before.

To thicken the plot, these cells show the same kind of unpredictability as Lorenz' weather and Henon's stellar orbits. Any particular cell may be rotating clockwise or counterclockwise. Each will always be spinning in the opposite direction of its neighbors, so the system can fall into one of the two states in Figure 2.37. The actual selection of one state over another displays, you guessed it, sensitive dependence on initial conditions.

Figure 2.36. A conservative linear system (a frictionless pendulum swinging free).

Like the child at rest on a swing, the system has "forgotten" its past and fallen into a stable state. But wait—it hasn't quite forgotten. The very fact that it is in state A rather than state B is a memory of some tiny perturbation that made it decide which one to settle into. Here, though, the system has become spontaneously more complex rather than less complex.

Other self-organizing systems include certain chemical reactions, electrical circuits, and geological materials. The most interesting self-organizing systems are biological organisms, which continually evolve toward higher organizational complexity.

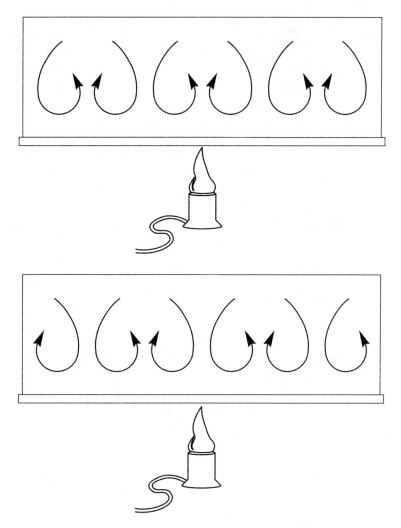

Figure 2.37. Bénard heat convection cells can rotate in one of two possible states.

Turn up the heat under our aquarium some more, and after another critical point in time, the system falls into that crazy random fractalization called turbulence. Physicists now understand that an entire spectrum of complex behaviors, some chaotic, some highly regular, arise in what was previously called *chaos.* Many other physical and chemical systems progress through a similar series of radical behavior changes, fluctuating from linear order to chaotic complexity and back again. Figure 2.38 shows a typical illustration of modern physics at work. Perhaps you'd better show these to your friend back at the playground.

153

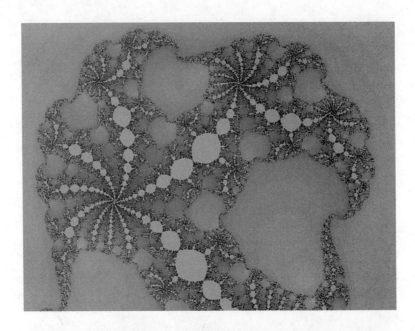

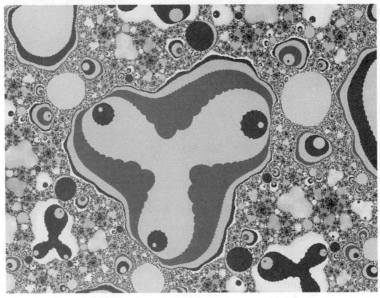

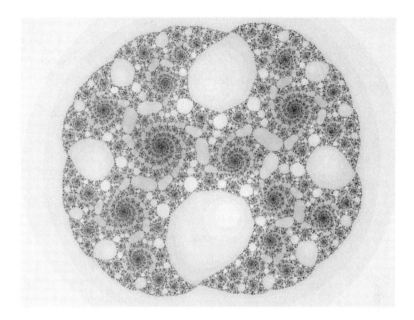

Figure 2.38. Phase transition boundaries of a ferromagnetic material from magnetic to nonmagnetic states.

You Can Do It: Magnetism Fractals

The magnetism fractal types in FRACTINT are some of the most visually stunning and complex images you'll ever see on your computer screen. They were discovered by Yang and Lee, two physicists researching the phase transitions of ferromagnetic substances from a magnetic to a nonmagnetic state.

(Don't have FRACTINT yet? Repeat the following mantra: "FRACTINT is free. FRACTINT is easy to get. I will like FRACTINT. I must get FRACTINT. FRACTINT is free. FRACTINT is easy to get. I will like FRACTINT. I must get FRACTINT...." Now turn to the Introduction and immediately follow the instructions for acquiring FRACTINT.)

continues

1. Start FRACTINT and choose the best 256-color video mode you've got. (EGA folks, choose a 2-color mode. With these fractals, you either want lots of color or no color at all.)

2. Press T and choose the **magnet1m** fractal type.

3. Just leave all the parameters at zero for now. For later reference, the **Real and Imaginary Perturbations** will skew and rearrange the set in weird ways. Press Enter to start generating.

Aside from being an infinitely detailed landscape of strange boundaries, this set is actually a map of infinitely many other sets. A map of sets like this is called a *Mandelbrot Set* (not to be confused with *THE Mandelbrot Set*), and the sets of which it is a map are called its *Julia Sets*. You'll learn more about this business of infinite maps in Chapter 5.

For casual exploration, you only need to know that when you see a part of this set that looks interesting, you can access an entire world of similar shapes by pressing the Spacebar. Try it:

4. Zoom in to any region near the edge of the big blue lake—I personally like the thin strip to the left of it. (Use Page Up and the arrow keys to zoom, and then press Enter.)

5. After this image appears (or sooner, if it you have a slow computer and don't want to wait), press the spacebar to see the Julia Set corresponding to the point in the middle of the screen.

You can imagine that by pressing the spacebar, you are zooming infinitely far into the set to see what a single point on it looks like up close. Quite an interesting looking "point"!

6. Zoom once more into part of this Julia Set. Unless you've picked an unusually boring region, you'll find intricate spiraling bubbles and other weird stuff.

(As you probably noticed, these fractals take a good long time to appear, unless you have an extraordinarily fast computer. While you're waiting, contemplate how important quick computers are to cutting-edge science. While you're still waiting, contemplate how fast your next computer is going to be when you buy it.)

Yang and Lee were rather surprised to find this kind of complexity lurking at the boundaries of an innocent little magnetic renormalization transformation.

7. Don't forget to press + or - to color cycle and touch the Enter key a few times. Try some of the Ctrl+function key combinations.

The new cross-disciplinary *science of complexity* has heralded a dawn of understanding to real-world, irreversible, self-organizing systems. Children pushing swings in the air are no longer beyond scientific understanding; such dissipative nonlinear systems contain a wealth of patterns. Fractals and chaos have supplied us with the vision to see those patterns.

The most grand application of complexity science may be deciphering the self-organization of the universe itself out of a mysterious *singularity* at the beginning of time. This *Big Bang*, suggested by the expanding motion of galaxies and the presence of a residual radiation emanating from all parts of the sky, has been both a physical and philosophical puzzle since the middle of this century. Scientists such as Ilya Prigonine of the University of Brussels have suggested that the same mechanisms that create order in living systems and heated fish tanks may be at the heart of the Big Bang. New conceptions of the production of entropy and order, time irreversibility, and chaotic instability may offer the tools to comprehend the origins of physical existence itself.

Physiology

Is it possible that mathematical pathology, i.e. chaos, is health? And that mathematical health, which is the predictability and differentiability of this kind of a structure, is disease? …When you reach an equilibrium in biology, you're dead.
— Arnold Mandell, psychiatrist (quoted by James Gleick in *Chaos*), 1986

Fractals, chaos, and complexity balance on the thin line between harmony and dissonance. They come to life and survive when rhythms fall in or out of sync. So do you. *Dynamical systems* are systems in motion, like a swingset or a chemical reaction or a turbulent fluid—or your heart and brain.

157

If your physicist friend had held back the throes of panic and taken a closer look when you started pushing the swing with your own clumsy rhythm, he might have been surprised. In the laboratory, a *pushed pendulum* shows erratic, inconstant behaviors: settling into apparent regularity only to leap suddenly into a chaotic tumult of motion and then return to near-perfect timekeeping motion. This sort of behavior is what strikes fear in the heart of physicists.

But real children on swings—even clumsy, uncoordinated ones—just don't do that. Why? What fends off chaos in this complex dynamical system? It turns out that the same mathematical guardian angel who protects children from heart attacks keeps them from flying off the swingset. Her name is *mode locking*.

Theoretically, when you give a frictionless pendulum a little push, it remembers that push forever. The perfectly rhythmic swing goes that much higher until the next *perturbation*, such as another push with your finger, comes along. As anyone who has heard "Daddy, push me *again!*" knows, real dynamical systems quickly forget perturbations and return to their original behavior.

Once again, time is showing off its arrow. If a system quickly returns to its state prior to perturbation, you cannot tell the perturbation ever happened by looking at the system. Even with an accurate mathematical model that would enable you to predict the future of the system, you still can't predict the past. Dissipative nonlinear systems are almost always *time irreversible*, and this arrow of time is what makes them capable of sustained rhythm in the face of chaos.

Mode locking is the tendency to fall back into a behavior pattern called an *attractor*, even when external perturbations knock the system off the attractor momentarily. Your heart does not remember perturbations, nor do your lungs. If they did, you'd have been dead the first time you got a shock by rubbing your feet on the carpet and touching your sister's nose. Life is rhythm.

But it's a special kind of rhythm, a rhythm where resistive friction is always dragging it toward rest and almost-coordinated pushes are always pumping it back into sync. Graphs of heartbeats and brainwaves are not smooth pulsations, but fractals with a dimension nearer to two than one. They thrive on chaos, and sicken with smoothness. When this measure of dimensional roughness falls closer to linearity, a heart attack or seizure is probably on its way.

Modern physiologists and psychiatrists are using chaos theory to diagnose *dynamical diseases* that arise when fractal rhythms fall out of sync. Schizophrenia appears to fall in this category, as do some forms epilepsy, asthma, hyperventilation, and (of course) arrhythmia. Similar fractal cycles apparently rule our hourly, daily, and monthly body rhythms as well.

Not all the body's fractals are spread out in time, however. The human lung has been cited by Benoit Mandelbrot as being "of excellent geometric design." To Mandelbrot, that means a perfect fractal. In fact, the bronchi are a special kind of superfractal: at the 15th level of detail, they change from near perfect self-similarity to almost-but-not-quite self-similar branching. By performing this fancy physiological feat, they manage to achieve a fractal dimension of 3—filling space entirely—while still leaving room for the capillaries, which also have a fractal dimension of 3.

Figure 2.39. A two-dimensional model of bronchial branching. (LUNGS).

You Can Do It: The Breath of Life

If you filled your lungs with plastic, let it harden, and dissolved all the tissue away, you'd see an amazingly dense network of fractal bronchi filling space with near-perfect regularity and efficiency. Because you probably aren't going to do that, you might like to view a simulated two-dimensional bronchial network with FractalVision.

1. Run FractalVision and **Load** the example **Template** called LUNGS.

2. Select **Draw** to watch the bronchi develop.

continues

If you wait long enough, this model will draw 15 levels of branching. Incredibly, your lungs go down several more levels than that, until the bronchi are nearly microscopic.

Like trees, lungs maintain a fixed ratio of surface area to volume. Leonardo da Vinci explained it like this: "All the branches of a tree at every stage of its height when put together are equal in thickness to the trunk [below them]." In practical terms, this means that air passing in and out of our lungs meets no greater resistance going though millions of tiny bronchial tubes than it did going through a few large ones. This geometric relationship enables us to breathe with less than infinite effort.

3. To confirm that these lungs would eventually fill space, select **Clear** and then **Paint**. The microscopic capillaries fill every bit of area not already taken up by larger bronchi.

4. Take a deep breath and get some oxygen to those brain cells.

Where has this chapter taken us? Hydrology, meteorology, botany, geology, astronomy, climatology, economics, chemistry, physics, physiology—yet, we've only sampled a few of the fields where fractals have found application. A zoologist in Rhode Island is exploring fractal flocking behavior in birds, entomologists in France are examining dynamical self-organizing behavior in insects, materials scientists are studying chaotic surface tension in Scandinavian rock formations, American geometricians are uncovering hidden patterns in the music of Bach and Mozart through fractal analysis. Fractals are not a separate field of study, but a new geometric language for describing the universe.

In Chapter 3, you'll explore a fractal model of the entire human body. You'll also take apart the fractal from Australian population biologist Robert May that gave *chaos* theory its name. Meanwhile, keep pushing that swing.

Fractals
from the Real World

Plate 1. The images on the following pages are more than pretty pictures. They are working models of nature's form and function, and the software used to create them is included with this book. You can design plants, clouds, mountains, rivers, and even galaxies by visually modeling the actual forces that form them.

Plate 2. I drew the lower shapes, and FractalVision drew the rest using my geometric "genetic code". This demonstrates how little information is actually needed to grow a richly detailed tree. Note how the maple tree and maple leaf grow from very similar genetic material, while the pine is quite different.

Plate 3. Grass going to seed

Plate 4. Ferns

Plate 5. Roots and shoots

Plate 6. Blossoming cherry
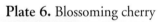

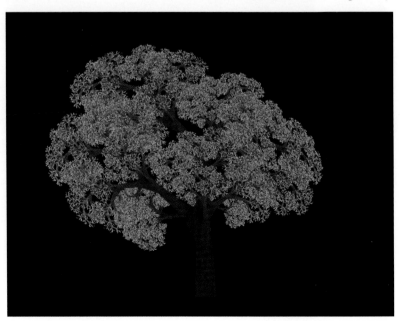

Plates 7 and 8. Self-similarity—the resemblance of each part to the whole—appears in nature when similar forces act on many levels of scale. Rivers have bends within bends, and mountains have rises and dips within peaks and valleys.

  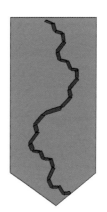 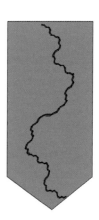

Plates 9 and 10. Most weather is made up of fractals, from snowflakes to hurricanes. To make these clouds, I sketched the movement of air masses under various conditions. Cumulus arise from warm air moving upward. When there is little vertical motion, stratus appear. High winds often produce wispy cirrus.

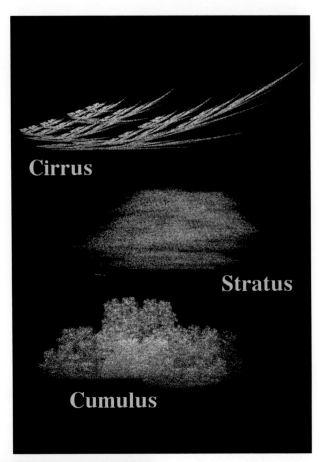

Cirrus

Stratus

Cumulus

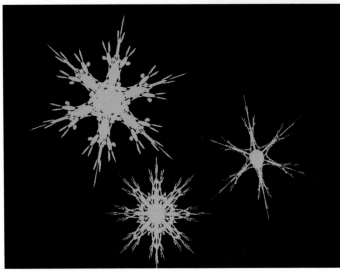

Plates 11 and 12. The fractal geometry of nature extends far beyond Earth. From the shape of continents and the chaotic orbits of stars in spiral galaxies, to galactic clusters within meta-galactic clusters, you find fractals throughout the universe.

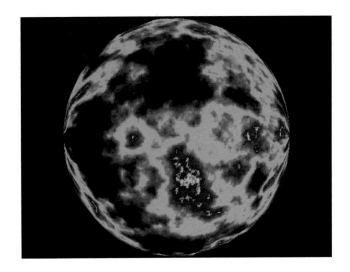

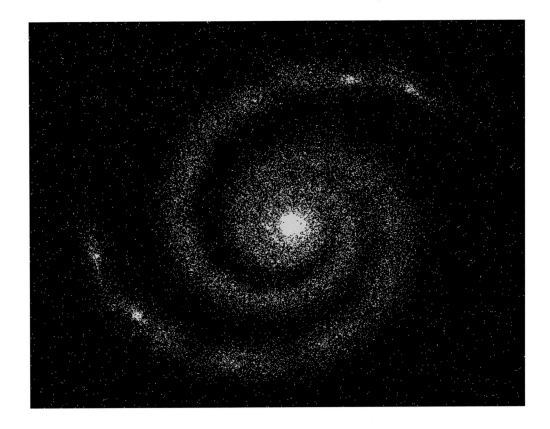

Plates 13 and 14. These models were created with a 3-D version of FractalVision and imported into Autodesk 3-D Studio for rendering.

Plates 15 and 16. Realism need not be confined to reality, as these 3-D extensions of Sierpinski's famed triangle prove.

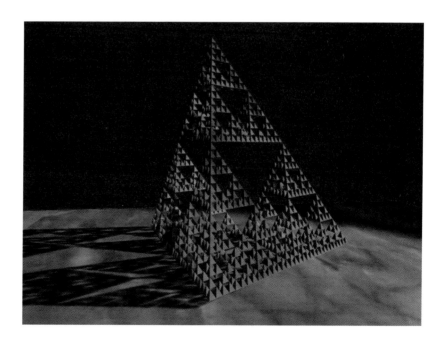

The History of Fractals and Chaos
A Nonlinear Timeline

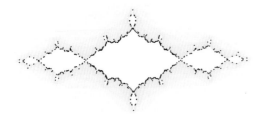

Plate 17.
Mathematicians such as Julia and Verhulst unwittingly lay the foundations of Chaos.

Plate 18.
Sierpinski, Koch, Housdorff, and others stumble into a land between dimensions.

Plate 19.
Mandelbrot finds deeply cyclic behavior in commodities prices.

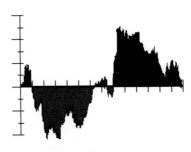

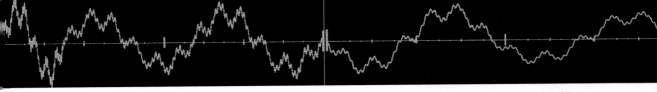

1653   1853   1953   1963

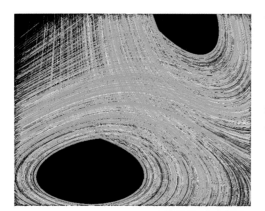

Plate 20.
Meteorologist
Lorenz discovers
*The Butterfly
Effect* in a model
of climate vari-
ability.

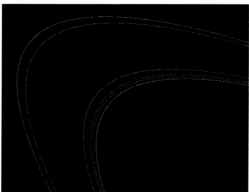

Plate 21.
Astronomer
Henon uses a
strange attractor
to explain
galactic star
orbits.

Plate 22.
Botanist
Lindenmayer
creates the first
computer-
generated plant
models.

1963   1966   1969

Plate 23. Davis and Knuth assemble a collection of *dragon curves* and *cellular automata.*

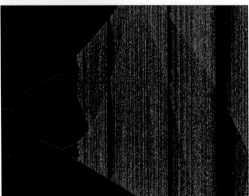

Plate 24. Biologist May explores *bifurcation* in population dynamics

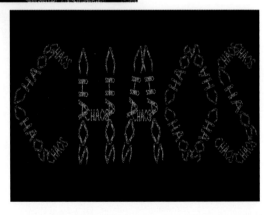

Plate 25. Yorke finds a name for the orderly disorder described by Lorenz and Smale.

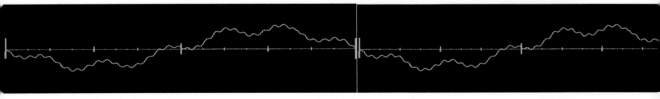

1969   1972   1975

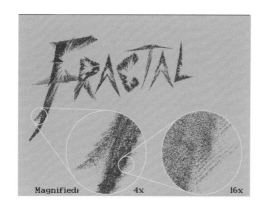

Magnified: 4x   16x

Plate 26.
Mandelbrot coins the word fractal for the geometry of nature.

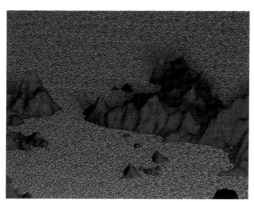

Plate 27.
Computer artist Voss models realistic mountains and coastlines.

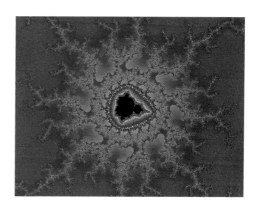

Plate 28.
Magnificent, complex beauty arises from the simple equation of the Mandelbrot Set.

1975   1978   1981

Plate 29. Hubbard and Devany use graphics to reveal fractals hidden in traditional math.

Plate 30. Barnsley develops *IFS* (Iterated Function Systems), which can represent any image with fractals.

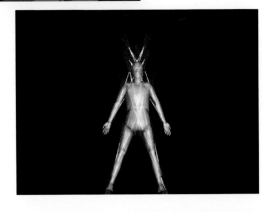

Plate 31. Human health is related to chaotic fractal rhythms in the body.

1981   1984   1987

Plate 32.
Revolutions in
chemistry,
biology, geology,
and physics
mature into a sci-
ence of
complexity.

Plate 33.
Applications of
fractals include
video image
compression
and special
effects.

Plate 34. Chaos
is found in all
branches of
science, from
animal behavior
to urban
development.

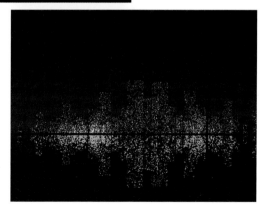

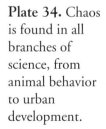

1987   1990   1993

Fractals from Unreal Worlds

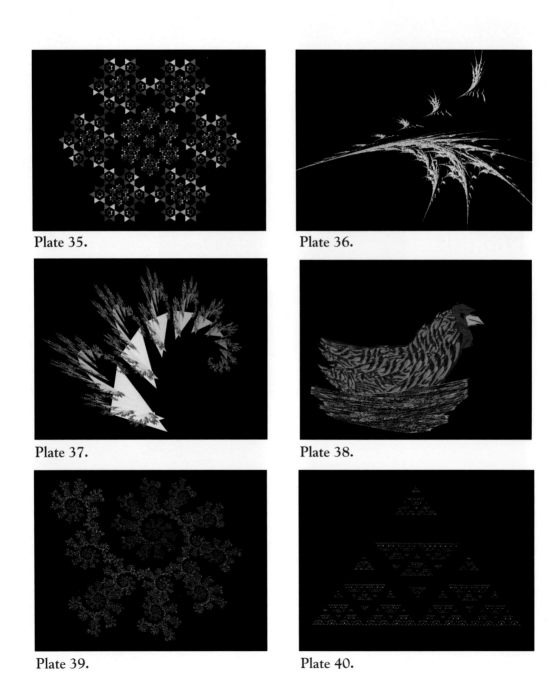

Plate 35.

Plate 36.

Plate 37.

Plate 38.

Plate 39.

Plate 40.

The Philosophy of Fractals

U ntil recently, "geometry" meant the study of abstract, simple shapes that are seldom seen in nature: lines, polygons, and perfectly smooth curves. These austere linear forms contain their own harsh lessons about the universe. Fractals, on the other hand, reveal quite another view of the structure of our world. In this chapter, you'll explore the ideas and implications behind this radical new geometry.

You'll also experience the onset of chaos and discover its true origins as well as its intimate relationship with fractals. You'll discover that "Period Three Implies Chaos" and learn how this fact may radically alter the way you see your everyday world.

Be prepared for some unfamiliar territory. Once you catch on to nonlinear thinking, some of your favorite old ideas may start to sound a bit suspect. You'll probably also find that your deepest intuitions are not as unscientific as they seem.

Keeping Control

In the mind's eye, a fractal is a way of seeing infinity.

—James Gleick, *Chaos*, 1986

Straight lines, graceful arcs, smooth curves, perfect circles, and regular polygons: these classical geometric shapes all have much in common. Even though some are not straight, they're all considered linear. Why? If you magnify the edge of any linear shape, you'll see a line (called a tangent). With nonlinear shapes like fractals, you can magnify and magnify forever, and you'll still see intricate detail (Figure 3.1).

You Can Do It: You Can See Forever...

You can zoom into the endless detail of fractals for yourself:

1. **Load** any sample template (like F-RACTAL).

2. **Paint** by pressing I or clicking the menu choice with the right mouse button. The paint continues to spray on-screen, filling in ever finer detail as it goes, until you press Esc.

3. **Clear**, then **Grow** any number of times (up to a hundred or so, where the program runs out of memory space).

4. **Paint** with I again. The enlarged shape may take quite a while to fill, but it exhibits intricate detail when it does.

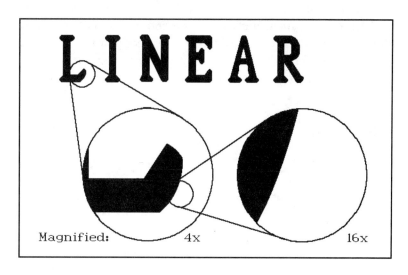

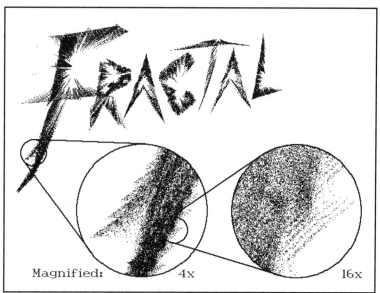

Figure 3.1. Smooth curves look like lines when magnified enough, but fractals don't (F-RACTAL).

Most of our mathematics depends on finding tangent lines and is mostly useless with nonlinear shapes. Unfortunately, the geometry of nature is mostly nonlinear. (See Chapter 2, "Fractals in the Real World" for many examples.) This in and of itself is a bit disturbing, but its implications are even more alarming.

Gaining Control

I look at mathematics pretty globally. It represents the ultimate structure and order. And I associate doing mathematics with control.
—Paul Erdös, mathematician, quoted by Paul Hoffman, "The Man Who Loves Only Numbers," *The Atlantic*, 1990

Science as we know it strives to predict and control nature. In short, scientists want to make some measurement now and use that information to predict what we'll see later. Better yet, if we can control that variable, we can control that predictable future, too.

One way to visualize this process is to draw a graph with the *measured* or *controlled variable* (the force used to push a box, for instance) on the horizontal axis. On the vertical axis, you graph the *result*, or *dependent variable* (how far the box moves). You could push harder, measure the results, and plot the relationship between these two variables. Later, you might want to move a similar box, and your graph would tell you how hard to push.

If your "Force vs. Distance" graph resembles a line or a linear curve, prediction and control are easy. You can even predict results that you didn't actually measure. For instance, you might use 5, 10, 15, and 20 lbs. of force in your experiment (Figure 3.2). If the curve were a simple line, you could easily predict how many feet you'd move the box if you push with 7.5 lbs. of force by looking halfway between the 5 and 10 lb. readings. This is called *interpolation*.

If you're really brave, you can predict the results of exerting 25 lbs. of force by extending the line (*extrapolation*). This is risky, because you're never quite sure if the line might suddenly change because of a slippery spot on the floor (or other unknowns) just past the 20 lb. distance (Figure 3.3). Scientists mistrust (yet use) extrapolation, but they usually consider interpolation safe and dependable.

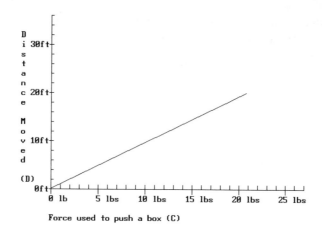

Figure 3.2. A linear graph relating the amount of force needed to push a box a distance across the floor (LINEAR1).

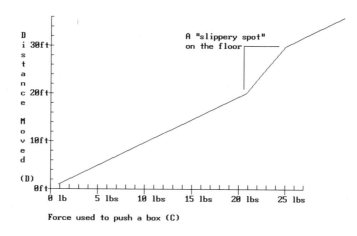

Figure 3.3. The dangers of extrapolation: a slippery spot on the floor changes the graph unexpectedly (LINEAR2).

Interpolation works for any linear shape. You can approximate a parabola, arc, sinusoid, or any other smooth curve with many tiny line segments because the transition from point to point is smooth and predictable. (Figure 3.4 is a curve constructed from tiny line segments.) Scientists or mathematicians spend much of their time differentiating curves to find those smooth linear transitions, or *tangents*, between points.

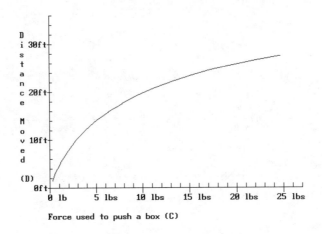

Figure 3.4. A linear curve, composed of tiny line segments (LINEAR3).

Because the transitions are smooth, you know that 5.00001 lbs. of force moves the box almost exactly the same distance as 5 lbs. does. In other words, a tiny change in the controlled variable creates a tiny change in the dependent variable. This is profoundly important. If this weren't true, the whole game would be foolish: interpolation and extrapolation wouldn't work, and the world would appear to behave very strangely. If 5 lbs. of force moved a box 10 ft., 10 lbs. moved it 20 ft., and 7.5 lbs. moved it 170 ft., control would be tricky at best.

The situation could be even worse. If a 5 lb. force moved a box 10 ft., but 5.001 lbs. moved it 25 ft. and 5.002 lbs. moved it 2 ft., prediction and control would be out of the question. You could try to devise a precise pushing machine, but perfect precision does not exist. Even if you could choose reliably between 5.0001 and 5.0002 lbs., could you choose between 5.0001001 and 5.0001002?

Unless you know that a tiny change in your control won't produce a big change in the results, science as we know it is futile. Fortunately, boxes sliding across floors—and many other phenomena—do act in a generally predictable fashion. Many curves are linear. Fractals, however, are not.

Losing Control

It is not certain that everything is uncertain.

—Blaise Pascal, *Penseés,* 1670

Figure 3.5 is a curve in which a tiny change in horizontal position (the controlled variable) can mean a large difference in vertical position. Even in Figure 3.6, where the same curve is magnified, it's still hard to pin down an exact vertical location at any given horizontal position. The fact is, you could indefinitely magnify the curve, and the vertical prediction would never narrow down to a manageable range.

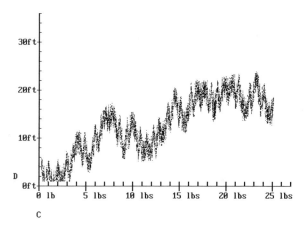

Figure 3.5. A nonlinear curve (NONLIN1).

Yet, a direct correspondence exists between the C and D axes. This could be the graph of a natural phenomenon in which every possible value of C completely determines a unique value for D. Still, you could never hope to predict D based on observation or control of C, unless you had an ideal instrument with absolutely perfect precision.

Graphs like Figures 3.5 and 3.6, in which a tiny difference in a controlled variable can create a large difference in the result, are not difficult to devise. Many such curves fail to yield to prediction and control.

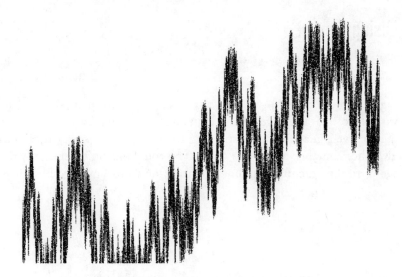

Figure 3.6. The same curve as Figure 3.5, magnified several times (NONLIN1).

Of course, not all fractal curves misbehave quite so much. Figure 3.7 is a nonlinear curve, but it is still predictable in the sense that a small change in the x-axis always corresponds to a small change in the y-axis—it looks like a continuous, gently changing curve. If this were the "pushing the box" graph, a negligible difference would exist between the results of 5 lbs. of force and 5.0001 lbs.

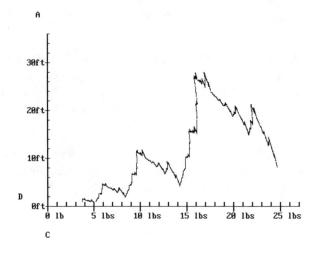

Figure 3.7. A smooth nonlinear curve (NONLIN2).

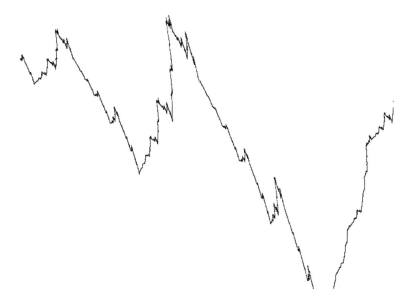

Figure 3.8. The same curve as Figure 3.7, magnified several times (NONLIN2).

You would almost think that you could use interpolation and extrapolation to make predictions based on this curve. You may remember, in fact, that the previous chapter presented a simple program for fractal interpolation.

Out of Control

The "control of nature" is a phrase conceived in arrogance, born of the Neanderthal age of biology and philosophy, when it was supposed that nature exists for the convenience of man.
—Rachel Carson, *Silent Spring*

In practice, almost all traditional mathematical techniques for interpolation go belly up with fractals. To interpolate between two points, you must be able to find the tangent line that connects them—not just see it visually, but actually find its rate of change, or slope. When you magnify the curve to discover that tangent (Figure 3.8), you don't get a nice line. Like all fractals, it simply has no tangent lines. The only way to approximate or predict the slope at a given point is to draw the curve in its entirety and eyeball a guess. There are ways to be a bit more rigorous about it, but the predictive value of fractal interpolation is suspect at best.

Extrapolation is even more out of the question. Without any tangent line to extrapolate, you can never make predictions about parts of the curve you haven't actually measured (or simulated on a computer).

The problem with prediction lies in the flexibility of fractals. The INTERPO program in Chapter 2 works by playing the fractal equivalent of "connect the dots." This is useful for reconstructing a realistic picture of a data set, but doesn't offer any information about where any hidden "dots" may lie. The fractal curve could just as easily be made to pass exactly through an extra point at (.1,.2) as through one at (50,55), while still fitting all other data points with perfect accuracy. Any prediction is therefore entirely arbitrary.

Linear curves wield their power, then, by imposing constraints on where unseen data might fall. Because they must, by definition, change gradually, they cannot zoom all of a sudden up to a distant part of the plane to include a stray data point. When you use linear curves to model reality, you must assume that nature shows a similar kind of constraint. You cross your fingers and hope any data points that don't land near your curve are errors on your part and not the result of some deep flexibility in nature. If Nature really was infinitely flexible and able to jump suddenly away from smoothness on a whim, your only choice for modeling her would be with those unruly and unpredictable fractals.

You Can Do It: Linear and Nonlinear Curves

You can see the inner workings of the curves in Figures 3.2 through 3.8…

1. **Load** the LINEAR1 **Template**. The graph labels are set as text captions, and the template is a single line segment. You don't need to **Draw** or **Paint** anything—a line is a line.

If you're dying to see what a line with a crook in it looks like, you could **Load** the LINEAR2 **Template**. Then again, let's not and say we did.

2. **Load** the LINEAR3 **Template** instead. Here, the seed shape is a little line segment and the curve is defined by another small line segment turned downward just a bit.

3. **Draw** and the curve zips across the screen. (FractalVision can make linear shapes, too.)

If you were to make the line segments that compose this curve exceedingly tiny, you would also have to decrease the angle between adjacent parts of the curve until it was equally minute. I will spare you the actual execution of such a fascinating exercise and move on to the nonlinear curve in Figure 3.6.

4. **Clear** the picture and **Load** the NONLIN1 **Template**. This is similar to the "sine wave" fractal in Chapter 1, "A History of Fractals and Chaos," and the mountain horizon simulation in Chapter 2.

5. **Draw** and watch the curve collapse to nearly infinite detail.

As the segments that define the curve become smaller, the angle between adjacent segments does not decrease at all. Therefore, the sketch becomes more discontinuous as it comes closer to approximating the fractal curve. Contrast this to the linear curve, which becomes more continuous as you more closely approximate the smooth curve.

Consequently, this nonlinear curve does not smooth out when magnified.

6. **Clear** and **Paint** to see the curve without the successive approximations in the way.

7. **Clear**, select **Grow** a few times, and **Paint** again. The curve is just as ragged as before.

The same infinite discontinuity lies hidden in Figure 3.7, even though the curve looks continuous at first glance.

8. **Clear**, **Load** the NONLIN2 **Template**, and **Paint**.

9. **Clear**, **Grow** several times, and **Paint** once more. It's not any smoother than it was before.

The appearance of continuity in a linear curve means that upon closer inspection, irregularities straighten themselves out. Nonlinear curves can look continuous, but that visual continuity is an illusion. They're jagged through and through.

No Hope

Do you think you can take over the universe and improve it?
I do not believe it can be done....
The world is ruled by letting things take their course.
It cannot be ruled by interfering.

—Lao Tzu, *Tao Te Ching*, 600 BC

Unfortunately for those of us who like to control things, most of the natural world does not conform easily to linear equations. Nonlinear, fractal forms are the rule rather than the exception. As Benoit Mandelbrot put it in *The Fractal Geometry of Nature*, "Clouds are not spheres, mountains are not cones, coastlines are not circles, and bark is not smooth...." Our mathematical techniques have enjoyed great success in predicting the few exceptional phenomena that are almost linear, such as the streaming paths of projectiles, planets, and particles. More chaotic (and immediately useful) subjects such as the weather, earthquakes, fluid flow, and formative dynamics stubbornly elude prediction.

Fractals do not necessarily offer hope that we can control these elusive phenomena. On the contrary, we are just beginning to understand that chaos and unpredictability are more deeply embedded in nature than we ever imagined. Fractals do, however, provide powerful tools for modeling and visualizing nonlinear systems.

Patterns in Space and Time

We cannot produce order on the world-wide scale of everyday life without first having a clear picture of order itself, in the realm of ordinary objects. And this requires a completely new view of geometry.... Space must be considered an almost living entity... a kind of stuff which, according to the recursive structures that are built up in it, becomes progressively more and more alive.

—Christopher Alexander, architect, *The Nature of Order*, 1986

It's usually safe to assume that you use more words to describe a complicated pattern than a simple one—the going rate for a good picture being about a kiloword, before inflation. You aren't going to run up much of a phone bill telling a friend in Kansas how to plant a row of peas with 100 seeds three inches apart. You might pay

Ma Bell's offspring a pretty penny, however, if you want to describe the location of every seed in your garden. Conveying enough information to accurately reproduce a realistic picture of even a single plant would take hours.

Or would it? The visual and structural complexity of an object isn't always directly related to the length of a set of instructions needed to reproduce it. If you could describe a single seed well enough for your friend to reproduce it, perhaps she could grow the complex plant from that.

The following exercises in algorithmic gardening are admittedly a bit far-fetched. Your patience with the planting pays off at harvest time, when you can expect to reap a deeper understanding of information and its relationship to physical form.

Planning and Planting

Space the seeds at two-foot intervals in rows 36 to 42 inches apart.
—*The Encyclopedia of Organic Gardening,* 1978

Imagine that you needed to provide your gardener, Mr. Greenthumb, with a short set of instructions, telling him where to plant some seedlings. Your gardener isn't particularly acute in the above-the-neck department and requires extraordinarily explicit instructions. For example, you might hand him a sheet that says:

Plant a tree, walk east 10 ft., and repeat until you reach the edge of the field.

If he followed your instructions, he would finish the job with a row of evenly-spaced trees in a line running east to west. Now imagine that your gardener cannot read. You would have to go out and show him how to get started, and then tell him to precisely repeat your actions until he was done. Figure 3.9 shows the field after you plant the first two trees, showing Mr. Greenthumb what you had in mind.

Figure 3.9. The first two trees in a row that you plant (TREELINE).

In Figure 3.10, he has faithfully repeated your work to plant 14 trees.

Figure 3.10. The same pattern as Figure 3.9, continued by your gardener, Mr. Greenthumb (TREELINE).

Now look at a slightly more complex set of instructions:

1. Plant two trees, one on each side of the field.

2. Plant a tree halfway between those two.

3. Plant trees halfway between the trees that are already in the ground.

4. Repeat step 3 until the trees are too dense to plant any more.

This again produces a single line of evenly spaced trees (though it involves a bit more running around for the tree planter). You might picture this technique with a diagram like Figure 3.11. The top shape points to the first three trees, and the bottom copies show where to put the next two. When Mr. G. continues this pattern, a tree is planted at each arrow in Figure 3.12.

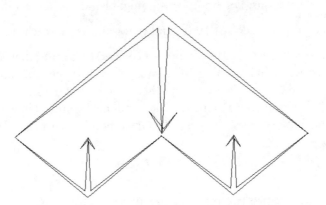

Figure 3.11. Diagram of an alternative technique for planting a line of trees (LINE2).

These repetitive procedures take the results of the last step to do the next: locations of previously planted trees are used to determine the next planting spots. This type of repetition is called *iteration*, and instructions of this type are *iterative*.

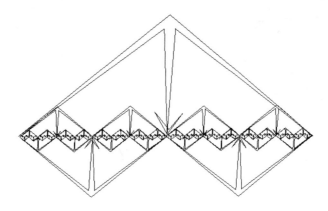

Figure 3.12. The same pattern as Figure 3.11, taken further (LINE2).

You Can Do It: Your Electronic Gardener

Fractal templates are basically a visual language for describing iteration on the computer screen. You can use FractalVision software to explore a wide variety of iterative procedures in a visual way.

1. **Load** the TREELINE **Template** to transform your computer into an electronic Mr. Greenthumb, with the screen as his "field."

The template is simply a visual way of representing the previous four-step set of instructions. The seed shape shows where to begin, and the copy is "10 ft. east."

2. **Draw** to repeat the pattern and "plant a row."

You can think of a line as a fractal as well, because every part of a line resembles the whole. Here's a fractal template that builds a line from self-similarity:

3. **Load** the LINE2 **Template**, **Clear**, and **Draw**.

As you read the following section, you might like to follow along with FractalVision as it plays the role of Mr. Greenthumb. Simply **Load** each **Template** to supply him with his instructions, and **Draw** to put him to work.

Predicting Patterns

Nature, to be commanded, must be obeyed.

—Francis Bacon, *Novum Organum*

You would think simple iterative instructions tend to create simple, predictable patterns. This certainly applies for the instructions you've seen so far. For example, if you select a particular point in the field, you can immediately tell whether or not a tree will sprout there without having to go through the whole planting process. If the point is due east of the starting point, it falls on the tree line. Otherwise, it does not.

Furthermore, if you walked in a straight line in any direction across the field, you could easily predict when you would bump into a tree. Even before the trees were planted, any high school geometry student could write equations describing your walking line and the planting line. You could apply simple algebra to solve those equations and find the intersection of the two lines.

You can make this sort of prediction for other tree planting patterns, too. For example, suppose you gave your tree planter the following instructions, represented visually by Figure 3.13:

1. Plant a tree, turn 5 degrees right, and walk forward 10 ft..

2. Repeat step 1 for a while (say, fifteen times).

You know that Mr. Greenthumb, however humble of mind, is unerringly diligent in carrying out your command. Can you predict where a person walking across the field along a straight path will encounter trees when the gardener's task is completed? Again, you don't need to plant (or draw) the trees to make such a prediction. The resulting pattern is a simple arc, and you can solve the equation of a circle to find the intersection. (It isn't necessary to work through the math here. The point is that you wouldn't need more than simple geometry and algebra.) Each predicted intersection is marked with an X in Figure 3.13.

Figure 3.13. Visual instructions for planting trees in a semicircle (ARC).

Of course, neither algebra nor Mr. G. will let us down. Figure 3.14 reveals that our predictions were on the mark.

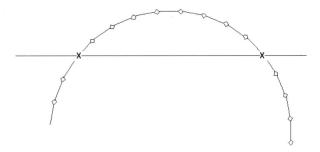

Figure 3.14. The pattern in Figure 3.13, after Mr. G. has planted 15 trees (ARC).

Adding a Dimension

If you shut your doors to all errors truth will be shut out.

—Rabindranath Tagore, *Stray Birds*, 1916

So far, I've used only examples where the trees fall on a continuous line or curve. Figure 3.15 is an example of a more useful tree planting pattern. If the instructions were written rather than visual, they would read something like this:

1. Plant a tree.

2. Plant another 10 ft. due east of the first, and another 10 ft. due south of the first.

3. Repeat step 2 for every tree planted.

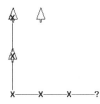

Figure 3.15. Instructions to plant an evenly spaced grid of trees. It's easy to predict that trees will be planted where the ? and Xes are (TREEGRID).

177

This eventually creates a "grid" of trees. As with the other examples so far, it's easy to predict whether any particular point in the field will contain a tree. If the point is an even multiple of 10 ft. east and south of the start, a tree will be there. We know Mr. G. will plant a tree on the ? because it is 20 ft. east and 30 ft. south of the start. Figure 3.16 confirms this.

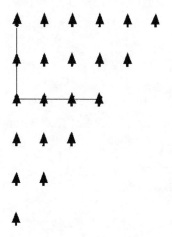

Figure 3.16. The results of the "instructions" in Figure 3.15 (TREEGRID).

> All these grids and lines aren't very exciting, are they? Imagine when books on geometric modeling covered lines and boxes from cover to cover. Not to worry, though. All this predictability and orderliness is about to collapse under its own weight. I'll return to the juicy stuff soon, I promise. Just one more grid—and watch closely…

The following instructions also create an evenly spaced grid:

1. Evenly divide the field into four sections.

2. Divide each of those into four sections again.

3. Keep going until the sections are about 10 ft. (a good tree spacing) apart.

4. Plant trees in the center of each section.

Figure 3.17 expresses this approach visually. Xes mark where the trees are planted. In the bottom-left corner, I predicted the location of several trees (with small Xes and a ?) based on the tree spacing we defined.

Are you convinced yet that most iterative instructions are predictable? Well, lines, smooth curves, and grids are. Startlingly, almost nothing else is.

You Can Do It: Dangerous Deviations

For a visual demonstration, try modifying the template that produced Figure 3.17:

1. **Load** the X-GRID **Template**.

2. Select **Next Part** until the handle is on the X in the bottom-left corner.

3. Select any combination of **Grow, Shrink, Skew, Spin, Squish**, or **Stretch** from the menu. Perhaps even move the part over a bit.

4. **Clear** and **Draw**.

Modify any part of the template any way you like, then **Clear** and **Draw** again. Unless you chance upon the grid arrangement (or one of a few linear patterns like ARC), your pattern will appear chaotic.

In Figures 3.18 and 3.19, I introduce some slight variations to the grid-making instructions used to create Figure 3.17. Now can you predict whether the ? falls on a tree? Does any formula describe the final pattern in which we could "solve" an intersection with a line across the field? No.

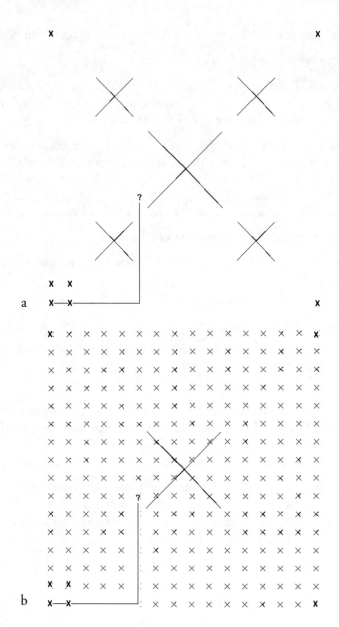

Figure 3.17. Another method of defining a grid (X-GRID).

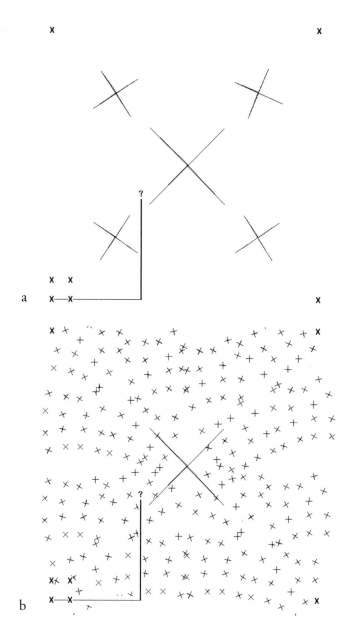

Figure 3.18. A slight rotation has been added to Figure 3.17 (X-GRID with Spin added).

181

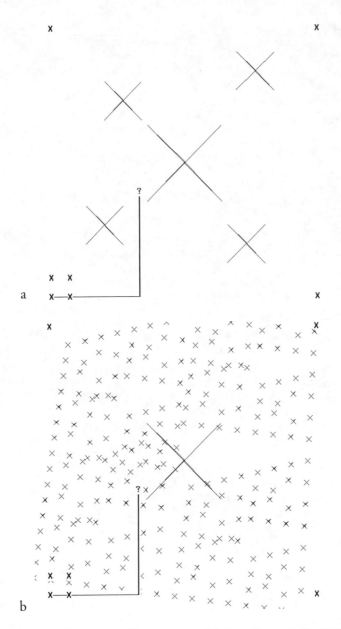

Figure 3.19. A small amount of movement added to Figure 3.17 (X-GRID with Move added).

The template is no more complex than it was before I modified it. The instructions to draw the Xes on-screen could be written down almost as briefly as the previous instructions to draw a grid. Those simple, known instructions were followed precisely by a digital computer. Yet you cannot predict whether an X falls on a given point without proceeding through the entire procedure from start to finish. The only way to know where the trees fall is to simulate the entire planting process.

The Iterative Universe

We scientists…had built up our concepts (and prejudices) about the characteristic behavior of natural systems by observing artificial systems, systems which were chosen precisely for their regularity! This total regularity was a prerequisite for the mathematical description of the process. Only the advent of powerful computers freed us from this restriction. Computers—generally suspected of impressing total order and discipline on every facet of life—have made possible this better understanding of harmony and chaos.
—Gert Eilenberger, physicist, *The Beauty of Fractals*, 1986

Almost all iterative instructions produce unpredictable results. Mathematics and science are based on lines, smooth curves, and grids. Why? Certainly not because they are typical patterns found in nature. We have clung to these few unusual shapes simply because they are the only ones that we know how to predict and control.

FractalVision software is purely a visual language for instructing the computer where to place dots on-screen. It does not contain any "secret formula" that transforms every pattern into a fractal. In fact, you can build any pattern that you can describe as a series of repeated transformations. The program creates mostly fractals, only because fractals are by far the easiest shapes to make. In this light, it isn't surprising that nature is filled with fractals. One must be very clever to find the few shapes that are not fractals.

The people who discovered grids and smooth curves many hundreds of years ago knew that they were exceptional forms. They also doubted that any but a few of nature's secrets could be unlocked with linear mathematics. Today, however, we have become so enamored with the successes of linearity that we tend to forget its limitations. Predicting the path of projectiles and light rays with linear equations makes perfect sense because they obviously travel in linear paths. But it doesn't make sense to use linear equations for predicting the behavior of forms like hurricanes and plants. This fact might have been obvious to Plato or Descartes, who were only beginning to explore linearity. Now we are so adept with (and dependent on) linear equations, it is often hard to admit that they aren't Nature's own favorites.

The unpredictability of nonlinear iterative systems does not make them any more attractive. Even when we are in complete control, as with our precise instructions to an obedient tree planter, we still can't predict the results.

This fact is worth repeating before I discuss its dramatic implications:

Even when we have precise control over an iterative process, we cannot predict its effects at any specific place and time.

If iterative processes were common, this would imply that we are often unable to know the outcome of even our own most perfectly controlled actions. You might hope iteration isn't very common.

But it is. Iteration simply means using the current state of a system over and over to create the next state. A secretary iterates every time he follows the same procedure to organize an office that he used yesterday. A driver iterates when the same rule forces her to respond to several road signs or to stop at subsequent red lights. A broker who always tries to buy low and sell high helps create an iterative market. Is it surprising, then, that traffic flow and stock prices are more easily simulated with fractal graphs than with linear ones?

Now, what if the universe follows certain constant laws (as scientists are eager to demonstrate), and each moment transforms the immediate past into the immediate future according to these laws? If this is so, the universe itself is an iterative system. This would not bode well for any ambitious species that wished to use technology to control and predict anything. If we had complete control over the entire universe, along with omniscient knowledge of its current state, we still could not predict the future.

Our best hope would be to build a magical computer that could "simulate" the future faster than it happened. Of course, such a computer would need to contain more components than the universe itself and run faster than time. And as we learned in lesson 1, even the tiniest error in precision might produce a huge error in the result, so our universe simulator would need to be infinitely accurate as well.

Fractals Without Iteration

If the doors of perception were cleansed every thing would appear to man as it is, infinite. For man has closed himself up, till he sees all things thro' narrow chinks of his cavern.
—William Blake, *The Marriage of Heaven and Hell*, 1790

The vast majority of iterative systems take the result of one operation and feed it to the next, manufacturing unpredictability and fractal complexity in the process. If that isn't bad enough, many systems that don't seem to involve iteration still produce complex, unpredictable fractals.

For instance, look at the program in the next **For Programmers Only** box. It involves no iteration, no repeated feeding of the results of a function back into the same function. You could read enough of it over the phone in 30 seconds to tell a computer-literate friend how to reproduce the images it makes. In spite of the fact that it's the shortest program in this book and the only one that doesn't use iteration as a shortcut to complexity, it produces the most visually complex fractals of the lot. (Figure 3.20)

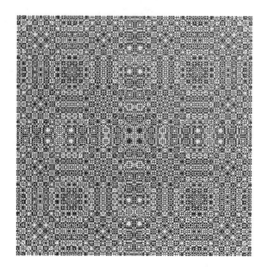

a

continues

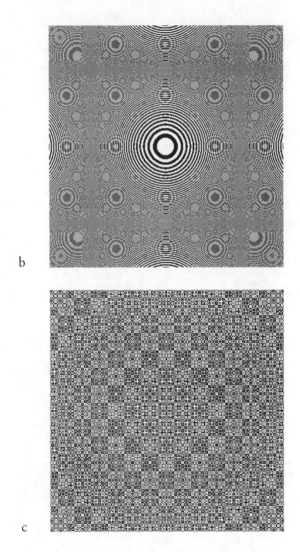

b

c

Figure 3.20. A few of the patterns produced by the MOIRE program.

You Can Do It: Moiré Patterns

Programmers will want to play with the source code, but anyone can see the results of this simple algorithm. Simply type MOIRE at the DOS prompt and watch the show. Unless you have a fast 486, I recommend selecting CGA low-resolution 4-color mode for maximum speed. The larger pixels also make intricate patterns easier to discern.

For Programmers Only: Interfering with Reality

Algorithmic simplicity can create visual and geometric complexity. You could actually make this program considerably shorter by removing seven of the eight `putpixel()` commands and adjusting the loop to pass over the whole square instead of an eighth of it. This amplifies the "image compression" involved in packing all those pictures into this tiny little program, but it slows things down in the bargain. In this case, speed matters more than compactness.

Speaking of speed, if you've got a snappy 486 and VGA graphics, try changing the `setvideomode(1, 1)` to `setvideomode(6, 1)` and changing the `SIZE` definition to `200` or `300` instead of `100`. More resolution, more colors. Ooo, Aaaah.

Fooling around with any of the parameters and loop values in this program provides you with entirely new universes of intricate designs.

Listing 3.1. A program to create intricate fractal interference patterns without iteration.

```
/* MOIRE.C
 *
 * This program creates color moire patterns
 */
```

continues

Listing 3.1. continued

```c
#include <stdio.h>        /* Standard input/output libraries */
#include <stdlib.h>

#define MAIN             /* See Appendix D for header files */
#include "fv.h"          /* and compile instructions */

#define SIZE 100         /* change to 200 if you use VGA */

void main(void)
{   int a, i, j, x, y,   /* counters for looping */
        c,               /* color to make each circle */
        cx, cy,          /* x,y center of the screen */
        vidmode;         /* video mode */
    char str[16];
    vidmode = pickmode(detectmode()); /* confirm video mode */
    if (setvidmode(vidmode, 1) != 1)
    {   printf("\nUnable to set graphics mode.\n");
        exit(0);
    }
    cx = scrnx / 2;  cy = scrny / 2;  /* find screen center */
    for (a = 1; a < 32765; a++)               /* main loop */
    {   if (kbhit())          /* pause if user presses a key */
        {   if (getch() == 27) break;       /* quit if Esc */
            getch();
        }
        for (x = a, i = 0;    /* scan a triangular slice of */
             i <= SIZE;       /* the screen, pixel by pixel */
             x += a, i++)

/* Try changing x in the next line
 * to (x << 4) or (x >> 4) for more patterns */

            for (y = x, j = i; j <= SIZE; y += a, j++)
            {                             /* draw circles! */
                c = (((long) x * x +
                      (long) y * y) >> 10) % ncolors;

    /* Draw eight pie slices to fill a square region.
     * We can get away with this speed-up trick,
```

```
        * since circles and squares have eight-way symmetry */
            {   putpixel(cx + i, cy + j, c);
                putpixel(cx + j, cy + i, c);
                putpixel(cx + j, cy - i, c);
                putpixel(cx + i, cy - j, c);
                putpixel(cx - i, cy - j, c);
                putpixel(cx - j, cy - i, c);
                putpixel(cx - j, cy + i, c);
                putpixel(cx - i, cy + j, c);
            }
        }
    }
    settextmode();   /* close down graphics, and quit */
    closedown();
}
```

All this program does is draw one set of tiny concentric circles, identical to the ripple that occurs when you throw a rock into a pond. To create the next picture, it draws a slightly smaller set of concentric circles and completely erases the old set. Where do all the patterns come from, and why do most of them show fractal detail? Believe it or not, they originate from the structure of your computer screen. More specifically, what you see is the interference pattern between the circles drawn by the program and the square grid of pixels that composes your display.

You've probably seen similar effects appear when two window screens (the old-fashioned kind of "windows" and "screens," that is) are rotated next to one another, or in moiré fabric, a fabric with an irregular, wavy finish. Viewing moiré patterns was a fad in the late nineteenth century, but we now take them a bit more seriously. They show many of the same characteristics of chaotic dynamical systems: a small change in the size of the grid can produce a large change in the pattern. Orderly patterns suddenly pop up among complex self-reflective ones. Many patterns retain a consistent appearance over many levels of scale.

If the interference of two perfectly linear grids creates fractals and the interference between smooth linear curves makes fractals, how likely is it that any system in the real world is not going to produce complex, unpredictable fractals? How many wave-like patterns are interfering with one another every time you make a sound or take a step? You get the idea.

This all sounds like fun to fractal nuts like me, but it might bother a few people who are more intent on keeping things under control. And the worst is yet to come…

Chaos

Now, at the end of this century, more and more scientists have come to think, as we do, that many fundamental processes shaping nature are irreversible and stochastic; that the deterministic and reversible laws describing the elementary interactions may not be telling the whole story. This leads to a new vision of matter, one no longer passive, as described in the mechanical world view, but associated with spontaneous activity. This change is so deep that we believe we can truly speak of a new dialogue of man with nature.

—Grégoire Nicolis and Ilya Prigogine, *Exploring Complexity*, 1989

Throughout this book, I've shied away from equations. Interactive visuals almost always lend a better intuitive understanding of the subject at hand. There is a danger in hiding all my equations in the back of the book and the **For Programmers Only** boxes, however. The risk is that you might think that those magical formulas are as complex as the images they produce. They aren't.

To prove it, and to bring the hidden magic out in the open, I'd like to take you on a journey through the innards of one simple mathematical equation. Our travels begin in the familiar land of linearity and end up at the far reaches of chaos.

Population Growth

Evolution is chaos with feedback.

Joseph Ford, physicist, (quoted by Clifford Pickover, 1990)

$$p_2 = rp\,(1 - p)$$

A new value for the variable p equals r times *the old p* times the quantity 1 minus *the old p*. In the 1970s, Robert May picked this equation as a simple model for population growth. Every organism reproduces at a certain rate (call it r); therefore, each generation increases by the current population (call it p) times the rate of growth.

Of course, a petri dish or ecological niche only has so much room for organisms to multiply before space and food start limiting growth. A theoretical maximum population does exist, and for convenience May scaled p as a percentage of that maximum. So when the population is 50 percent of the maximum, he would say that $p = 0.50$. When the population is only 20 percent of the maximum, $p = 0.20$, and so on.

As each generation begets the next, the population not only increases by a certain amount (r times x), but also decreases according to how close it is to the maximum. If $p = 1.00$, or 100 percent, all new babies would die from lack of space and food. If the population is lower, then more babies survive. An obvious estimate for this factor is $1 - p$, the difference between the maximum population and the current population.

So May ended up with the new population (p_2) equaling the rate of growth (r) times the current population (p) times the difference between the maximum population and the current population ($1 - p$).

$$p_2 = rp\,(1 - p)$$

May then asked, "What happens to the population over time?" and "How does the population growth pattern depend on the growth rate?" Figures 3.21 through 3.24 are graphs of population growth for various values of r, from 100 percent to 250 percent. The leftmost dot in each graph represents the initial population (set to 10 percent), and each successive dot's vertical position indicates the population size for the next generation.

r = 1.00002

Figure 3.21. Population over time with 100 percent growth rate.

Figure 3.22. Population over time with 150 percent growth rate.

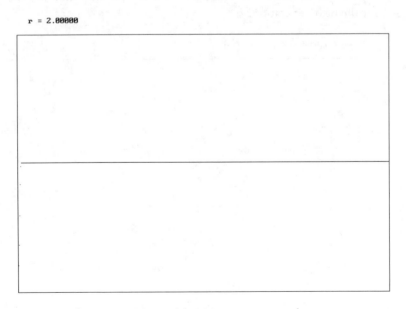

Figure 3.23. Population over time with 200 percent growth rate.

r = 2.50000

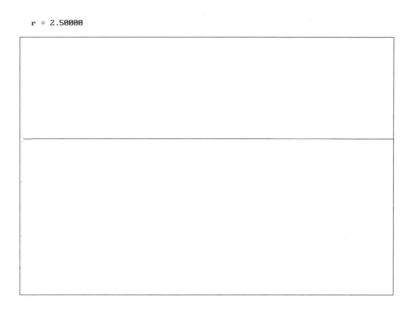

Figure 3.24. Population over time with 250 percent growth rate.

As May expected, the population quickly stabilizes at a certain carrying capacity. Up to a certain point, a higher rate of growth means a larger stable population. As the growth rate approaches 300 percent, the size of the stable population remains close to 70 percent.

Things Get Weird

One should never place one's trust in the future. It doesn't deserve it.
— Andre Chamson, *On Ne Voit Pas Les Coeurs*

Nice simple equation. Nice simple results.

But May didn't stop at 300 percent growth rate. He wanted to know what happens at 350 percent or 400 percent. What if the critters have big litters? He discovered that at values of *r* between 300 and 345 percent the population did not level off at a stable number, but hopped rhythmically between two different values (Figure 3.25).

Between 346 percent and 354 percent, the population skips among four different values (Figure 3.26).

r = 3.20000

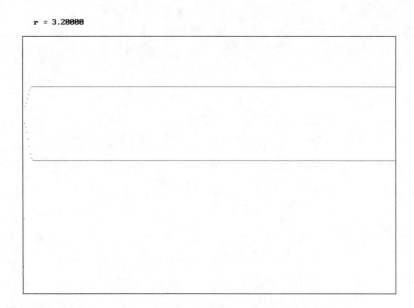

Figure 3.25. Population over time with 320 percent growth rate.

r = 3.50000

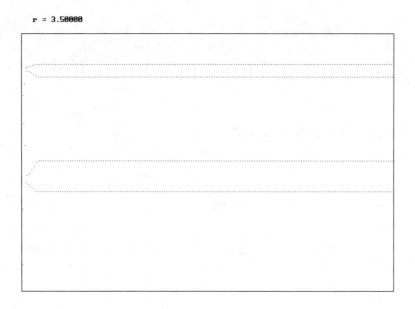

Figure 3.26. Population over time with 350 percent growth rate.

Between 355 percent and 356 percent, it jumps among eight different values (Figure 3.27).

r = 3.55000

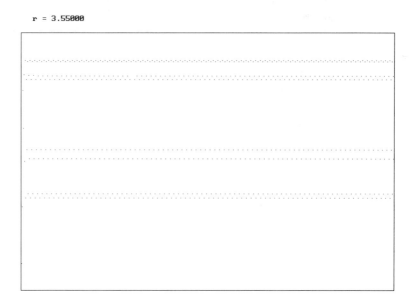

Figure 3.27. Population over time with 355 percent growth rate.

If $r = 3.566$, the population dances among sixteen different values (Figure 3.28).

Then, somewhere around $r = 3.58$, things start getting weird, but just a little weird at first (Figure 3.29).

Was the population cycling regularly among a large number of values, or was it just flitting around at random within several ranges of values? By the time r reached 370 percent, all hell broke loose (Figure 3.30). The population level careened about wildly between a high point and low point. May could not find any stable pattern at all.

Even more strangely, at certain values of r the equation suddenly behaves itself and the population once again cycles reliably among a few stable levels. When $r = 3.74$, a cycle of five population levels popped up. For r values from 383 percent to 384 percent, a cycle of period three appears (Figure 3.31). In each case, the number of population levels bifurcates into twice as many, then the period repeatedly doubles, more quickly each time. Eventually, the number of cycles and the speed at which that number changes become so great that it all looks random again.

At 400 percent, the population level is completely unpredictable, varying all the way from the maximum to a single lone critter and back, without apparent rhyme or reason (Figure 3.32). In a model that seemed predictable at first, using the simplest possible equation, Robert May found both perfect order and total chaos.

r = 3.56600

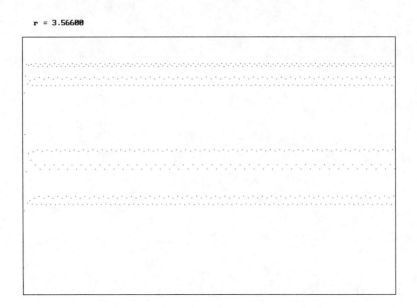

Figure 3.28. Population over time with a 356.6 percent growth rate.

r = 3.58000

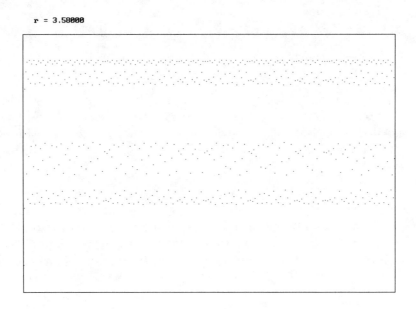

Figure 3.29. Population growth with a 358 percent growth rate.

r = 3.70000

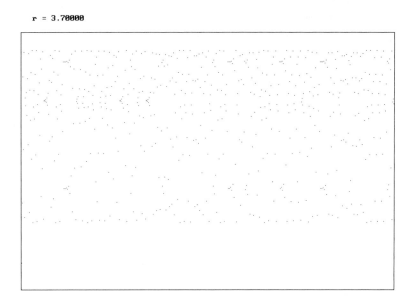

Figure 3.30. Population growth with a 370 percent growth rate.

r = 3.84000

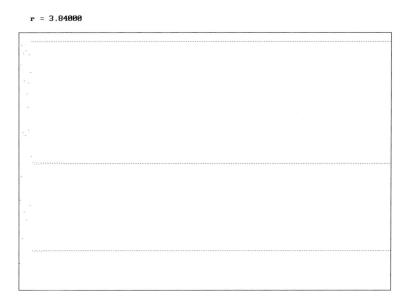

Figure 3.31. Population growth with a 384 percent growth rate.

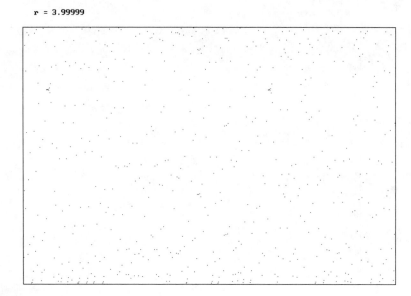

Figure 3.32. Population growth with a 400 percent growth rate.

You Can Do It: The Onset of Chaos

You can look over Robert May's shoulder as he discovers unexpected chaos in his bifurcation equation. The BIF program included with this book is an interactive computer "movie" of $rp(1 - p)$. May actually worked this out on a hand calculator, back in the technological "Dark Ages" of the early 1970s.

1. Type BIF at the DOS prompt (or start BIF.EXE from Windows or another graphics DOS shell).

The curve you see on-screen is the same as Figure 3.21. The first dot on the left is the initial population, and the line of dots indicates a stable population level.

2. Press any key to start the movie. *r* slowly increases and so does the stable population level.

Using the keys on your numeric keypad, you can control the speed at which r changes by pressing the asterisk (*) key to speed up and the slash (/) key to slow down. I strongly recommend that you keep the line moving at a painfully slow pace for now, but you might need to press * once on some computers for the line to look like it's moving at all.

3. Try pressing the minus (-) key to reverse the movie by decreasing r. The line obediently moves downward.

4. Press plus (+) to make r increase again. The line moves up. You have control of the growth rate, and you can therefore predict and control the population level. You can pretend you are a famous experimental biologist (the name Jehovah comes to mind).

Let r climb slowly. When it gets close to 3.00, what happens to the first few generations? At exactly 3.00, the line splits into two, as the population begins hopping between two stable levels.

5. Just before r reaches 3.4, press / at least once to slow the movie down. You won't want to miss this.

Bifurcation. Bifurcation. Bifurcation. She's breaking up…chaos.

Yet within the chaos, you can see a wealth of strange patterns. Stable periodic populations pop up when you least expect them, sometimes for a fraction of a second, sometimes longer.

6. Try the - and + keys again. You still have control over the growth rate, but can you predict the results of your control? I just don't think so.

7. If r is still creeping along through chaos, you might want to press * to speed up until you reach $r = 3.8$ or so, and then press / to slow down again.

At 3.83, a cycle of period three begins. But chaos is always at the threshold. The first few generations keep losing it and pulling themselves together again. Then comes bifurcation and the descent into the maelstrom.

8. You can switch to a God's-eye view of the entire movie by pressing M for map.

continues

Now the left side of the screen represents the beginning of the movie ($r = 1.0$), and the right side represents the end ($r = 4.0$). The generations do not progress across the screen; instead, they bounce up and down on the vertical stripe that represents a particular value of r. The coloring is the same as before, with red representing the first generation, green representing the next, and so on. Bright white represents the population level of the 150th generation, the last one computed.

Here you see the whole movie at once: on the left, a rapid stabilization to a single population level, which becomes greater as you move to the right. Then the generations start stabilizing at two levels, then four, then eight. On the right, chaos takes turns with order, always giving order the shorter turn.

In the next **You Can Do It** box, you'll get a chance to zoom in and explore the landscape represented by this map.

May wondered if real populations could act like his model. Could a species settle into stable population levels at one reproductive rate and vary randomly between a high and low at another? Data from populations in the wild did show similar patterns, but researchers had assumed the unstable populations would eventually reach an equilibrium and stabilize. May's model brought this interpretation into some doubt.

The Shape of Nature

Mysterious in the light of day,
Nature retains her veil, despite our clamors:
That which she doth not willingly display
Cannot be wrenched from her with levers, screws, and hammers.

—Johann Wolfgang von Goethe, *Faust*

Theorists of all persuasions preferred to make a sharp distinction between the equations that modeled a system's behavior and the random noise that messed up everyone's measurements. They saw randomness as a dressing curtain put up by Nature to hide her pure form. The mathematician's job was to sketch the smooth and lovely curves that scientists could glimpse only through the screen. May's equation seemed to suggest that the shape of Nature herself might include chaotic irregularity—that if scientists were able to peek around the screen, they might unveil a form more ragged than the gentle curves they adored.

If scientists regarded the bizarre behavior of $rp(1-p)$ as shocking, mathematicians took it like a shot glass of napalm. Field researchers are accustomed to all sorts of strange and unexpected noise, and it did not seem all that improbable to find the same kind of noise in a theory as they found in the real world. Mathematicians, on the other hand, don't usually encounter randomness unless they work hard to create it.

If certain mathematical procedures produced pseudorandom numbers, all the better for the statisticians. But certainly *that* kind of equation was an entirely different breed from the regular sort, which were respectably stable and smooth. May's equation was a mathematical werewolf, a gentlemanly curve that transformed at the stroke of 3.0 into an unruly monster. That calm and chaos could live together in Nature's body was frightening. That they could be inseparably interwoven in the pure abstract unity of a single mathematical equation was inconceivable.

Perhaps one renegade curve could be tolerated or ignored. But a troublemaking mathematician/philosopher named James Yorke analyzed $rp(1-p)$ in depth and came up with a conclusion that would make any ordinary mathematician shiver. He proved that any equation consisting of only a single changeable parameter and cycling among three stable states at any point would necessarily show cycles of all other possible sizes and lengths, along with completely chaotic behavior. Yorke's legendary paper, *Period Three Implies Chaos*, gave a new science of chaos its name.

Figure 3.33 shows a "map" of $rp(1-p)$ with each vertical slice representing the behavior for one value of r. Although this shape is an abstraction (a real observer would see only a single slice for any given population experiment), it is a tidy way to visualize how the equation bobs in and out of chaos as r changes.

Equations that at first glance bear absolutely no relationship to $rp(1-p)$ show nearly identical behaviors. Figure 3.34 is a map of $r \sin(\pi x)$, for example. The *sin* function gives the height of a point as it moves around a circle, and π is the ratio between the diameter and circumference of a circle. This trigonometric equation, called Fiegenbaum's bifurcation equation after the mathemetician who discovered its deep similarities to May's equation, has nothing whatsoever to do with $rp(1-p)$, at least in theory. But the map of its behavior shows the same wanton dance of randomness and order. As Figure 3.35 shows, this dance continues even in the minute details of the bifurcation equations.

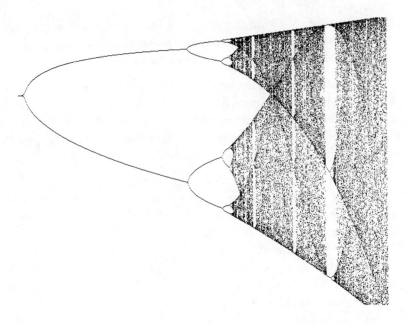

Figure 3.33. A map of the equation $rp(1 - p)$ for $r = 3$ (left) to $r = 4$ (right). I left out the first few iterations to make the bifurcations more obvious.

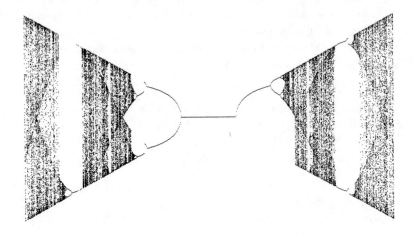

Figure 3.34. A map of the equation $r \sin(\pi x)$ for $r = -2$ (left) to 2 (right).

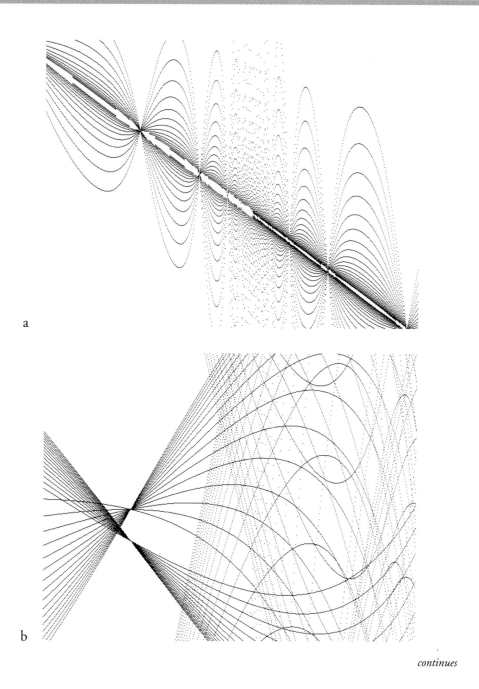

a

b

continues

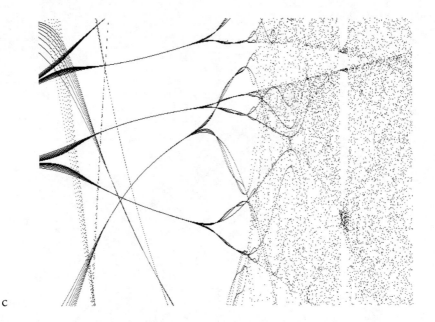

c

Figure 3.35. Some highly magnified details of Figure 3.33.

You Can Do It: Chaos Up Close

The previous **You Can Do It** and **For Programmers Only** boxes show you how to explore bifurcation with the BIF program. If you have FRACTINT (which I hope you do because it is fabulous free fractal fun—turn to the introduction to find out how you can get yours today…), you can use the zoom feature to become even more intimate with the bifurcation equations.

1. Run FRACTINT and choose your favorite video mode. Resolution and colors don't make much difference this time —in fact, using 2-color (black and white, or monochrome) modes often helps bring out fine details.

2. Press T and select the fractal type **bifurcation**.

3. Press Enter to accept the default parameter. (**Filter cycles** is the number of iterations to skip before plotting on-screen. If you had set this to 1, you would see the same map that the BIF program displayed.)

4. Zoom in with Page Up or a mouse.

Can you find the places pictured in Figure 3.35? (Hint: I turned up the number of iterations by pressing X and changing the **Maximum iterations** setting to 1,000 or so.)

Here's how to explore a different bifurcation equation, the $r\sin(\pi x)$ mentioned previously:

5. Press T and select the *bif=sinpi* fractal type.

As you zoom in, you'll notice the details of this one are often quite different in structure than the other. For example, the orderly part of the curve often jumps suddenly from one value to another, which never happened in the first bifurcation type.

For Programmers Only: Making Mathematical Movies

The following program makes a movie of $rp(1-p)$. By adding the eleven lines starting with /*****/ and commenting out the lines right after them, you can make a movie of $r\sin(\pi x)$ instead. You might also try some other equations of your own.

Listing 3.2. An interactive movie of May's population bifurcation equation.

```
/* BIF.C
 *
 * This program is an interactive movie of
 * Robert May's bifurcation equation rp(1-p).
 *
 * To make a movie of Feigenbaum's bifurcation
```

continues

Listing 3.2. continued

```
 * equation r sin(pi x) instead, add the lines starting
 * with /***** and take out the lines after them.
 */

#include <stdio.h>        /* Standard input/output */
#include <stdlib.h>
#include <math.h>         /* for the fabs() function */

#define MAIN             /* See Appendix D for compile */
#include "fv.h"          /* instructions & header file info. */

#define ESC 27           /* The Escape key code */
#define drawclr 7        /* Color to make the text */

int lastp[650];          /* array for erasing last fram */

void main(void)
{    int vidmode, i, j;  /* video mode and counters */
     float r, p, jump;   /* r, p, and change in r each frame */
     char str[40],       /* string for display */
          a = 0;         /* for keyboard reading */
     vidmode = pickmode(detectmode());   /* get video mode */
     printf("\n\n");
     printf("This program plots the equation rp(1-p) to"
            " simulate biological growth.\n");
     printf("The height of the leftmost dot represents"
            " the initial population level,\n");
     printf("with successive generations to the right.  "
            "You will see a movie of\n");
     printf("what happens with increasing values of r, "
            "the reproductive rate.\n");
     printf("\nPress any key to continue. . .");
     getch();
     if (vidmode > 6) vidmode = 6;  /* don't use super-VGA */
     if (setvidmode(vidmode, 1) != 1)
     {    printf("\nUnable to set graphics mode.\n");
          exit(0);
     }
```

```
/*****/ /* r = -2.01, jump = 0.001; */    /* see note above */
r = 0.99, jump = 0.001;  /* initialize everything */
    for (i = 0; i < scrnx; i++) lastp[i] = 0;
    setcolor(drawclr);
    while(a != ESC)          /* keep on until user hits Esc */
    {   sprintf(str, "r = %7.5f  (jump = %8.6f) ", r, jump);
        moveto(0, 1);          /* print values on screen */
        outtext(str);
        for (i = 0, p = 0.1; i < scrnx; i++)  /* iterate */
        {
            putpixel(i, lastp[i], 0); /* erase and redraw */

/*****/  /* putpixel(i,
                    lastp[i] = (scrny / 2) + 25 -
                    (p / 4) * (scrny - 50),
                    i & 8 + 8); */


            putpixel(i,
                    lastp[i] = scrny - p * (scrny - 50),
                    i % 8 + 8);

/*****/  /* p = r * sin(3.14159265 * p); */


            p = r * p * (1 - p);   /* the formula itself */
        }
        if (kbhit())              /* process keystroke */
        {   switch(a = getch())
            {   case '+':              /* make time go forward */
                    jump = fabs(jump);
                    break;
                case '-':              /* make time go backward */
                    jump = -fabs(jump);
                    break;
                case '*': jump *= 10.0;   /* go faster */
                    break;
                case '/': jump /= 10.0;   /* go slower */
                    break;
                case 'M':   /* display map of all behaviors */
```

continues

Listing 3.2. continued

```
              case 'm':
                      clearscreen();
                      moveto(0, 1);

/*****/               /* outtext("This is a map of r sin(pi p)"
                              " for r=-2 (left)"
                              " to r=2 (right)"); */
/*****/               /* for (r = -2.0, i = 0; r < 2.0;
                              r += 4.0 / (float) scrnx, i++) */

                      outtext("This is a map of rp(1 - p),"
                              " for r = 1 (left)"
                              " to r = 4 (right).");
                      for (r = 1.0, i = 0; r < 4.0;
                              r += 3.0 / (float) scrnx, i++)
                      {   for(j = 0, p = 0.1; j < 160; j++)
                          {
/*****/                   /* p = r * sin(3.14159265 * p);*/
/*****/                   /* putpixel(i,
                                      (scrny / 2) + 25 -
                                      (p / 4) *
                                      (scrny - 50),
                                  j % 8 + 1); */

                          p = r * p * (1 - p);
                          putpixel(i,
                                  scrny - p *
                                  (scrny - 50),
                                  j % 8 + 1);
                          }

/*****/               /* putpixel(i,
                                  (scrny / 2) + 25 -
                                  (p / 4) * (scrny - 50),
                                  15); */

                      putpixel(i,
                              scrny - p * (scrny - 50),
                              15);
```

```
                            if (kbhit() && (getch() == ESC)) break;
                    }
                    moveto(0, 20);
                    outtext("Press any key to continue.");
                    getch();
                    clearscreen();

/*****/             /* r = -2.01; */

                    r = 0.99;
                    break;
            case ' ':                      /* pause */
                    getch();
                    break;
            }
        }
        r += jump;                         /* increment r */

/*****/ /* if ((r >= 2.0) || (r <= -2.0)) */

        if ((r >= 4.0) || (r <= 1.0))   /* pause if done */
        {   moveto(0, 20);
            outtext("Press any key to start, or Esc to quit."
                    "                                      ");
            a = getch();

/*****/  /* r = -2.0; */

            r = 1.0;              /* start at r = 1 */
            jump = fabs(jump);   /* make jump positive */
            moveto(0, 20);       /* display meaning of keys */
            outtext("*=faster  /=slower  +=forward  -=backward"
                    " Space=pause  M=map  Esc=quit");
        }
    }
    settextmode();        /* Close down graphics */
    closedown();
}
```

Chaotic fractals and smooth linearity are not strangers, but strange bedfellows. Just as Nature's calm is punctuated by storms, the atmosphere of mathematics is troubled by chaos. In Chapter 2, you saw heroic scientists falter in their quest to predict and control a threatening Nature. It is now apparent that even the pure realm of abstraction is not a haven from the dangerous and unexpected. We have failed to tame our own mental creations; even thinking is not safe.

Wholes in the Parts

Appreciating the harmonious structure of any architecture is one thing; admiring the wildness of nature is quite another. In terms of aesthetic values, the new mathematics of fractal geometry brought hard science in tune with the peculiarly modern feeling for untamed, uncivilized, undomesticated nature.

—James Gleick, *Chaos*, 1986

Shapes like those in Figure 3.36 present themselves as an entirely new form of creation. They remind one of organic forms, yet seem dramatically "unnatural." They show none of the predictable symmetry of modern artifacts, yet an unerring orderliness marks them as "high tech."

Figure 3.36. Fractals often appear organic, yet unnatural (ZOOMBIRD, VOR-TEX, and REACH).

Fractals, then, seem to be an intriguing mix of painstaking technological precision and another, more mysterious "natural" element. What is that element? What makes forms as abstract as Figure 3.36 somehow seem organic?

The heart of the matter lies in self-reflection. As many examples in Chapter 2 show, natural forms often reveal transformed copies of the whole in every part. Shapes you create with FractalVision software have this property, too. This emerges not only in the process of the geometric iteration used to draw them, but also in the mood and feeling of the completed pictures.

You Can Do It: A New World

As these shapes paint themselves before your eyes, you may sense that they represent a profound departure from ordinary works of art and science.

1. **Load** the REACH **Template**.

2. **Paint**. If this were a Rorschach test, what would you see?

3. **Load** the VORTEX example, **Clear**, and **Paint**. Here, a sense of depth exists, even though the transformations that define the shape are entirely two-dimensional. Where does that sense of depth originate?

4. Finally, **Load** the ZOOMBIRD example, **Clear**, and **Paint** once more. The sense of depth and motion is even stronger with this shape.

The feeling of motion and space that these shapes convey comes partly from the illusion of distance. The "birds" and the "ground" in ZOOMBIRD have the same geometry as telephone poles along a road vanishing into the distance. Couple this visual experience of infinity with intricate self-reflective detail, and your brain immediately associates the resulting images with the three-dimensional organic world.

However, the specific forms are entirely unfamiliar and artificial. Thus arises the psychology of fractals, a subtle confusion of the real and the fantastic. Depending on the fractal, the net result may strike one with awe, aesthetic pleasure, or haunting unease.

A Fractal Human

…fractal monsters are the very substance of our flesh!

—Benoit Mandelbrot, *The Fractal Geometry of Nature*, 1982

With techniques explained in Chapter 4, "The Art of Fractal Modeling," you can create a fractal with any shape that can be drawn by a "regular" drawing program. (This fact has been rigorously proven by mathematician John Elton.) Therefore, any form can be drawn in two very different ways:

■ The standard approach is to build it from individual, separate shapes or strokes.

■ The fractal way is to define its parts as iterative reflections of the whole.

Just as you can draw something in two ways, you can also see something in two ways: as an aggregation of separate parts or as an interlaced network of self-reflection. Though the physical form being seen is the same in both cases, the experience of seeing is remarkably different.

When you create a drawing or representation of something, you can never include every detail present in the original. The job of both artist and scientist is to capture the "important" aspects of reality in their representations. The way in which one sees a subject has a profound influence on which details are included and which are left out. The tools you use can also dramatically influence the portrait.

For example, in a sketch of the human body, a child's crayon drawing includes very different elements than a medical illustration. An impressionist reveals one side of the human form, while a cubist unveils another.

How would a human body look if drawn with the tools of fractal geometry? In Figure 3.37, a rough sketch of the human form is covered with six copies of itself. Each copy represents a major anatomical feature of "FracMan."

Now imagine that each of the six parts of the body are divided into six parts in the same fashion, and the pattern continued to infinity. Figure 3.38 illustrates what a human would look like if each member of the body was a miniature reflection of the body itself. At first glance, it doesn't appear very realistic. However, you may be surprised when you examine it more closely. You'll find that many details have appeared that were absent from the seed-plus-copies sketch. For example, "hands" and "feet" have appeared on the end of each limb, complete with fingers and toes. (There are five, but they're hard to count at this magnification.)

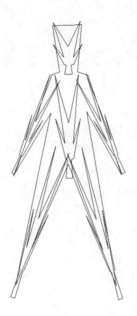

Figure 3.37. A rough sketch of the human form, covered with six copies of itself (BODY).

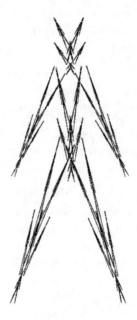

Figure 3.38. "FracMan," a fractal sketch of the human body (BODY).

You Can Do It: FracMan

The fractal way of seeing a human body may be a bit scary at first, but you may be surprised by the accuracy of FracMan's self-reflective geometry.

1. **Load** the BODY **Template**.

The seed approximates the proportions of a human figure. To instruct the computer about how the body is organized, six copies of the seed are included: arms, legs, torso, and head.

2. **Paint** the portrait by pressing I or clicking **Paint** with the right mouse button.

I've used colors to show how various parts of the body are reflected in the rest. The largest muscles are tinted orange (as reflections of the legs), extremities are pink-purple (the color of the head), and lifting muscles are green (like the forearms).

By coloring all parts of the body except one with the background color (making them invisible), you can more clearly see the whole-body reflections of any one part.

3. Press Esc to stop **Paint**ing, select **Clear**, and **Adjust**.

4. Press A to choose **Color** A, the background color. The seed turns black and disappears.

5. Press = to **Color All Levels**. When the handle is on the seed, this colors the entire fractal with the current color. Everything but the handle turns black.

6. Press Tab to grab the Next Part. You can tell it's the torso from the location of the handle, even though you just made the template itself invisible.

7. Press Tab once more to grab the head.

8. Select **Color** B by pressing B. The head turns red.

9. Select **Color All Levels** by pressing =. When you are on any part other than the seed, this applies the current color to that part only at all levels of detail. The seed also turns red.

continues

10. **Accept** your changes by pressing Enter, and **Paint** again by pressing I.

You see only the various parts of the body that correspond geometrically to the head—all the most sensitive, highly enervated parts of the body.

11. Repeat steps 3 through 10 to show only the arms, legs, or torso. If you prefer, simply **Load** the ARMS, LEGS, TORSO, and HEAD **Template**s.

In the next **You Can Do It** box, you'll see FracMan do some calisthenics.

In fact, though this "FracMan" doesn't look much like a person as seen from the outside, it does show a strong resemblance to an acupuncture chart. This isn't too surprising, because the sciences of acupuncture and reflexology (among others) are based on the premise that parts of the body are reflections of the whole.

It is surprising that so simple a mathematical model could reproduce so many details of our anatomy. For example, all the major joints in the body are geometric reflections of the waist. To create Figure 3.39a, I simply pivoted the torso a bit. The neck, elbows, wrists, fingers, knees, ankles, and toes all bent automatically as "reflections" of the waist, as did even the jaw and genitals.

When I tilt FracMan's neck (Figure 3.39b), the corresponding wrist and ankle joints tilt with it. Figures 3.39c and 3.39d show how the jaw, forearm, and calf muscles move as reflections of the arms.

A New View of You

If we wish to understand the nature of the Universe we have an inner hidden advantage: we are ourselves little portions of the universe and so carry the answer within us.

—Jacques Boivin, *The Heart Single Field Theory*

This all suggests a very different view of the body than that implicit in most Western medicine. Is your head something that sits on top of your neck or is it a field of "headness" that permeates your entire body, shining strongest above your shoulders and in your hands, feet, and genitals? These areas have more in common than geometry. They are control centers for the four basic human activities—communication, creativity, locomotion, and reproduction. To see all these reflections highlighted together, take a look at Figure 3.40a, which portrays an archetypal "head-body"—not just a skull, brain, and face, but a "body of sensation and self-expression."

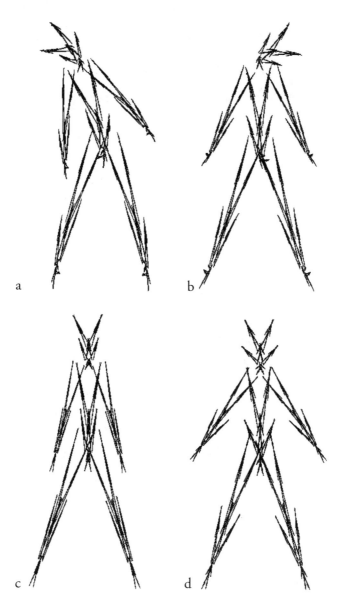

Figure 3.39. Fractal calisthenics (BEND, TILT, FLEX-IN, and FLEX-OUT).

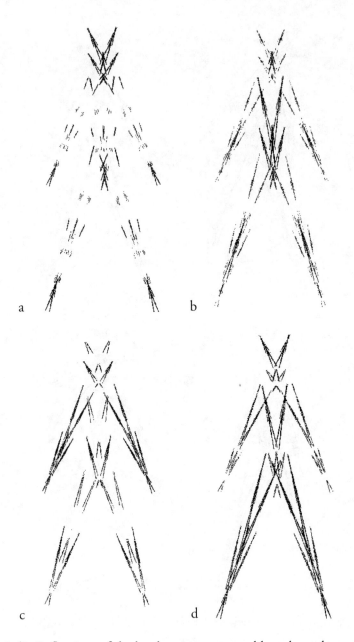

Figure 3.40. Reflections of the head, torso, arms, and legs throughout the body (HEAD, TORSO, ARMS, and LEGS).

Figures 3.40b, 3.40c, and 3.40d depict a whole-body view of torso, arms, and legs. Notice the reflections: thighs become brow, abdominals, and biceps—all of the largest muscles in their respective parts. Feet become head-top, shoulders, and hips, where we bear our burdens. Walking and carrying are rhythmic dances of this whole-body "leg." What archetypal roles do arms and torso mirror throughout the whole?

You Can Do It: Fractal Calisthenics

Sometimes, you just gotta dance…

1. **Clear** any picture you might have on-screen from previous templates, then **Load** the BEND **Template**.

This is the BODY **Template** from the last **You Can Do It** box, with the torso rotated and the head moved and rotated to line up with it.

2. **Paint** and notice how all the major joints of the body now bend slightly. They are all geometric reflections of the waist.

3. Press Esc to stop **Paint**ing, and **Load** the TILT **Template**. I rotated just the head —this time, to the right.

4. **Paint** again. (You don't need to **Clear** first. I've placed this template next to the other one so you can compare the two pictures side by side.)

This time, only the wrists, ankles, and genitals bend. The knees and elbows are not reflections of the neck. Interestingly enough, the wrists and ankles are complex joints capable of twisting in two directions. The knees and elbows don't show the same flexibility.

Just as the waist and neck reflect throughout the body as joints, the arms and legs correspond to muscles. To see the arm-like muscles in action…

5. **Clear** and **Load** the FLEX-IN **Template**. To create this one, I simply pulled the arms in closer to the body.

6. **Paint**, and the calves, forearms, abdominals, and jaw all become tense.

continues

7. Without **Clearing**, **Load** the FLEX-OUT **Template** and **Paint**. All those same muscles relax and spread out.

If FracMan's parts were connected the way ours are, his muscles and joints would move together. The human body is an inseparable microcosm, and even a fractal model fails to capture the intimate interplay of motion involved in a single gesture.

Thinking Fractal

The major problems in the world are the result of the difference between the way nature works and the way man thinks.

—Gregory Bateson, Lindisfarn, Long Island, 1976

This "fractal way of seeing" has already led to an entirely different experience of the human body. Such experiences of self-reflection arise from more than just physical laws and genetic codes. Poets and philosophers throughout the ages have hinted about seemingly separate things being reflections of each other and of themselves.

The body examples demonstrate the incredible difference between the grid-like and fractal mind sets. If we have actually developed an intuitive sense of our environment and ourselves as separate atomistic units, we cannot help but feel the rift that separates us from all else. Feelings and activities such as love and cooperation must reach across a void, and the very structure of the universe seems to keep that chasm open and unbridgeable. Just as a head thinks, a heart beats, and legs walk in independent rhythms, so must I maintain my own greedy separation from all others to have any identity at all.

When you begin to think fractal, the world is a very different place indeed. Each part of that world is defined not by its division from others, but by its resonance with a greater whole. Separation becomes a ridiculous idea when one's identity is gained by a unique transformation, rather than a greedy withdrawal. Just as every part of the body synchronizes with and permeates all others, my individuality is strengthened rather than threatened through giving and cooperation.

Remember, the difference between these two experiences is not in the physical forms that surround us. Just as any shape can be drawn with a pencil or with fractals, any physical world can be experienced either as distinct units or a self-reflective whole.

Be warned, however, that a nonlinear environment (like FractalVision software) can affect your intuition—even more than books about "holographic paradigms" or "the enfolded order." Reading about the "world in a grain of sand" is one thing, but taking a magnifying glass to the beach and looking down at a tiny copy of the top of your own head is quite another.

Fractal Faces

There's no art
To find the mind's construction in the face.

—William Shakespeare, *Macbeth*

As a final exercise in fractal philosophy, take a closer look at that head. If the head is a reflection of the body, it should be possible to reconstruct the essentials of a face from the same six elements arranged in about the same relationship.

Beginning with Figure 3.41a, an upside-down FracMan, I fattened his limbs to make Figure 3.41b. Tilting the "legs" and elevating the "torso" to become a nose produced the bird-like Figure 3.41c. Introspection made me think that the "torso" of my head is the tongue, not the nose. Also, as mentioned earlier, the head-top should be a reflection of the feet. When I tried this arrangement, I produced a clown-like Figure 3.41d, which had all the basic parts, more or less in the right places: eyes with irises appeared as reflections of the mouth and tongue and a new "nose" popped up unexpectedly as some second-level reflections of the jaw and eyes. A little adjustment and I produced Figure 3.41e, a reasonable mapping of the structure (if not the outward appearance) of a face.

Figure 3.42 depicts how slight changes reflect throughout the "expression." Tilting the eyes made the nose and mouth weepy (Figure 3.42a), and a creepy smile produced demonic eyes and eyebrows to match (Figure 3.42b).

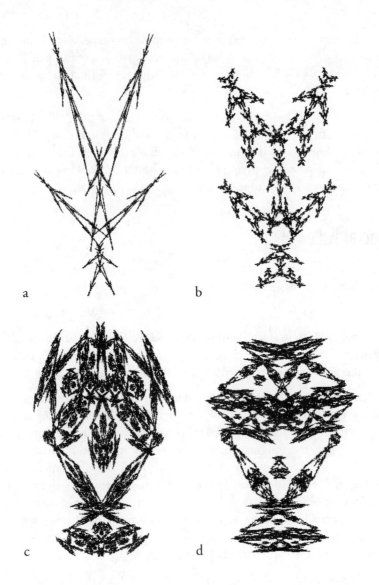

a b

c d

e

Figure 3.41. An upside-down FracMan becomes a face (FACE1, FACE2, FACE3, FACE4, and FACE5).

Figure 3.42. Expressions on a fractal face (WEEPY and CREEPY).

You Can Do It: Fractal Faces

To follow along with the transformation of a body into a face:

1. **Load** the FACE1 through FACE5 **Template**s one by one.

2. **Paint** each of them, **Clear**ing the picture between examples.

3. To see fractal facial expressions, **Load**, **Clear**, and **Paint** WEEPY and CREEPY. Can you put a different expression on FracMan's face?

A Philosophy for the Real World

Once you get over the hump, you understand the paradigm, you can start actually measuring things and thinking about things differently. You have a new vision. It's not the same as the old vision at all—it's much broader.

—Christopher Schulz, seismologist and geologist,
(quoted in James Gleick's *Chaos*, 1986)

Fractals are a powerful tool for real-world modeling. That power comes not only from superficial resemblance to natural forms, but also from deep harmony with the inner workings of the universe. You have seen that:

■ The same iterative processes that form the self-reflective shapes of nature also render it inherently unpredictable and uncontrollable.

■ You can find the fundamental irregularity of nature in the purely abstract realm of mathematical equations as well.

■ Most simple instructions lead to deep complexity, even when carried out with rigid precision.

■ Fractal geometry implies a radically different view of the world than linear geometry—a view where the identity of objects arises from relationship rather than separation.

This new view of the world is consistent with both scientific experiment and everyday observation and can describe any form that can be described by more traditional patterns of thought. In most cases, you can model the appearance and structure of the real world more easily and succinctly with fractals than with linear shapes.

And it's about time you got your hands dirty making some of those real-world models yourself. In the next chapter, you will learn the nitty-gritty of building fractals with FractalVision software.

4

The Art of Fractal Modeling

I n the first three chapters of this book, I presented a great number of fractal models, from plants to planets. Now it's your turn. To create your own fractals, you'll learn how to control the fractal template as a painter controls his brush. As with any new skill, you can develop it by yourself with enough practice, but a few rules and tips will give you a head start.

If you've tried to strike out on your own with FractalVision software, you probably found your own fractal designs surprising. The result of a particular fractal template is always fascinating, but often not quite what you had in mind. As you learned in Chapter 2, "Fractals in the Real World," and Chapter 3, "The Philosophy of Fractals," predicting where any specific point will fall in a fractal is impossible, even in theory.

You can, however, gain control of the overall shape of the whole fractal. Although traditional paint and draw programs require subjects to be broken into many separate pieces, fractal design demands that you work with the entire subject at once. To wield this type of holistic control, you will need to develop a new intuition.

This chapter is intended to supply you with that intuition by leading you through hands-on fractal design projects. Follow along, and soon you'll be able to "fractalize" anything you can see or imagine. When you do discover new and surprising shapes, you'll know how to fine-tune them to evoke their unique qualities.

Ideally, you should switch on your computer and follow along with the design process as you go. In case you prefer (as I do) to read through computer books while sitting outside in the shade sipping lemonade, I've explained and illustrated everything. The actual step-by-step instructions for using the software are confined to the **You Can Do It** boxes. (If you can, however, go ahead and bring your laptop with you to the lawn chair.)

Building Fractals From the Ground Up

If the properties we assign to the natural world are partly expressions of the way we think and our capacity for understanding, then the introduction of new tools such as the computer will change those properties. The computer, like the microscope, expands our senses. The world made visible by the computer seems limitless.
—Clifford Pickover, *Computers, Pattern, Chaos, and Beauty,* 1990

Before you design your first model, it may be useful to review some key points about fractal design from the preceding chapters.

In theory, fractals are infinitely detailed. In practice, however, you can only approximate infinite detail by defining a seed shape, placing reduced copies of that shape, and continuing the pattern repeatedly. The seed shape and its copies compose a fractal template.

There are two ways to create a fractal from a fractal template: You can either draw successive approximations level by level, or paint the infinite level fractal on-screen all at once. These techniques correspond to the **Draw** and **Paint** commands in FractalVision software.

In Chapter 2, I presented a general procedure for fractal modeling:

1. Look for self-reflection and find its limits.

2. Find the relationship between one level of scale and the next.

3. Create a seed shape to mirror the largest or smallest level of scale.

4. Place transformed copies of the seed to reflect the next level of scale.

5. Select a level of detail to match your observations.

6. Continue the pattern to see your results.

7. Fine-tune your shape to match your observations.

The two approaches embodied in FractalVision's **Draw** and **Paint** commands also entail two different techniques of fractal design. Beginning with the successive-approximation approach, you'll soon be ready to step into infinity and learn the all-at-once approach.

Drawing a Plant

To create a little flower is the labor of ages.
—William Blake, *The Marriage of Heaven and Hell,* 1790

Trees and plants are the easiest fractal models to create, and because of the immense variety of plants in the world, you have a lot of leeway in what you call "realistic."

For starters, let's draw a tree. The seed shape will obviously be the trunk, and the copies of the seed will be the first level of branches. You can make the trunk any shape you like. In Figure 4.1, I've gone a bit beyond a common rectangle shape and created the twisty trunk of an apple or an oak tree.

Figure 4.1. The seed shape—soon to become the trunk of a tree—can be any polygon (OAK).

You Can Do It: Shaping a New Seed

Run the FractalVision software (see the Introduction of this book for operating instructions).

As you may have noticed, the white handle always holds either a part of the template—a copy of the seed or the whole seed itself—or a corner point on the seed shape. Use **Next Part** to grab the parts and place, size, and spin them; use **NextPoint** to grab the points and change the shape of the seed. When the handle is on a part, it appears as an upside-down T; when the handle is on a point, is appears as a plus sign (+).

The **New** command creates all new parts or all new points, depending on what the handle is holding. When you start FractalVision, the handle is on the seed part. Before you grab a corner point and make a new shape, you should eliminate all the copies of the seed. This will make it easier to see and work with the corner points of the seed shape.

1. Select **New** and press 0 (this informs FractalVision that you want zero copies of the seed, so only the seed shape remains).

2. Select **NextPoint** to grab a corner point on the seed shape.

3. Select **New**. When you're hanging on to a corner of the seed shape, this command enables you to create a new shape from scratch.

4. If you have a mouse, you can sketch a shape by clicking the left button where you want each corner to appear. After you place the last corner, click the right button.

If you don't have a mouse, press the number of corners you want on your shape and a regular polygon with that many sides will appear. (If the number you choose is less than 6, press Enter to verify that this number isn't the first digit of a larger number.)

5. If you are using a mouse and you want to move some of the corners to adjust the shape, simply point to the corner you want to move, hold down the left button while you drag it around, and release.

If you don't have a mouse or if the points are too close together for FractalVision to determine which one you're trying to grab, you can use the **NextPoint** command to grab corners and the arrow keys to move them.

The **Grow**, **Shrink**, **Spin**, **Skew**, **Stretch**, and **Squish** commands also will change the overall shape of the seed when the handle rests on a corner point. You may want to experiment with a few of these commands to get a feel for their operation.

In the next **You Can Do It** box, you'll place the branches on your trunk.

After you make a seed shape, create copies and place them where the first level of branches would go on a tree. In Figure 4.2, I have placed four branches, all of them smaller than the main trunk and rotated to match the angle of the part of the trunk where they are attached.

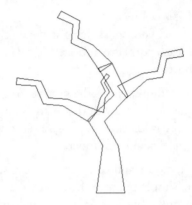

Figure 4.2. Four copies of the trunk define the branching pattern of a tree (OAK).

When FractalVision continues my branching pattern, it produces Figure 4.3.

Figure 4.3. The tree defined in Figure 4.2 to the eighth level of detail (OAK).

Figures 4.4 and 4.5 illustrate the results of slightly different branching patterns.

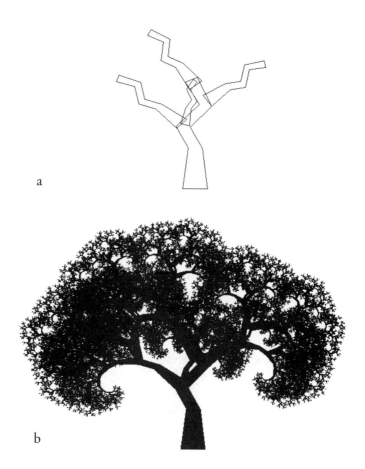

a

b

Figure 4.4. Slightly larger branches produce a fuller tree (OAK2).

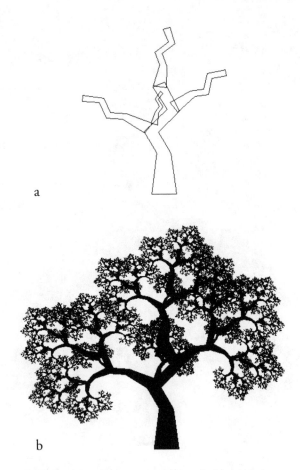

Figure 4.5. Tilting the top of the tree makes all the branches curve, too (OAK3).

You Can Do It: Placing Copies of the Seed

To place your branches:

1. Select **Next Part** and then select **New**.

2. If you have a mouse, you can place copies of the seed by pointing and clicking the left button. Although the copies won't have any rotation

(you will add that later), for now, plop three or four of them on the screen and press the right mouse button when you're done.

If you aren't using a mouse, type a number (4, for example) to create a corresponding number of seed copies to automatically arrange in a circle around the seed.

3. Use **Next Part**, the arrow keys, and the **Spin** command to place the branches where you want them. Use **Shrink** and **Grow** to adjust their sizes.

    Alternatively, you can do this with the mouse by grabbing and dragging the center of a part with the left button to move it and grabbing the top of the longest pole of the handle to spin and size it (this takes a bit of practice and a steady hand).

    I usually combine the mouse and keyboard techniques by using the mouse to get the parts approximately where I want them, and the keyboard to fine-tune them. By selecting **Precision**, you can move and spin in very small increments to get everything just right. Select **Precision** again for gross movements. (Note that you cannot size and spin with the mouse when fine precision is on.)

4. Select **Draw** to watch your tree grow.

5. Select **Clear** and use **Next Part**, **Grow**, **Shrink**, and **Spin** to change the branches slightly, then **Draw** again. (Can you mimic Figures 4.4 and 4.5? If you would like to see my version of these templates, they're called OAK, OAK2, and OAK3 and they are included on the disk that accompanies this book.)

All that remains between you and a complete fractal model of a tree are some picky adjustments: the level of detail, coloring, shading. Figure 4.6 shows the effect of setting the level of detail. Level 0 is the seed, and Level 1 is the first level of branches that you created. Subsequent levels repeat the pattern for branches and branchlettes.

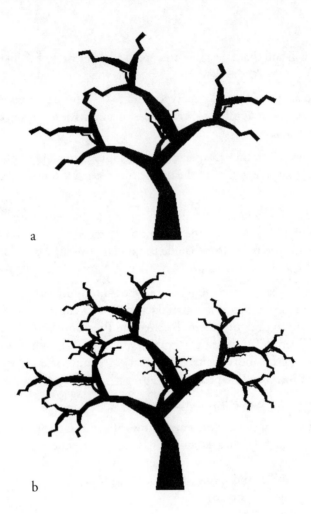

a

b

Figure 4.6. The oak tree with level-of-detail settings from 2 (a) to 5 (d) (OAK).

Drawing a detailed tree can take quite some time: *each* level of detail adds four branches to every existing branch, taking almost four times as long as the previous level of detail to complete. If the level of detail or the number of parts is greater than 5 or 6, even the fastest computer will keep you waiting for a while.

Fortunately with FractalVision's **Paint** command, you can skip to the infinite level. By drawing the first few levels and then painting the infinite level on top of that, you can quickly produce an image that is nearly identical to Level 14 or 15. Figure 4.7, for example, is identical to Figure 4.6d except that the infinite level has been sprayed on top of it. (Inquiring minds will discover the magic behind this business of "skipping to the infinite level" in Chapter 5, "The Math Behind the Magic.")

Figure 4.7. You can save a lot of time by drawing only up to the fifth level of detail and then painting the "infinite" level (OAK).

The final adjustments that you can make are coloring and shading. Although you'll have to crank up the machine to see color (or turn to the color plates in the middle of the book), shading we can do.

The two types of shading, or fill, that are used most often are *outline* (0% fill, Figure 4.8a), and *solid* (100% fill, Figure 4.8b). On some computers, 0% fill will draw much faster than 100% fill, so you might want to design a model using outlines and then change to solid fill for the final image.

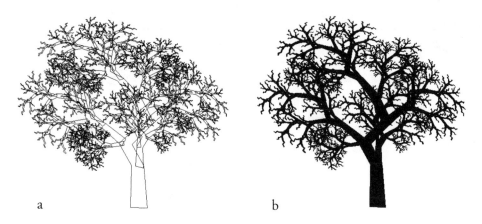

a   b

Figure 4.8. The tree as an outline produced with 0% fill (a). The tree as a solid produced with 100% fill (b) (APPLE).

You can also fill shapes with a random haze varying from 10% to 90%. For a tree, this would add a bark-like texture (Figure 4.9). This is also handy when you want transparency and a gaseous look, as with the clouds in Chapter 2.

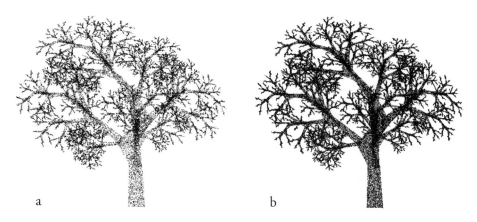

a   b

Figure 4.9. An apple tree with 25% fill (a) and 75% fill (b) (APPLE).

You Can Do It: The Adjust Panel

FractalVision features one master control panel that adjusts the level of detail, coloring, and shading.

1. **Load** the **Template** named OAK, and **Clear** the picture so you can see the template.

2. Select **NextPoint** and immediately select **Next Part**. This is a shortcut to put the handle on the seed part without going through the other parts first.

3. Select **Adjust** to access a menu-like control panel:

```
ADJUST DETAILS:


ACTION            KEY
 Next Part        Tab
 Color All Levels  =
 Color All Parts   \
 Fill All Parts    ¦
 Blend Colors      .
 Accept           Esc


                111111
        0123456789012345
 Level  ■---------------


        0%    50%  100%
 Fill   ████████████


 Colors A  B  C  D  E
        F  G  H  I  J
        K  L  M  N  O  P


        0%    50%   100%
 Red    ████
 Green  ███
 Blue   ■
```

(If you have a CGA or Hercules adapter, you will only see **Colors A** and **B**, and the **Red/Green/Blue** controls won't be there. Also, your color settings may differ if you did not begin this session with the STARTUP template which comes up when you start FractalVision.)

You can only adjust one part (the part that the handle is currently on) of the template at a time. (The **Color All Parts** and **Fill All Parts** menu choices are exceptions to this rule, and I'll discuss these momentarily.)

Currently, the handle rests on the seed. Because the seed is brown, **Color B** is selected (it has a white circle around it). The dotted line to the right of the word **Level** is also brown. The **Red/Green/Blue** settings define the brown color: **Red** is set at around 30%, and **Green** is set at about 10%.

Now, look at the settings for another part, a copy of the seed.

4. Select **Next Part**.

A progression of colors appears by the word **Level**. These are the colors for this copy of the seed at each level of detail. The first few levels (trunk and branches) are brown, and the last few (foliage) are green. The white rectangle indicates that the current **Level** of detail is 6.

The template colors always reflect the color at the current level of detail, so this branch is green.

5. Press the letter J to change the current color to violet. The white oval is now around **Color J**, and the block under **Level 6** turns violet. The **Red/Green/Blue** settings also now define violet instead of green.

   Notice that the other branches on the tree didn't change, and that the colors for this part at levels 0 through 5 didn't change either. If you wanted to make this part violet at all levels of detail, you would now select **Color All Levels**. However, proceed to Step 6 instead.

6. Select **Color All Parts** to change all the branches to violet at **Level 6**.

7. Select **Accept**, and then **Draw**. All the branches at **Level 6** are now violet instead of green.

That might seem like a lot to learn just to change the color of the foliage, and it was. Don't worry, however, if you didn't catch everything. You'll have

continues

241

plenty of opportunities to familiarize yourself with the **Adjust** panel as you cruise through the remaining **You Can Do It** boxes in this chapter.

For now, just hop back in there and go through each of the basic operations once.

8. Try each of the operations in the following question and answer section: select **Clear** and **Adjust** and do the operation, and select **Accept** and **Draw** to see the result.

Answering Questions

The FractalVision **Adjust** panel gives you complete control over the coloring and shading of every part of your template, at every level of detail. I'm sure you have many questions about how to harness this impressive array of features. I'll answer your questions, if you pretend that you asked them. All the following instructions assume that you have already chosen **Adjust** from the main menu.

Level of Detail

Q: How do I set the level of detail? (Example: I want to draw only the first few levels of branches on a tree.)

A: Type a number from 0 to 15, use the arrow keys, or click the **Level** setting you want with the mouse.

Color Assignment

Q: How do I change the color of a part at one level of detail? (Example: I want to make only the very tip of each branch white.)

A: Select that level of detail, then select **Next Part** until the handle is on the part you want to color. Finally, pick the color by pressing a letter or clicking on the color with the mouse.

Q: How do I change the color of a part at all levels of detail? (Example: I want to make all left-branching sticks and twigs a different color than the right-branching sticks and twigs.)

A: Use **Next Part** to grab the part you want to color, pick the color you want, and then select **Color All Levels**.

Q: How do I change the color of all parts at a single level? (Example: I want to make all the Level 5 foliage yellow.)

A: Pick that level by pressing a number, select the color by pressing a letter, then select **Color All Parts**.

Q: How do I change the whole template—all parts and all levels—to one color? (Example: I want the entire tree to be brown.)

A: Select **Next Part** until the handle rests on the seed shape, then select **Color All Levels**. Because the seed is Level zero on all the parts, every part takes on the color at every level.

Red/Green/Blue Palette Adjustment

Q: How do I mix a new custom color? (Example: I want to make everything that's green bright orange instead, but no orange appears on the **Colors** palette.)

A: Pick the color you want to replace by pressing its letter, then use the mouse or arrow keys to change the **Red**, **Green**, and **Blue** settings. (You can make bright orange, for example, by setting **Red** to 100%, **Green** to 70%, and **Blue** to 0%.)

Fill, or Shading

Q: How do I draw a single part as an outline only? (Example: I want the seed part to be an outline, but the rest of the tree to stay filled.)

A: Use **Next Part** to grab the part and change the **Fill** setting to 0%. You can either click 0% fill with the mouse or use the up/down arrows to move to **Fill** and the left arrow to decrease the setting to 0%. (Shortcut: Press Home instead of the left arrow to skip to 0%.)

Q: How do I make a single part draw as a filled solid? (Example: I changed my mind, and I want the seed to be solid again.)

A: Set the **Fill** for that part to 100%. As a short cut, use the End key instead of the right arrow to skip to 100%.

Q: How do I draw everything as an outline or a solid? (Example: I want the entire tree to be hollow, or I want the entire tree filled.)

A: Set the **Fill** for any part to 0% (for outline) or 100% (for solid), then select **Fill All Parts**.

Q: How do I fill the shapes with random haze rather than just outline or solid? (Example: I want a bark-like texture on the tree.)

A: Change the **Fill** setting to anything other than 0% or 100%. The higher the setting, the denser the fill.

As you explore the rest of this chapter, you might want to refer back to this question and answer section. Remember that you'll need a bit of experience to master these powerful and flexible coloring and shading options.

Drawing A Still Life

Intuition is not something that is given. I've trained my intuition to accept as obvious shapes which were initially rejected as absurd, and I find everyone else can do the same.

—Benoit Mandelbrot, (quoted in *Chaos* by James Gleick, 1985)

So far in this chapter you've investigated almost every control used in FractalVision software. As all this information sinks in, you may experience a shift in the way you see and work with fractal templates. Shapes that once surprised you will begin to become obvious. In pursuit of this subtle shift in intuition, I'll guide you through the design of another fractal drawing. Following the tradition of many great artists before you, you'll be drawing a still life—a terra-cotta pot filled with dried grass.

You will usually start a fractal model with a previously designed template that features a similar color palette (and possibly a similar seed shape) to what you're after. For instance, you can start designing a tree by loading an existing tree so you don't have to mix all the greens and browns from scratch. The trunk and branches may even be reusable with only slight modification. In this case, start with the template in Figure 4.10.

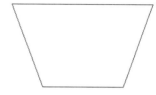

Figure 4.10. You will grow the grass from this pot (POT).

How do you make grass grow out of the pot? The old-fashioned way requires you to draw the grass as a separate set of objects. The fractal way, of course, is to create the grass from copies of the pot itself. In Figure 4.11, one miniature pot grows into a blade of grass (or something vaguely resembling a blade of grass, anyway). Because the minipot is thinner and higher than the original, the grass shoots upward and thins out as it grows.

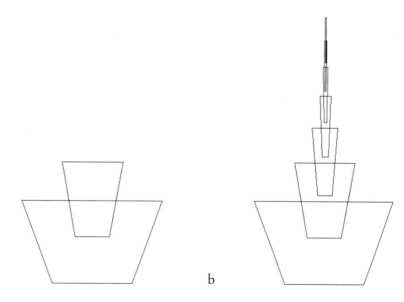

a   b

Figure 4.11. Copies of the pot grow up from it (POT).

One blade of grass, however, just won't do it. Figure 4.12 adds two more copies of the seed. The three copies become nine, twenty-seven, seventy-two, and more when the pattern continues.

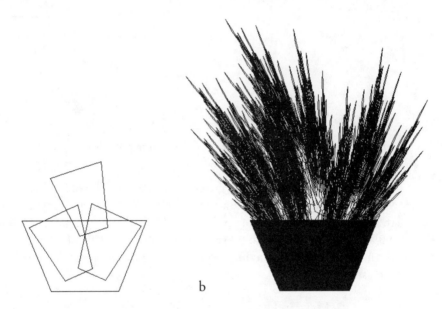

a   b

Figure 4.12. Three copies of the seed multiply to become a full pot of grass (POTGRASS).

You Can Do It: Pot and Grass

Usually, you can find a template with a palette and seed close to what you need. This time, however, you might as well learn to make your own from square one.

1. Select **Next Part** and **New**, then press 0 to kill all copies of the seed so you can see the seed shape by itself.

2. Select **NextPoint** and **New**, then press 4 and Enter. (This is square one.)

3. Select **Spin** four times to line up the square with the top and bottom of the screen.

4. Select **Shrink** or **Grow** until the square is about one-quarter the width of the screen—small enough to leave room for something to grow from the top.

5. Select **NextPoint** until the handle rests on the top-left corner of the square, and press the left arrow three times.

6. Select **NextPoint** again and press the right arrow three times. Your pot should now resemble Figure 4.10.

To grow the grass, you need to add some copies of the seed.

7. Select **Next Part** and **Insert.** You could also have selected **New** and entered the number 1, but pressing the Insert key is faster when you want to add just one part.

8. Using the arrow keys or the mouse, move the new copy of the seed to the position shown in Figure 4.11.

9. Select **Grow** and **Squish** four times each. The quick way to do this is to press ****[[[.

10. Select **Draw** and **View.** Again, the result should resemble Figure 4.11. (Until you selected **View**, the seed shape may seem to disappear. This happens because the template was drawn with an XOR operation. If you don't know what that is, trust me that the disappearance of the seed is an unavoidable illusion caused by displaying the template atop the drawing. When in doubt, use **View** to see how the picture really looks and **Clear** to see how the template really looks. Selecting **Restore** puts the picture back after you **Clear** it.)

11. **Clear** the picture and **Insert** twice to get two more parts.

12. Use **Next Part**, the arrow keys, and **Spin** to arrange the new parts as shown in Figure 4.12. Notice that the new parts are identical to the part that the handle was on when you **Insert**ed, so you don't need to **Grow** and **Squish** them.

13. Select **Draw** and **View** again to check your work. Twiddle and fiddle until you your picture resembles Figure 4.12.

continues

247

Now, set up the colors you need for the dried grass and terra cotta:

14. Select **Adjust.**

15. Select **Color** B by pressing the letter B. Always start with B as your first usable color because color A is the background color of the screen.

16. With the mouse or arrow keys, adjust the **Red** setting to 75%, **Green** to approximately 30%, and **Blue** to 0%. Adjust these percentages until the pot looks like terra cotta to you. If you find terra cotta too tame, make the pot a brilliant magenta or an aquamarine instead.

Dried grass might be yellowish-orange at the tip and greenish at the base of the stem. Between the tip and the base, you should gradually blend the two colors. You can do that.

17. Select **Color** C and create green with **Red** at 10%, **Green** at 75%, and **Blue** at 0%.

18. Select Color H and create yellow-orange with **Red** at 90%, **Green** at 75%, and **Blue** at 0%.

19. Select **Blend Colors.** When FractalVision asks you "Blend from H to what color?" press the letter C. Poof! It automatically computes a gradation from green to yellow-orange.

Now comes the hard part: assigning those colors to the right levels and parts of the template. You could use a lot of coloring schemes for this image, but for now, designate all the grass at Level 1 to be green, the next level to be green-yellow, and so on. Here's how to set that up:

20. Select **Next Part** once if the handle is on the seed. It's easier to see what you're doing if the handle isn't on the seed because the seed only has one level by definition.

21. Press 1 and then C. This sets the current part to Color C at Level 1.

22. To make all the other parts the same color at Level 1, select **Color All Parts.**

23. Press 2 and then D and select **Color All Parts** again by pressing \.

24. Keep going. Press these keys in order: 3 E \ 4 F \ 5 G \ 6 H \.

25. The pot is Level 0. Give it the right color by pressing 0 and then B.

26. Set the **Level** back to a guess at what you'll want it to be for the finished drawing: press 6.

27. Select **Accept** (press Esc) to return to the main menu, and **Draw.**

If you didn't follow all that (or don't want to follow all that), you can **Load** the **Template** named POT to start at Figure 4.11 or POTGRASS for the completed template in Figure 4.12.

For a bit of spit and polish, you may want to use coloring to differentiate the individual blades a bit more.

28. Select **Clear** and press Tab (**Next Part**) until the handle rests on the leftmost copy of the seed.

29. Select **Adjust** and press D to change Level 6 for this part to a greenish color.

30. Select **Accept** and **Draw.**

Finally, add the pot:

31. Select **Adjust** and press 0 to set the level to zero, and use the arrow keys or the mouse to set the **Fill** to 100%.

32. Select **Accept** and **Draw.** Finis. **Save** it.

This fractal masterpiece may not end up in the Louvre, but if you persevered through the steps of its creation, you've gained quite a bit of fractal drawing experience. You've also started building a designer's vocabulary. Think of "squish and rise" as a phrase in the visual language of fractals. You now know that any time a shape is squeezed and raised repeatedly, you'll see a set of thin spreading needles. With a little spin here and there and some different colors, you can use the same geometric pattern for fractal explosions and starburst shapes. Similarly, you can modify the branching pattern for the oak tree that you learned earlier to create branching structures of all types, from shrubs to bronchial passages.

As you sculpt fractal galaxies, letters, fish, and chickens (!) in the rest of this chapter, you will build your vocabulary to include spirals, zooms, sparks, and feathery textures. Once you've seen the basic visual formula for taking a spiral or a zoom into the distance, you'll be able to recognize and model those patterns wherever you encounter them.

Drawing Design Review

Whatever can be done once can always be repeated.

—Louise Young, *The Mystery of Matter*

Here's a review of the steps for fractal drawing (you can often switch the order in which you do these):

1. Set up (or load) the palette of colors with which you think you want to work.

2. Define a seed shape out of which the rest of the design will arise.

3. Think, "How can I transform the seed to *move toward* the shape I'm after?" Insert copies that progress one step toward the eventual shape. For example, if you want the shape to "thin out," squish a copy; if you want it to "zoom in," place a shrunken copy in the middle of the seed.

4. Try various levels of detail and touch up your copies as you see the results.

5. When the basic shape is just right, adjust your colors and shading.

6. Fine-tune it, then draw and save it.

7. Add any accents and extras by drawing or painting over your original drawing.

Up to this point, you've been building fractals level by level with FractalVision's **Draw** command. The most powerful design techniques, including fractal image compression, spray the entire fractal on-screen at once at the infinite level (the **Paint** command). Traditional computer rendering techniques stop at a few thousand lines or a few million pixels. Infinity is where serious fractal design begins.

Collage: The Whole Fractal at Once

Graphics systems founded on traditional geometry are great for creating pictures of man-made objects, such as bricks, wheels, roads, buildings, and cogs. However, they don't work well at all when the problem is to encode a sunset, a tree, a lump of mud, or the intricate structure of a black spleenwort fern.... We need a richer library of geometrical shapes. These shapes need to be flexible and controllable so that they can be made to conform to clouds, mosses, feathers, leaves, and faces, not to mention waving sunflowers and glaring arctic wolves. Fractal geometry provides just such a collection of shapes.

—Michael Barnsley, "A Better Way to Compress Images," *BYTE*, 1988

The collage theorem is a Golden Rule of fractal design:

> **If you completely cover the seed with copies of itself, with no holes or "overhangs," the resulting fractal will always look like the seed itself.**

To see how this works, examine the fractal template in Figure 4.13. The seed is a square, and the template contains four minisquares. The smaller squares cover the larger one completely, leaving no holes—they don't hang over the edges of the big square either. When you continue this pattern, each level completely covers up the next larger level, re-creating the original shape (Figure 4.14). Regardless of how many levels you descend, even to the infinite level of FractalVision's **Paint** command, you'll end up with the same square.

You can re-create any shape by covering it exactly with copies of itself. Figure 4.15 illustrates how you can also completely tile a triangle with four miniatures of itself.

Figure 4.16 is a more complex example, where some of the copies overlap. This overlap doesn't change the shape of the resulting fractal as long as the copies don't hang over the edge of the seed.

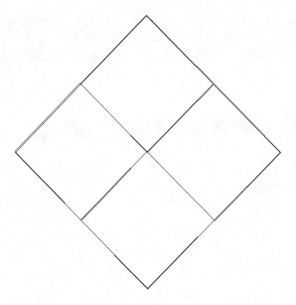

Figure 4.13. You can tile a square with four copies of itself (SQUARE).

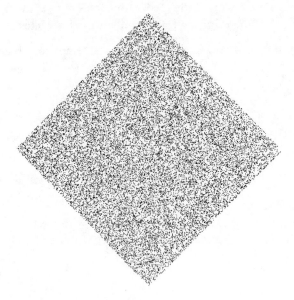

Figure 4.14. By continuing the pattern, you can reproduce a square as an infinitely detailed fractal (SQUARE).

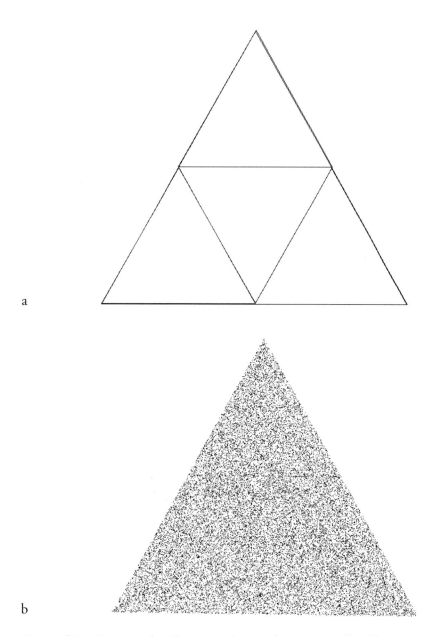

a

b

Figure 4.15. You can also tile a triangle with four copies of itself and reproduce it perfectly with a fractal (TRIANGLE).

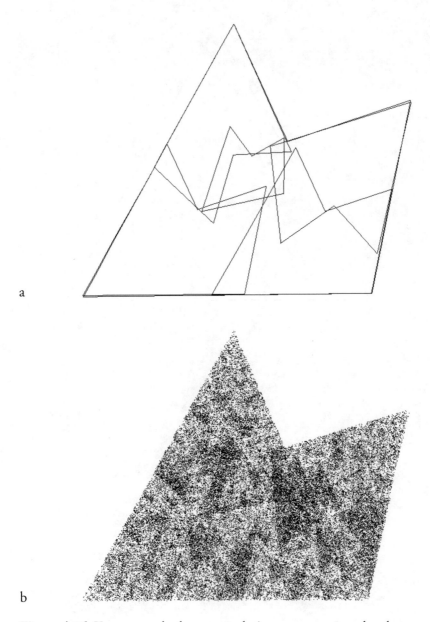

a

b

Figure 4.16. You can apply the same technique to more complex shapes (COLLAGE).

You Can Do It: Fractal Collage

Run FractalVision and try to make a fractal collage using the following steps:

1. Select **NextPoint**, then select **New**.

2. If you are using a mouse, sketch a shape from your imagination by pointing where you want each corner point and clicking the left button. Then click the right button when you're done. (If you aren't using a mouse, press the number of points you want and move them with the arrow keys and the **NextPoint** command.)

3. Select **Next Part** and **New**. Use the same procedure to place a few copies of the seed (five or six, for example).

4. Finally, use the mouse and/or menu to resize and place the copies to completely cover the shape as perfectly as you can.

5. When you **Paint** or **Draw**, you should see the same shape filled. The more accurate your collage, the closer the final image will resemble your seed.

Tiling Variations

We should remark the grace and fascination that there is even in the incidentals of Nature's processes. When a loaf of bread, for instance, is in the oven, cracks appear in it here and there; and these flaws, though not intended in the baking, have a rightness of their own, and sharpen the appetite.

—Marcus Aurelius, *Mediations*, second century A.D.

What if you left small holes or overhanging edges when you tiled a shape? They would appear throughout the fractal at all levels. You can control the accents and details of your fractal by learning to predict these "side effects" and employing them on purpose. Figure 4.17 illustrates the result of shrinking one of the copies while leaving the others intact. This action opens a crack in the square, which then propagates through the whole fractal.

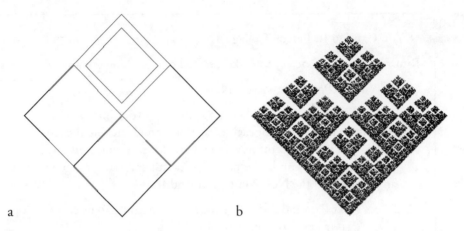

a   b

Figure 4.17. By shrinking one of the tiles in Figure 4.13, you can introduce fractal cracks (SHRINKSQ).

In Figure 4.18, I have enlarged the same copy until it hangs over the edge of the seed. Again, the aberration is reflected in each part at every level.

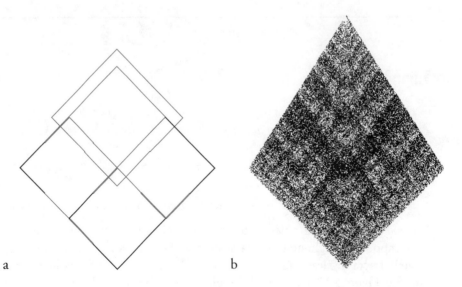

a   b

Figure 4.18. Enlarge a tile to hang over the edge of the original square, and a fractal arrowhead grows from one corner (GROWSQ).

Figures 4.19 through 4.21 show the effects of spinning, stretching, and skewing the same tile. Each type of transformation is carried to infinity in a predictable way.

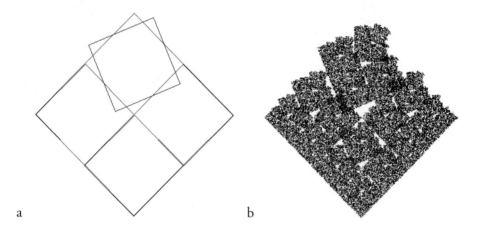

a   b

Figure 4.19. Spinning a tile creates a spiral overhang on the corner (SPINSQ).

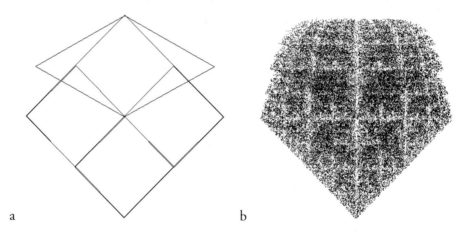

a   b

Figure 4.20. Stretching a tile widens the entire top (STRETCHSQ).

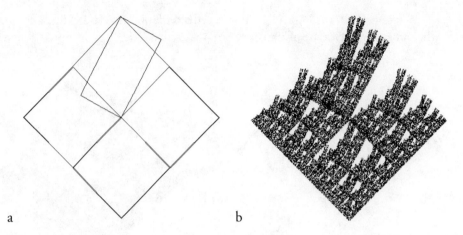

a   b

Figure 4.21. Skewing the tile forms sweeping, curved points (SKEWSQ).

You Can Do It: Controlled Tiling

Starting with the SQUARE and TRIANGLE examples, introduce some different kinds of holes and overhangs, and notice how they reflect in the finished shape. Use the following steps as an exercise:

1. **Clear** the picture and **Load** the **Template** named SQUARE.

2. Select **Next Part** until the handle appears on the top copy of the seed.

3. Select **Shrink** twice and **Paint**. (This re-creates Figure 4.17.)

4. Select **Clear** and **Shrink** once or twice more. Can you anticipate what shape will appear before you **Paint** it?

5. Select **Paint**. How close is the result to the shape you predicted? The same cracking pattern appears, but the cracks are larger.

Imagine an effect you'd like to create and try to produce it. Try another. This exercise is worth an hour or two of playtime. Controlled tiling is the foundation of almost all the fancy tricks that I'll show you later.

Don't be discouraged, however, if you can't seem to gain control over your results just yet. As you continue to practice, you'll develop an eye for tiling and a feel for the mouse and the keyboard. Fractals training works on your intuition more than your hands, and that may take a few sessions to develop.

6. **Clear, Load** the TRI1 example, and **Paint.** (This shape was created by modifying the four-tile triangle in Figure 4.15.)

7. Without **Clear**ing, **Load** the TRIANGLE template, which is a triangle perfectly tiled with four copies of itself.

8. Can you change this template so that it will re-create the image on-screen? Try it and select **Paint** to check your work.

I recommend that you repeat steps 6 through 8 for the TRI2 and TRI3 templates, each of which is a modified version of TRIANGLE. **Paint** with each of them, then re**Load** TRIANGLE and try to modify it and reproduce the shape.

This may be the hardest exercise in the whole book, but it's also the most important. When you become reasonably adept at tiling control, you will find that creating real-world fractal models is a breeze.

Generally, irregular shapes (see Figure 4.16) require more copies to cover them, while simple shapes (like Figures 4.13 and 4.15) can be tiled with very few copies. Irregular shapes are also harder to tile without an overlap between copies. This overlap doesn't change the outline of the resulting fractal, but it can create shading variations within the shape.

This effect is clearly shown in Figure 4.16. Unlike the square and triangle, which both filled uniformly, this shape fills with a complex shading pattern. Where does the pattern originate? When two copies overlap, the overlapped areas within the fractal appear "denser" than the unoverlapped areas. When you **Paint**, these dense spots are reflected throughout the shape, just as holes and overhangs are. If you pay careful attention to the placement of the overlap, you can control the shading pattern.

It's easy to tile simple shapes such as squares and triangles with copies of themselves. But the power of the collage theorem enables you to reconstruct shapes as grand and intricate as an entire galaxy…

Painting the Galaxy

Geometry is concerned with making our spatial intuitions objective.... Fractal geometry is an extension of classical geometry. It can be used to make precise models of physical structures from ferns to galaxies.

—Michael Barnsley, *Fractals Everywhere*, 1988

Figure 4.22 is an artist's rendering of the Milky Way. The artist is me.

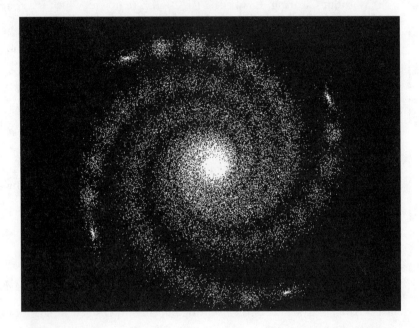

Figure 4.22. You can put the Milky Way into your computer (GALAXY2).

Unlike the galaxy you modeled in Chapter 2, this one has several spiral arms. To view this the fractal way, you can imagine that the cluster of stars at the end of each arm is a copy of the whole galaxy. If you clipped off those end clusters (with metagalactic pruning shears), the remaining portion of the galaxy would resemble a copy of the whole as well. In Figure 4.23, I tiled a rough sketch of the galaxy with five copies of itself, four arm ends, and one galactic center.

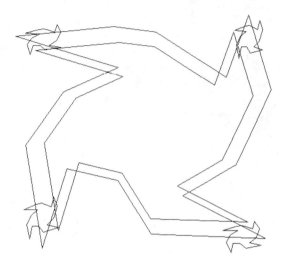

Figure 4.23. You can roughly tile a general outline of the galaxy with five copies of itself (GALAXY2A).

Figure 4.24 is the fractal defined by the template in Figure 4.23. I succeeded in modeling four radial arms, but this ain't no spiral galaxy if it don't spiral.

How do real galaxies spiral? If you know the answer to that question, you can put that knowledge to work in your model. You actually don't need to know the answer if you have a visual representation, however. Even if you weren't aware that real galaxies spin, you could see by looking at a picture like Figure 4.22 that the inside part of the galaxy is a *rotated* copy of the whole.

In this case, the geometry betrays the inner workings of the real system. When you delve into fractal image processing, you'll find that a well-defined "real system" isn't always available as a base for your fractal image. At that point, the fact that geometry itself is enough to create a fractal mimic will become all-important.

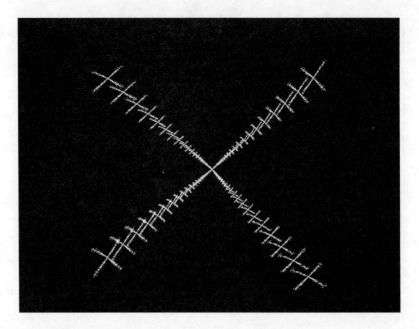

Figure 4.24. The fractal defined by the template in Figure 4.23 (GALAXY2A).

For the moment, however, you only need to concern yourself with getting those arms to spiral one way or the other. Both the physical laws of inertia and the geometric relationships in the picture suggest spinning the central copy of the seed (see Figure 4.25).

As a final step, add some randomness. No star cluster or galactic center is an exact copy of an entire galaxy. Figure 4.26 uses the same template as Figure 4.25, with 25% random displacement added to each dot.

How did I get from Figure 4.26 to Figure 4.22? Just by foolin' around. Although the step-by-step instructions and illustrations in this book may appear to be straightforward, real fractal design is no more linear than the models that derive from it. I whipped off Figure 4.26 from scratch in about five minutes, but the subtle alterations that turned Figure 4.26 into Figure 4.22 took the better part of an hour—and remember that I've used this software a lot longer than anyone else on the planet (or in this galaxy for that matter).

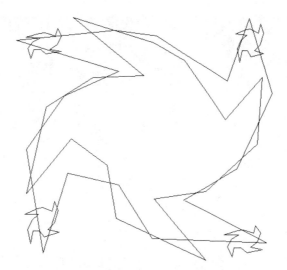

a

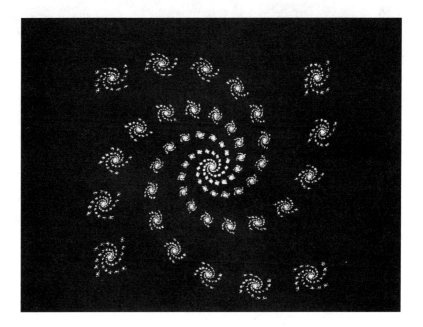

b

Figure 4.25. By spinning the central part of the template, you can create spiral arms (GALAXY2B).

Figure 4.26. The template in Figure 4.25, with 25% randomness added (GALAXY2B).

FractalVision is a powerful tool, but it won't design for you. A keen eye and a lot of practice aren't in danger of being replaced by fancy software in the near future. (Fortunately, you have more than 200 predesigned templates to use and learn from while you're practicing. Experience is the best teacher, but you can learn from the experiences of others, too.)

You Can Do It: The Milky Way

And now for some do-it-yourself galaxy building:

1. Select **NextPoint** and **New**, then use the left mouse button to sketch a vague semblance of a four-armed spiral galaxy. Click with the right button after you've placed all the corners with the left button.

Alternately, you can press the number 8 to make an octagon, then use **NextPoint** and the arrow keys (or mouse) to pull the arms. Using either method, the result should resemble something like the largest shape in Figure 4.23.

2. Select **Next Part** and **New**, then press the number 4 to arrange four copies of the seed around it.

3. Using the mouse (or the arrow keys-**Next Part** combination), pull the four copies in so that they are positioned approximately over the ends of the galactic arms.

4. **Shrink** and **Squish** each of them until they are the size of a small star cluster at the end of a galactic arm (say, a few thousand light years away).

5. Select **NextPoint** and then **Next Part** (a quick way to grab the seed part).

6. Select **Insert** and use the mouse or the arrow keys to place the new part in the center of the galaxy.

7. Select **Grow** a few times and **Spin** once or twice.

Before you look at the fractal you've created, make it the right color:

8. Select **Adjust**, press Tab (meaning **Next Part**) until the handle is on the seed, then press P and =, using **Color P** to **Color All Parts** of the template.

9. Press Esc to return to the main menu and **Paint**.

Now it's time to fuss and fiddle.

10. Use the **Next Part** command to grab any part that seems a little off, twiddle it with **Grow**, **Spin**, **Squish**, or **Shrink** or move it a bit with the arrow keys.

For these final adjustments, you'll probably want to select **Precision** once to resort to fine movements. The handle will shrink and all changes will use baby steps instead of giant steps.

11. Select **Clear** and **Paint** again to see what you've done. Continue to twiddle until your sense of perfection is fulfilled.

Advanced Design Techniques

Fractals are about looking closely and seeing more.

—Tim Wegner and Mark Peterson, *Fractal Creations*, 1991

Growing your own grass and sculpting your own galaxies is all well and good, but we can't all be botanists and cosmologists. For those of you who dabble in personal publishing, you can also apply fractals to arts and letters. I'll start with letters and then use fractal artistry to illustrate additional advanced fractal design tips.

Designing a Fractal Letter

Art is man's nature.

—Edmund Burke, 1791

The goal here is to create a fractal letter F. The F in the word *Fractal* at the beginning of Chapter 3 (see Figure 3.1) is one possibility, but I'll start with something a bit more conventional.

For the first step, shape the seed like the F you want. In Figure 4.27 I've used a caption of box-characters (a grid) as a guide for shaping the seed.

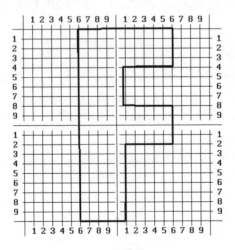

Figure 4.27. You can use the GRID template as a guide for lining up your seed shapes (GRID).

You Can Do It: Using a Caption Grid

The grid in Figure 4.27 is handy whenever you want a graph paper background to help you line up parts of your templates. Here's how to use it:

1. **Load** the GRID template.

2. Use **Next Part/New** and **NextPoint/New** to start a new template, and use the mouse and the arrow keys to line everything up with the grid in the background. You can **Draw**, **Paint**, and **Clear** without affecting the grid.

3. When you want to remove the grid, select **Extras**, then **Caption** and **ClearText**.

The next step is to tile the F with copies of itself. Many tilings are possible. One possibility appears in these examples. Figure 4.28 shows the first two copies in place—one in the upper part of the letter, one in the middle. To create Figure 4.29, I added two more copies right next to (and overlapping) the first two. Figure 4.30 completes the tiling by adding two more copies in the vertical part of the F. Figure 4.31 shows the resulting fractal shape.

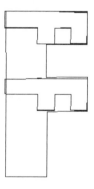

Figure 4.28. One way to tile an F with Fs is to start with two copies like this... (F-1)

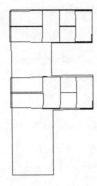

Figure 4.29. ...then add two more copies like this... (F-2)

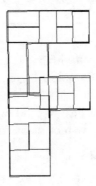

Figure 4.30. ...then add two more copies like this (F-3).

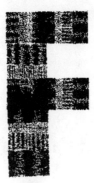

Figure 4.31. The resulting fractal reconstructs the original shape of the F (F-3).

You Can Do It: Fantastic Flying Fractal Fs

All the letters illustrated in this section look much more impressive on a color monitor than on a black-and-white page. To follow the development of a fractal letter, simply **Clear**, **Load**, and **Paint** each of the sample files specified in parentheses in the figure captions. (Press the letter I instead of P if you find your paintings come out too sparse.)

If you've worked your way through the previous **You Can Do It** boxes in this chapter, you should have enough experience to try designing more fractal letters of your own. (Hint: Be sure to peek at the example templates named CHAOS, YES!, and SPECIAL.)

Because the six copies overlap in some places, the fractal that results is not uniform in "density." If you don't want the vertical part (and its reflections) to be so faint, you can add another copy on top of that area to make it denser (see Figure 4.32). In Figure 4.33 you can see the reflections of the new copy.

Figure 4.32. By adding another copy over the faint area, you can make the density of the fractal more uniform (F-FIX).

I'll make sure you understand those reflections. Adding a copy produced a dense spot on the big F—the seed. But because that big F is tiled with copies of itself, a dense spot appeared on each of those mini-Fs, too. Those mini-Fs are tiled with even smaller Fs, which show even smaller dense spots, and so on to infinity. The light gray coloring doesn't go to the infinite level because I set the **Level** of detail to **3**.

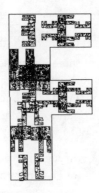

Figure 4.33. Here, only the reflections of the new part in Figure 4.32 are shown (F-FIX).

Another way to adjust the shading within a shape besides adding or rearranging copies is with FractalVision's **Fill** setting on the **Adjust** panel, which controls the relative density of the copies. By setting the fill for the bottom two copies of the F higher than the others, you can compensate for variations in density. The fractal in Figure 4.34 has the same textural pattern as Figure 4.31, but the shading is more consistent.

Figure 4.34. By adjusting the shading of the template in Figure 4.30, you can smooth the fractal density (F-FILL).

Now you're ready to add some fractal accents to your letter. If you extended the top of the F to the right, how would the whole shape look? To create Figure 4.35, I moved the top right points on the F over a bit. I then stretched the top two copies to fill the new seed shape. (I removed the extra copy in Figures 4.32 and 4.33.)

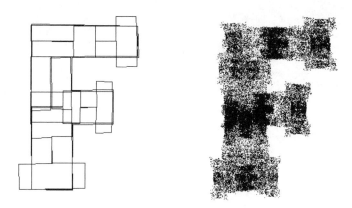

Figure 4.35. Once you have a basic shape, you can get fancy by adding fractal accents (F-FANCY).

Some of the accents appeared just in the right places to make a fancy Roman-style letter, but some are a bit off. In Figure 4.36, I shrank and lowered the two bottom copies and added two more copies to produce accents where you would expect them on a Roman F.

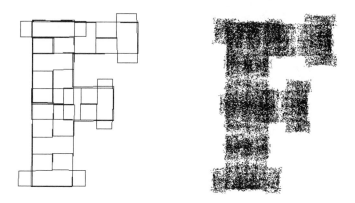

Figure 4.36. The serifs in a Roman-style F fit the fractal geometry of the letter (F-ROMAN).

Of course, these rather tame embellishments are only a beginning. You should try adding textures, accents, and variations of your own. Figure 4.37 will get you started. I created each letter by modifying the copies of the basic F shape.

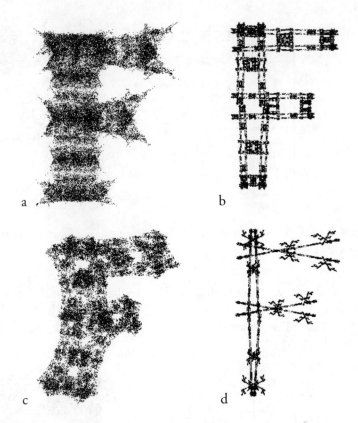

Figure 4.37. A few possibilities for fractal fonts effects: (a) F-FORKED, (b) F-STRUTS, (c) F-GOOFY, and (d) F-AXES.

Once you've designed a fractal shape, it's easy to add some dramatic zooming effects. The basic approach is to add one or more copies nearly the size of the seed yet offset from it just a bit. These added copies should be a different color from the rest to separate the effect from the original shape.

Although the figures printed here don't do them justice, the following illustrations are a few examples of a simple F as a starting shape. Color is essential to differentiate the letter from the zoom, so you'll want to look at these with FractalVision software. Figure 4.38a adds one shrunken and one offset copy for simple forward zoom. Figure 4.38b rotates the copy for a spiral zoom. Figure 4.38c uses two tilted copies to create an explosive or backward zoom effect. Figure 4.38d tilts and skews a copy to make the fractal "shine." Add these "F/X" to any fractal you create when you want a little extra razzle-dazzle.

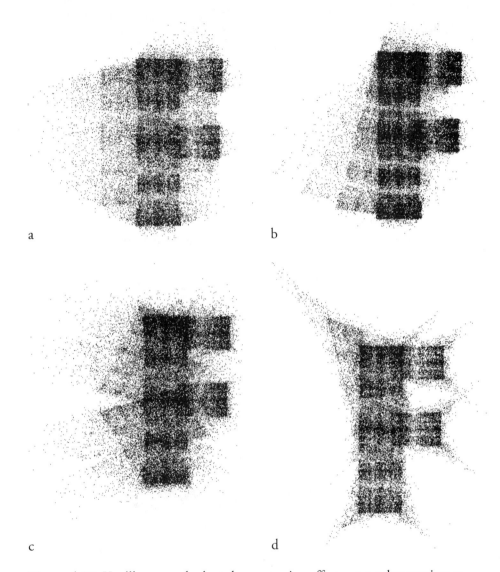

Figure 4.38. You'll want to look at these zooming effects on a color monitor to appreciate them and examine their construction: (a) F-ZOOM, (b) F-SWISH, (c) F-POW, and (d) F-SPARK.

Coloring Tips

Vision is the art of seeing things invisible.

—Jonathan Swift, 1711

Perhaps the biggest challenge of fractal design is learning to anticipate how parts of the template spread throughout the whole fractal on the way to infinity. To see more easily how parts reflect through the whole, you can use coloring to highlight each part separately. Figures 4.39 through 4.42 illustrate this technique.

The large fish consists of small fish (you are what you eat), but it isn't obvious in Figure 4.39 how those small fish come together to form the large fish's body. In Figures 4.40 through 4.42, I've colored all the reflections of the small fish black. I've colored the remaining parts of the template white to make them invisible.

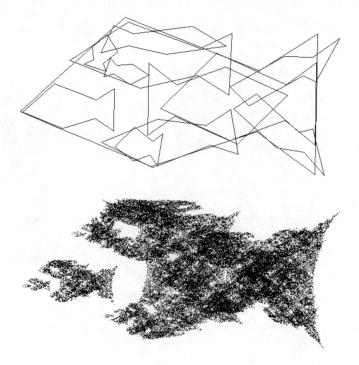

Figure 4.39. A fractal fish composed of its prey (BIGFISH).

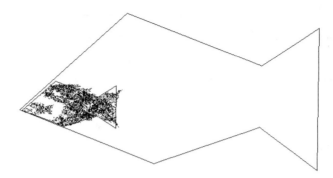

Figure 4.40. Level 1: The small fish highlighted by coloring.

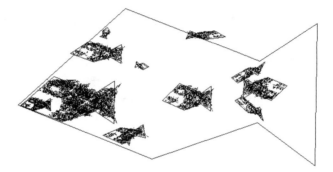

Figure 4.41. Level 2: Reflections of the small fish in the big fish's body.

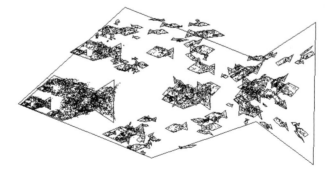

Figure 4.42. Level 3: Deeper reflections of the small fish.

You Can Do It: Big Fish, Little Fish, Yellow Fish, Blue Fish

If you have an EGA or VGA graphics adapter, you can employ two simple, fast coloring techniques to highlight the reflections of a particular copy of the seed at various levels of detail.

1. **Load** the BIGFISH example and notice the colors of the ten parts.

2. **Paint**, and select **Adjust** when it's done.

3. Use **Next Part** to move the handle to the "small fish" part of the template.

   You can see by the **Level** and **Colors** settings that the small fish part was **Color** F, down to **Level** 3 (the current **Level** of detail).

4. Now change the **Red** and **Green** settings (using the arrow keys or the mouse) to 100%, turning color F to bright white. The small fish and all its reflections (down to Level 3) leap out at you.

The "noses" of all the little fish that compose the big one are all shaded white, and the "mininoses" of the tiny fish that compose the little fish are white, too.

5. Tone down the **Red** and **Green** components of color F, and use **Next Part** to jump to another copy of the seed.

6. Again, you can see the reflections by setting the **Red**, **Green**, and **Blue** at 100% so they leap out. Restore the original **Red** and **Green** setting when you're through looking.

Viewing the parts of the fractal in this manner can be very useful when you're designing a complex fractal because you gain an immediate sense of the role each copy plays in the finished shape. Be sure, however, that each part has its own color (don't assign two parts **Color** B, for example).

You can also highlight reflections of a particular part at a particular level.

7. To try this, use **Next Part** to select the small fish part, then use the arrows or the mouse to select **Color** M. This will color **Level** 3 only.

8. Press **Enter** to return to the main menu, then **Clear** and **Paint**. The third-level reflections of the nose will all be colored, giving the fish bright pink spots.

Coloring variations like those outlined in the previous **You Can Do It** box can be a great help in developing an intuition for fractal design. Of course, you will also use them to color your finished shapes. The possibilities for coloring are limitless, but here are a few more handy suggestions:

- In general, start by giving each shape a different color, applied to all levels. This will make the role of the various parts more obvious when you're designing your shape.

- If another template or picture that you've made contains a palette of colors you want, load that file first, before you design your new fractal.

- Often, you'll want the first level of a part to stand out. Assign Level 1 of that part a bright color, and give the other levels a dimmer hue.

- You can eliminate certain levels by assigning them the background color (color A). For example, you might want to show only Level 2 reflections. To do this, assign all parts color A for Level 1, and each a different color for Level 2.

- Bright colors will show up much more than dimmer ones, which will affect the overall shading of your shape. If a part is too faint but just the right hue, try increasing the **Red**, **Green**, and **Blue** settings by equal amounts.

- Don't forget that red, green, and blue light sometimes add up differently than pigments. Table 4.1 lists some common colors and the formulas for creating them.

Table 4.1. Some common colors as created by combining red, green, and blue light.

Color	Component Colors
Yellow	100% red and 90% green
Orange	100% red and 45% green
Brown	40% red and 25% green
Purple	80% red and 80% blue
Pink	100% red, 90% green, and 90% blue
Aqua	80% blue and 70% green
Pine	40% green and 5% red
Gray	Equal amounts of red, green, and blue

Review of Collage Design

…you need a program that will perform an affine transformation on the picture or a portion of the picture. It needs to show the result of the transformation and give you the capability to change the transformation on the picture or a portion of the picture. It needs to show the result of the transformation parameters until you have the transformed version superimposed just as you want it on the original picture.… If this sounds like a very large undertaking, it is.

—Roger Stevens, *Fractal Programming in C*, 1989

The collage process so far includes:

1. Setting up your initial colors, or loading a file with the preset palette.

2. Moving points on the seed to approximate the shape you're after.

3. Tiling the seed with copies of itself, trying to avoid holes and overhang as much as possible, and painting to see the result.

4. Adjusting the shading and texture any of four ways by:

   ■ Rearranging the copies to change the amount of overlap between them.

   ■ Adding extra copies to fill faint areas.

   ■ Using the fill setting to adjust the relative density of the copies.

   ■ Brightening or dimming the colors of the copies by increasing or decreasing the red/green/blue settings.

5. Adding accents and highlights by changing the shape of the copies. You can move points on the seed shape to preview the first-level reflections of your planned changes.

6. Adding any appropriate special effects or extra details by inserting and arranging copies.

7. Adjusting your coloring and shading the way you want them, and painting your finished work.

As with the process outlined earlier for fractal drawing, you can often rearrange or skip some of these steps. Don't memorize the numbered list as if they were commandments from on high. Rather, you should use it as a reference until you feel comfortable without it.

Drawing Versus Painting

These clouds of points suggest sometimes fireworks or galaxies, strange and disquieting vegetable proliferations. A realm lies there of forms to explore, and harmonies to discover.

—David Ruelle, mathematician, (quoted in *Chaos* by James Gleick, 1986)

At this point, you've learned two approaches to fractal design employing different working techniques and software algorithms. I have differentiated these two approaches with the words *draw* and *paint*.

These new meanings of *draw* and *paint* have connections to the standard uses of the words in computer graphics. Ordinary "draw" programs (such as CorelDRAW, Micrografx Designer, and Arts & Letters) store images by assembling simple polygons and curves, much in the same spirit as FractalVision's **Draw** command. "Paint" programs store the whole image in one *bitmap* of points that is similar to FractalVision's **Paint** command.

The association, however, stops at these loose analogies. Both the **Draw** and **Paint** commands can produce either vector DXF files (compatible with draw programs) or PCX images (compatible with paint programs). My adoption of the words *draw* and *paint* is based more on the limitations of the English language than any deep connection to previous uses of the terms.

Having thus absolved myself of any guilt I might feel for further complicating the overwhelming hodgepodge of computer jargon, allow me to compare the uses of my new *paint* and *draw* techniques in depth. To minimize confusion with the old terms, I'll refer specifically to the FractalVision software commands.

Paint is most useful when you want to create subtle textures and rough edges. For bold, abstract, or intricate designs, you should use **Draw**.

When **Paint**ing, you are always dealing with the infinite level of detail (although you can pick out lower levels by coloring the shape). When **Draw**ing, you'll usually have many levels of detail. Therefore, you will need to pay more attention to the differences between levels and less attention to the differences between parts.

For example, you will color a typical **Draw**ing template differently than a normal **Paint**ing template. Instead of giving each part a different color for all levels, give each level its own color. All copies of the seed will be one color (red, for example) on Level 1, and another color (green, perhaps) on Level 2. This brings out distinctions between levels. Figures 4.43 and 4.44 use two alternating colors to bring out the levels in a leaf and a quilt design.

Figure 4.43. You can use alternating colors to visually separate the levels in a drawing (LEAF3).

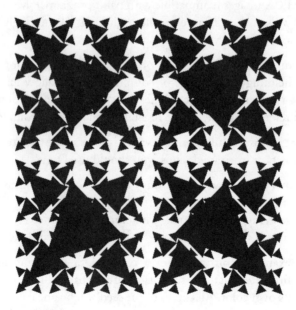

Figure 4.44. FractalVision's autoarrange feature can create abstract quilt-like designs by itself (QUILT).

You Can Do It: Automatic Design

With the fill set at 100% (as in Figure 4.33 and Figure 4.34), **Draw** produces bold, complex shapes. Through coloring, you can accentuate the overall form of each level in a design:

1. **Load** the LEAF3 sample file and **Draw** to see how this works.

2. Select **Adjust** and browse through the coloring selections with **Next Part**. (See how all the parts are colored the same—with a separate color for each level?)

This type of coloring is ideal for producing striking abstract designs. In fact, you can generate many beautiful patterns by simply selecting **New** and pressing a number.

1. From the main menu, select **Clear, NextPoint** and then **Next Part** (just press ' and Tab—this puts the handle on the seed).

2. Select **New** and press 4.

3. **Draw**.

You've just produced a quilt! What does **New 5** do? Try changing the **Level** setting on the **Adjust** menu to see simpler or more complex mosaics.

Table 4.2 illustrates that many of the guidelines for **Draw**ing are a bit different from those for **Paint**ing.

Table 4.2. A guideline comparison of Draw and Paint.

With Draw	With Paint
Let the seed show through so the second level won't cover up the first.	Try to cover the seed completely to reproduce its shape.
Try to overlap as little as possible, or the design gets too complex and garbled.	Overlapping copies create texture, but don't change the overall shape.

continues

Table 4.2. continued

With Draw	With Paint
Overhangs and holes will only reflect down to as many levels as you select.	Overhangs and holes will reflect throughout the shape at all levels.
Use **Blend Colors** on the **Adjust** menu to create a gradual progression from one level to the next.	Use **Blend Colors** for gradual changes between copies of the seed.

Figure 4.45 and 4.46 illustrate the differences between **Draw** and **Paint**.

Figure 4.45. I assigned a unique gray scale to each level in this Halloween face, displayed with the **Draw** command (GOUL).

Figure 4.46. When you use the **Paint** command, only the infinite level shows up (GOUL).

You Can Do It: The Ghost in the Machine

The GOUL template is a fanciful example that illustrates all these principles.

1. **Load** the **Template** GOUL.

2. **Draw** to see how holes and overlap "show through" to the previous level.

Also notice that I carefully chose the level of detail. One level less, and the shape wouldn't seem to "go to infinity." One level more, and the tiniest faces would muddy the image because the screen's resolution couldn't display them clearly. Finally, notice how I used a gradual blend of colors to show the progression from the giant face to the tiny ones.

3. **Clear** the picture and **Paint** with this same template.

continues

Only the finest level of detail shows up, and "holes" define the shape, while overlap adds texture. Because all parts are colored the same, no color distinctions exist between them. **Paint** can't show the color differences between levels the way **Draw** does because it only **Paint**s the infinite level.

When should you **Draw**, and when should you **Paint**? I don't have any clearcut rules, but these tips and examples should give you a sense for the merits of each approach.

Most real-world fractals lend themselves either to **Draw**ing or **Paint**ing, but seldom both. Therefore, I've used abstract designs to illustrate the difference between the two commands in Figures 4.47 through 4.53. In all these figures, I used the same template to produce both a **Draw**ing (a) and a **Paint**ing (b). You should use **Draw** when you want clear distinctions between elements in your picture. You can **Paint** the example in Figure 4.47, but it looks more pleasing with the concise lines of **Draw**.

Use **Draw** when you want to capture a particular level or show the progression from one level to the next. Figure 4.48 is an example of jumping, which sidetracks the intended image entirely, to the "infinite" level with **Paint**.

Use **Draw** when no holes or overhangs exist to define a **Paint**ing. In Figure 4.49, the copies perfectly cover the whole. **Draw** creates an intricate design; **Paint** simply shades the triangle.

Use **Paint** when you want a rich texture rather than patches of color. Figure 4.50 is very dramatic when **Paint**ed, but it loses some of its flavor when **Draw**n.

Use **Paint** when you need to go "all the way to infinity" to gain the effect you want. **Draw**ing a few levels of the example in Figure 4.51 barely hints at the swirling vortex that **Paint** produces.

Use either **Paint** or **Draw** when your shape is clearly defined by holes and edges and has little overlap between copies. The example in Figure 4.52 looks similar when **Paint**ed or **Draw**n.

Sometimes, you'll want to combine **Paint**ed and **Draw**n elements into one picture. **Paint**ed spray adds a flashy contrast to solidly **Draw**n shapes. Because **Paint** is really an infinite extension of **Draw**, you can often combine the two even with the same template. You've done this with trees, and it also works well in Figure 4.53.

Figure 4.47. Draw (a) brings out distinctions between elements more clearly than Paint (b) (PYRAMID).

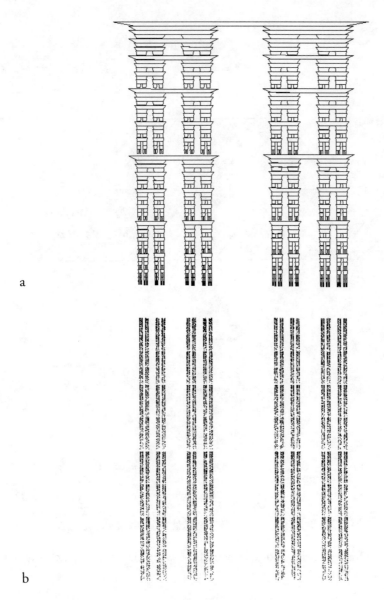

a

b

Figure 4.48. Sometimes the infinite level of **Paint** (b) is just too much (ARCHY).

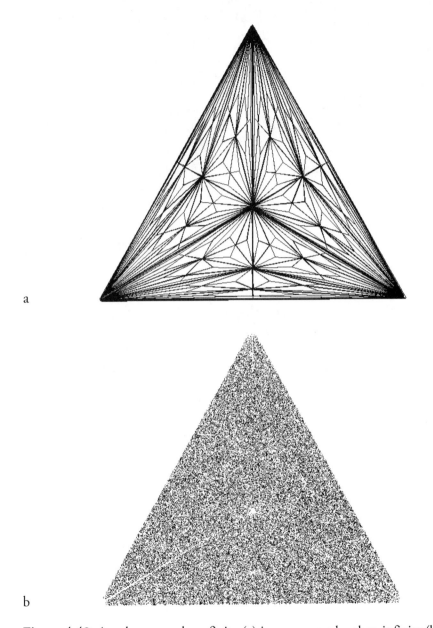

a

b

Figure 4.49. Another case where finity (a) is more complex than infinity (b) (GEM).

a

b

Figure 4.50. Paint (b) is better than **Draw** (a) when finery and texture are desirable (WEBS).

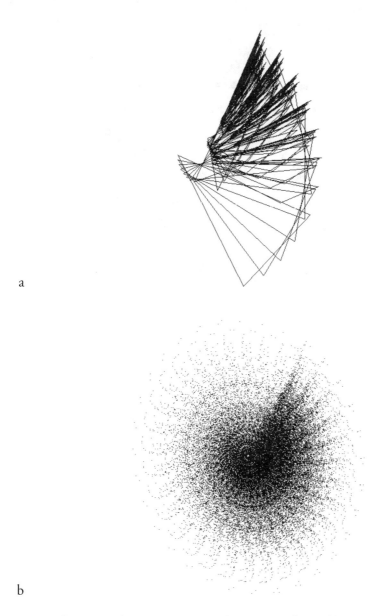

a

b

Figure 4.51. At other times, you need to go to infinity (b) to get anywhere at all (SHELL).

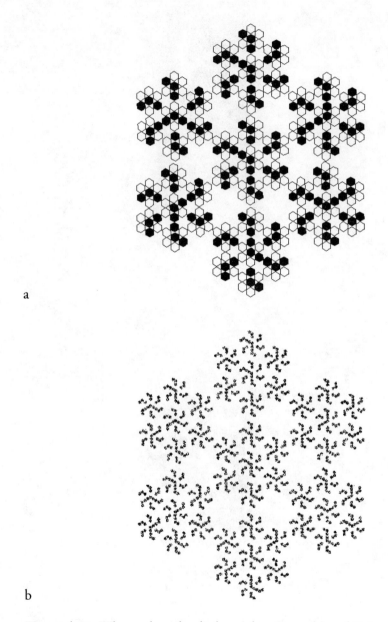

a

b

Figure 4.52. When a shape has little overlap, **Draw** (a) and **Paint** (b) both work well (HIVE).

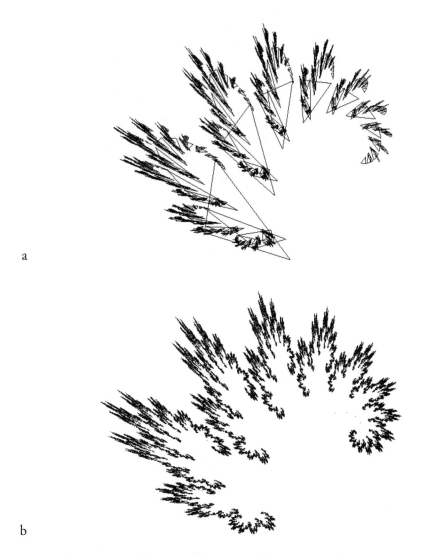

a

b

Figure 4.53. You could **Paint** (b) on top of the **Draw**ing (a) to complete the progression (FIRAL).

Figure 4.54 pulls everything together into a fairly complex fractal artwork. To create an image of a hen on her nest, I used three separate templates and most of the techniques I've covered so far.

Figure 4.54. You can combine templates and techniques to create complex images with varied textures (HEN, COMB, and NEST).

You Can Do It: Portrait of a Hen on Her Nest

The following steps will enable you to reconstruct the chicken. (You might also want to delve into the **Adjust** panel after **Load**ing each template to take a peek at how I set each of them up.)

1. **Clear** the picture, **Load** the **Template** named HEN, and **Paint**.

2. When done, **Load** the **Template** called COMB and **Draw**.

3. Finally, **Load** the **Template** NEST and **Draw** again.

4. Be sure to **Save** the **Picture** so you won't have to re-create it if you want to see it again.

You can gain some valuable experience by playing around with these three templates. Try **Draw**ing the HEN (rather than **Paint**ing her), experimenting with various **Fill** levels, or changing her **Colors**. Can you fluff the tail to make a turkey without giving it an elephant's nose?

HEN, COMB, and NEST also illustrate the importance of planning your palette of **Colors** very carefully. All three templates must use the same palette or the HEN's colors will change when you draw her COMB. If I had assigned each part of the HEN its own color, none would be left for the NEST (because only 16 colors can be displayed at once).

The palette is **Save**d with both the **Template** and **Picture** files. Consequently, you can change the palette associated with a template by **Load**ing a **Picture** that contains the **Colors** you want, and vice versa. To transfer a palette from one template to another, **Load** the first **Template**, **Save** a **Picture**, then **Load** the second **Template**, and **Load** the **Picture** again.

Image Processing

Using fractals to simulate landscapes and other natural effects is not new; it has been a primary application.... What is new is the ability to start with an actual image and find the fractals that will imitate it to any desired degree of accuracy. Since our method includes a compact way of representing these fractals, we end up with a highly compressed data set for reconstructing the original image.

—Michael Barnsley and Alan Sloan,
"A Better Way to Compress Images," *BYTE*, 1988

As the last few figures reveal, fractal design is not confined to the scientific models presented in Chapter 2, nor is it confined to intriguing abstractions. You can apply fractal collage to any shape whatsoever. Combine this information with the remarkable compression of visual information implicit in a fractal template, and you have a potential revolution in image processing.

In fact, that revolution has already started. Leading the insurrection are Michael Barnsley and Alan Sloan, founders of Iterated Systems in Norcross, Georgia. Sloan recognized the dramatic implications of Barnsley's mathematical work and spearheaded an effort to produce the first image compression system to employ fractals. Their technology, though still expensive (read: *thousands*), is now capable of turning video images into fractals at speeds approaching one frame per minute. Although this alone is certainly nothing amazing, the clincher is that the fractalized video is so compact that it can be transmitted through phone lines and played back at 30 frames per second on an ordinary 386 computer. (Image compression ratios can approach 50,000 to 1—the best ratio from any other form of image compression is approximately 100 to 1).

How do they do it? They employ the familiar collage techniques that you've been practicing for the past 40 pages, of course. You can compress images with FractalVision, too. To create Figure 4.55, I simply loaded a PCX picture of the mouse from Chapter 1 and tiled him with copies.

Figure 4.55. You can use fractal collage to compress any image by ratios of 10,000:1 or more (CARTOON1 and CARTOON2).

The most sophisticated fractal image processing machines rely on specialized hardware for recognizing the color boundaries of images and searching predefined libraries of fractals to match the patterns. Although current systems employ a distinct fractal for each color region in the image, compressing several colored regions into a single fractal is theoretically possible.

Figure 4.57, for example, is a single fractal template made by tiling part of the scanned image in Figure 4.56 with copies of itself. The copies were colored to match the various regions of color in the underlying image, and the resulting fractal (see Figure 4.58) approximates a multicolored section of the original picture.

Figure 4.56. A scanned image to be fractalized (HERON.PCX).

Fortunately, you have sophisticated hardware built into your head for recognizing color boundaries. By taking advantage of innate pattern-recognition systems, you can do a pretty good job creating fractals that match what you see on-screen. Once you've turned part of an image into a fractal, you can use the techniques discussed earlier in this chapter to add spectacular fractal effects.

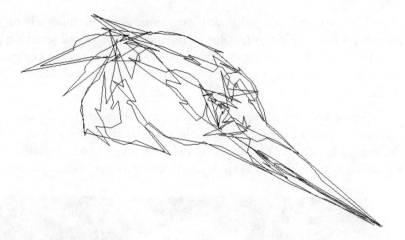

Figure 4.57. Part of the image has been tiled with copies of itself to make a fractal template (HERON).

Figure 4.58. The resulting fractal mimics a multicolored region of the picture (HERON).

Don't kid yourself, though. It took longer than a minute for me to tile the mouse and Mr. Heron by hand, and the quality of the results are barely acceptable for most video applications. You aren't going to sit down and convert all your PC Paintbrush files to FractalVision templates to save space on your hard disk. However, you can store the template in Figure 4.57 with less than 100 bytes and pop it up in your own programs with the Iterated Function System routines found in Chapter 5 and Appendix B, "Mathematics Review, Formulas, and Algorithms."

More importantly, working with fractal collage by hand gives you the best possible understanding of how fractal image processing works. Once fractal image compression hits the streets, you will have an advantage in assessing and utilizing the technology. Some points to keep in mind:

- Unlike bitmapped storage and compression, fractals are scalable. When you enlarge an image stored as fractals, you will not see the familiar blockiness of enlarged pixels, but complex detail at every level of scale.

- If fractals are carefully selected for their resemblance to the actual objects portrayed in the image, magnification may actually reveal realistic detail not present in the original picture. Even when these fractal artifacts are not realistic, they are much easier for the eye to overlook than a grid pattern.

- Fractal image compression is a *lossy* technique—the compressed image will be noticeably different than the original. It is, therefore, unsuitable for applications where every bit counts, such as medical imaging. In other applications, such as video animation, the loss in quality may go completely unnoticed.

- The quality of the compressed images is selectable. If you want a high-quality reproduction, you can use more fractals and/or more tiles per fractal (although you will surrender some compactness in the bargain). Naturally, a more accurate collage also takes more time to process.

- Image compression ratios also depend on the nature of the image to be compressed. Fractals work better with irregular and highly textured images than with smooth and orderly images.

- The advantages of fractal compression over other forms of compression also depend on the type of image. Fortunately, complex images that are the most inefficient for handling by traditional linear techniques are often the best candidates for fractal processing.

You Can Do It: Fractalizing an Image

The image and templates in Figures 4.55 through 4.58 are included, so you can see how fractal image compression works. The following steps fractalize the heron's head:

1. **Load** the **Picture** named HERON. (If you have another PCX image that you'd like to process, just **Load** it instead of the HERON picture.)

2. Select **NextPoint** and **New**, then use the mouse to sketch an outline of a part of the image you want to fractalize. (Try to select a region that you can image by composing it with copies of itself. Theoretically, you can tile any region this way, but you can tile some shapes a lot easier than others. Often it's better to start simply and use several templates to reproduce an area than to spend all night trying to tile a squiggly-wiggly with little squiggly-wigglies.)

3. Select **Next Part** and **New**, then press a fairly small number (2 or 3, for example) to generate starting copies.

4. Use the mouse and the **Grow**, **Shrink**, **Spin**, **Skew**, **Stretch**, and **Squish** commands to cover the largest parts of the seed first.

Be sure that any particular copy of the seed does not overlap regions of different colors.

5. Add more parts with **Insert**, then place and size them to fill the remaining holes.

6. **Clear** and **Paint** to check your work, and make alterations as necessary. You may want to re**Load** the **Picture** again for reference. (Be patient. It will take more twiddling and fiddling than you expect. That's why people charge big bucks for machines that do it automatically.)

7. **Adjust** the **Colors** to match the colored areas under the template.

8. **Save** the **Template**, and repeat these steps for other regions that you want to fractalize.

Nature's Favorite Design Technique

Individuality seems to be Nature's whole aim—and she cares nothing for individuals.

—Johann Wolfgang von Goethe, *Maxims and Reflections*

After all this talk about real-world fractal modeling and image processing, you might ask how Nature does it. Are the techniques used to sculpt a tree at all similar to the techniques you've learned for simulating one? Well, as with most yes/no questions, the answer is "yes…and no." One could say "yes" because real trees and galaxies take their form from hidden codes and forces manifesting as self-reflective shapes. Alternatively, another person could also say "no" because Nature does not plan ahead and devise those codes and forces specifically to achieve a premeditated effect. (Some would argue that God has the whole thing planned out, but that concept of planning is a bit more complex than ours—*design* and *chance* are listed as synonyms in the big thesaurus in the sky.)

So how do Nature and the Supreme Being design things? They modify what's there a bit, and see what happens. If it works, keep it; if it doesn't, let it die. Darwin called it *evolution*, or *natural selection*, but with the right software you can do the selecting yourself. (When people do it, we usually have the humility to call it *breeding* instead of *evolution*.) The following **You Can Do It** box steps you through the process, but first take a look at the simulated evolution of a fern and a tree.

I created the first image in Figure 4.59 with FractalVision software and exported it as IFS codes—geometric genetic codes that define the shape. (You'll get the mathematical scoop on IFS codes and how they work in Chapter 5.) The MUTATE program took these codes and randomly altered them slightly to create the right half of the figure.

In this case, I was in the position to choose which image was going to "survive," the original fern or the mutation. I picked the original (1)—the mutation met a quick and painless demise. MUTATE then produced another mutation (see Figure 4.60), and this time I let it live. The new fern then became the starting point for subsequent mutations (see Figure 4.61).

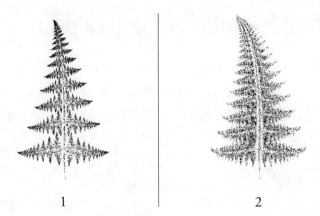

Figure 4.59. You design a fractal (1), and the MUTATE program randomly changes it (2) (FERN.IFS).

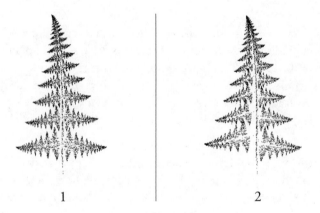

Figure 4.60. If you think the original is the fittest of the two, the mutant dies, and a new mutant is born (2).

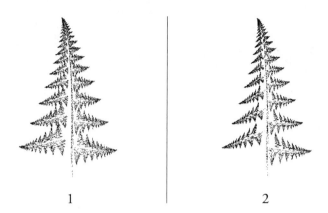

1   2

Figure 4.61. If you pick the mutant as the fittest, it replaces the original (1) and becomes the basis for new mutations (2).

How can you use mutation as a design technique? Simply choose the shapes that most closely match your design criteria. For example, you might begin with the maple tree in Figure 4.62 with the design goal of breeding a taller tree with a more open canopy. Figure 4.63 chronicles the controlled evolution of the species toward your goal. (Many unsuitable mutations were rejected, and these are not shown in the figures.) Several generations later, the superior specimen in Figure 4.64 has been developed.

Figure 4.62. Begin with an ordinary tree (MAPLE.IFS) to breed a taller maple.

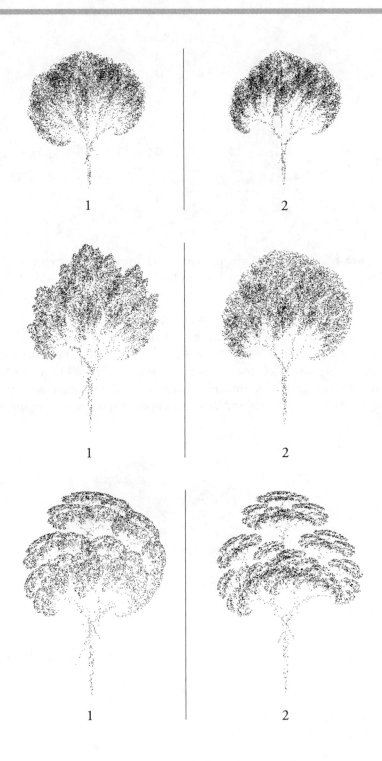

1

2

1

2

1

2

1   2

Figure 4.63. Choose the tallest and most attractive (from many ugly mutants not shown).

Figure 4.64. When the cream of the crop meets your satisfaction, save it for future breeding.

Fractals continually encourage us to pay attention to the whole more than the parts. Designing models with a "survival of the fittest" mentality takes this policy to its logical extreme. You can leave the piecemeal alterations of the design entirely to chance and direct your undivided attention to the overall form of the model. You know when it looks right, even if you have no idea how the individual parts were changed to make it that way. The most natural design technique is to forget about technique and concentrate on design.

You Can Do It: Breeding a Better Fractal

You can take any template from FractalVision and use if for breeding stock:

1. Start FractalVision and **Load** the **Template** you have in mind. If you don't have one in mind, try LEAF1.

2. Select **Paint** to see what it looks like.

The MUTATE program uses the **Paint** algorithm to display mutations (you may not see what you're used to seeing for templates that are normally **Draw**n). As discussed in Chapter 2, often you can add an extra part to make the trunk or stem of a plant show up with **Paint**. Even if your tree trunk doesn't show up in the MUTATE program, it will still be there when you finish breeding and import the model back into FractalVision.

3. Select **Save** and then select **IFS Codes**. Enter a filename (usually the same name as the template) to direct FractalVision to save the numerical codes that define the template in a small text file. The file will automatically be given the .IFS extension.

4. Select **Quit** and press Y.

5. At the DOS prompt, type MUTATE (or run MUTATE.EXE from a graphics shell).

6. When MUTATE asks for the name of the IFS file, type the name that you just saved under in FractalVision. (LEAF1, for example—there's no need to type a file extension.)

Your model now appears on the left side of the screen. The color will not be the same as your template—each part is given a different color to help you see the internal structure of the fractal. After it's done **Paint**ing, a mutation appears on the right. The numbers 1 and 2 appear under these images.

Think about what characteristics you'd like to breed into the model. You could go for something as straightforward as skinniness, or as subjective as beauty.

7. Which of the two images best suits your criteria? If it's the one on the left, press 1. If it's the one on the right, press 2.

If you pressed 1, the original image stays and a new mutation based on it appears on the right. If you pressed 2, the mutation you selected moves to the left side of the screen and a new mutation based on it comes up on the right.

8. Keep selecting until the image on the left is worth saving (or until you want to start over), then press Escape.

9. When MUTATE asks you for a filename, give it a different name than the original (unless you want to erase the original and replace it with the new one).

Notice that you can also specify the name of the input and output files on the command line. For example, you could have typed MUTATE LEAF1 NEWLEAF instead of MUTATE.

To get the design you bred back into FractalVision:

10. Start FractalVision and **Load** the original **Template** again.

You should load the old design because the IFS codes manipulated by MUTATE only describe the relationships between parts of the fractal and do not include the other information used by FractalVision, such as the seed shape, coloring, and shading.

11. Select **Load** and **IFS Codes**, and enter the name you have given the new mutant.

continues

12. **Save** the **Template** under the new name. The new template combines the old model's seed shape and coloring with the new model's geometry. You can now **Draw**, **Paint**, **Adjust**, and all that other FractalVision jazz with your well-bred fractal.

You can also exchange IFS files between MUTATE and FRACTINT. Refer to the section on exchanging images and data with other software in Appendix A, "FractalVision Software Reference," for details.

For Programmers Only: Unnatural Selection

The theory and algorithms for working with Iterated Function System Codes are covered in Chapter 5. You'll find the same paint() function documented more thoroughly in the IFS.C program there.

However, you can understand and experiment with this program without knowing anything about IFS by treating the transformation arrays as code numbers to be modified by a percentage of their value. What percentage and which ones to modify when are up to you. For example, you could increase control over breeding by changing only one of the variables at a time, instead of all six as I've done here. (Some other avenues to explore: bring in the draw() function from IFS.C in Chapter 5, or write a routine to select for some measurable quality in the image and automatically breed without user input.)

Listing 4.1. MUTATE.C. A program that randomly mutates output so you can breed for a desired quality.

```
/* MUTATE.C
 *
 * This program takes IFS codes output by
 * FractalVision or FRACTINT and
 * randomly mutates them, letting you choose
 * which mutations survive.
 */
```

```
#include <stdio.h>      /* For getch() */
#include <math.h>       /* For cos() and sin() */
#define MAIN            /* See Appendix D for compile  */
#include "fv.h"         /* instructions and header files */


#define drawclr 15      /* Color to make the dots */
#define NAMELEN 40      /* Maximum length of filename */
#define NTRANS 16       /* Maximum number of transformations */
#define COUNT 10000     /* Number of dots to paint */

int ntrans,             /* actual number of transformations */
    probsum[NTRANS];    /* cumulative probability of
                           each transformation */

float centerx1, centerx2, centery;     /* center of windows */
FILE *diskfile;                    /* file handle and filename */
char filename[NAMELEN];


        /* The tranformations that define the fractal */

float movex[NTRANS], movey[NTRANS],
      move2x[NTRANS], move2y[NTRANS],
      Ta[NTRANS],  Tb[NTRANS],  Tc[NTRANS],  Td[NTRANS],
      T2a[NTRANS], T2b[NTRANS], T2c[NTRANS], T2d[NTRANS],
      prob[NTRANS];

float mutate(float value);         /* function prototypes */
void saveifs(void);
void loadifs(void);
void draw(float a, float b, float c, float d,
          float mx, float my, int iter);
void paint(int mx, int my);

void main(int nargs, char **arg)
{   int vidmode, t;             /* video mode and a counter */
    char a = '2';                   /* for keyboard input */
    vidmode = pickmode(detectmode());     /* get video mode */
```

continues

307

Listing 4.1. continued

```
if (nargs > 1) strcpy(filename, arg[1]);
    else     /* if filename not on command line, ask for it */
    {   printf("\n\nThis program will mutate the "
            "genetic codes of a fractal,\n");
        printf("allowing you to select which "
            "mutations will survive.\n\n");
        printf("Enter the name of the "
            "IFS file to use (try MAPLE): ");
        scanf("%s", filename);
    }
    loadifs();                      /* read data from the file */
    if (setvidmode(vidmode, 1) != 1)
    {   printf("\nUnable to set graphics mode.\n");
        exit(0);
    }
    centerx1 = scrnx / 4;       /* compute middle of windows */
    centerx2 = centerx1 * 3;
    centery  = scrny / 2;
    setcolor(drawclr);                      /* set drawing color */
    drawline(scrnx / 2, 0, scrnx / 2, scrny - 1);
    while(1)                                /* main loop */
    {   if (a == '2')         /* if user picked the mutation, */
        {   for (t = 0; t < ntrans; t++) /* (or first time) */
            {   T2a[t] = Ta[t];       /* store the new codes */
                T2b[t] = Tb[t];
                T2c[t] = Tc[t];
                T2d[t] = Td[t];
                move2x[t] = movex[t];
                move2y[t] = movey[t];
            }                   /* put the left image on-screen */
            setclipregion(0, 0, scrnx / 2 - 1, scrny - 1);
            eraserect(0, 0, scrnx / 2 - 1, scrny - 1);
            paint(centerx1, centery);
            moveto(centerx1, scrny - 20);
            outtext("1");                   /* label it with a 1 */
            setclipregion(scrnx / 2 + 1, 0,
                        scrnx - 1, scrny - 1);
```

```
}
        else
     {   for (t = 0; t < ntrans; t++) /* reject mutation */
{   Ta[t] = T2a[t];    /* restore original codes */
                Tb[t] = T2b[t];
                Tc[t] = T2c[t];
                Td[t] = T2d[t];
                movex[t] = move2x[t];
                movey[t] = move2y[t];
            }
        }
        t = rand() % ntrans;    /* Mutate one transformation */
        Ta[t] = mutate(Ta[t]);
        Tb[t] = mutate(Tb[t]);
        Tc[t] = mutate(Tc[t]);
        Td[t] = mutate(Td[t]);
        movex[t] = mutate(movex[t]);
        movey[t] = mutate(movey[t]);
        eraserect(scrnx / 2 + 1, 0, scrnx - 1, scrny - 1);
        paint(centerx2, centery);   /* display right window */
        moveto(centerx2, scrny - 20);
        outtext("2");                         /* label it 2 */
        if ((a = getch()) == 27) break;    /* wait for key */
    }
    settextmode();
    closedown();                      /* close down the graphics */
    if (nargs > 2) strcpy(filename, arg[2]);  /* save codes */
    else
    {   printf("\n\nEnter the name of the output IFS file: ");
        scanf("%s", filename);
    }
    saveifs();
}

/* This routine takes a number and returns a
 * slightly different number.
 * By altering it, you can control the
 * size and direction of mutations.
 */
```

continues

Listing 4.1. continued

```c
float mutate(float value)
{    float delta, newval;
     delta = (float) rand() / (32768.0) + 0.6;
     newval = value * delta;
     return newval;
}


/* The following two routines load and
 * save FractalVision and FRACTINT compatible IFS codes
 * (they automatically add the .IFS extension)
 * Note that loadifs() only reads the very first set
 * of IFS codes in the file and ignores the name label.
 * Likewise, saveifs() only writes one set of codes per
 * file and gives them the same name as the file itself.
 */

void loadifs(void)
{    int i, psum = 0;
     float p;
     char str[NAMELEN + 15];
         strcpy(str, filename);
     strcat(str, ".IFS");
     if ((diskfile = fopen(str, "r")) == NULL)
     {   printf("Can't find a file named %s.", str);
         exit(0);
     }
     diskfile = fopen(str, "r");
     while(fgetc(diskfile) != '{');
     for (i = 0; i < NTRANS; i++)
     {   if (fscanf(diskfile, " %f %f %f %f %f %f %f\n",
                    Ta + i, Tb + i, Tc + i, Td + i,
                    movex + i, movey + i, prob + i) != 7)
             break;
         movex[i] *= -50.0;
         movey[i] *= -50.0;
         probsum[i] = (psum += (int) (prob[i] * 32768.0));
     }
     ntrans = i;
```

```
        fclose(diskfile);
}
void saveifs(void)
{   int i;
        char str[NAMELEN + 5];
        strcpy(str, filename);
    strcat(str, ".IFS");
    diskfile = fopen(str, "w");
    fprintf(diskfile, "\n %s {\n", filename);
    for (i = 0; i < ntrans; i++)
    {   fprintf(diskfile,
                " %.2f %.2f %.2f %.2f %.2f %.2f %.2f\n",
                T2a[i], T2b[i], T2c[i], T2d[i],
                move2x[i] / -50.0, move2y[i] / -50.0,
                prob[i]);
    }
    fprintf(diskfile, " }");
        fclose(diskfile);
}

/* The following routine is from
 * the IFS.C program (explained in Chapter 5) */

void paint(int mx, int my)
{   int t, j;
    unsigned long ct = 0;
    float x1 = 0.0, y1 = 0.0, x2, y2;
        while(!kbhit() && (++ct < COUNT))
    {   j = rand();
        for (t = 0; t < ntrans - 1; t++)
            if (j < probsum[t]) break;
                x2 = x1 * Ta[t] + y1 * Tb[t] + movex[t];
                y2 = x1 * Tc[t] + y1 * Td[t] + movey[t];
                x1 = x2, y1 = y2;
        if (ct > 8)
            putpixel((int) x2 + mx,
                    (int) y2 + my, (t + 2) % ncolors);

    }
}
```

In the past, people who wanted to do anything with fractals had to wade through graduate-level math books and pound the equations they found there into computer programs. Now, FractalVision software and the techniques covered in this chapter may give you all the power you'll ever need to work with fractals.

However, there are secrets hidden in those math books that you should know about. In fact, fractal imagery can reveal deep truths and practical applications that would otherwise remain hidden to anyone without a PhD in set theory.

In Chapter 5, I reveal the inner workings of FractalVision. All the equations and algorithms are presented, but everything is also explained visually and intuitively, so you can safely continue reading without donning your mathematical hip waders.

The Math Behind the Magic

I n this chapter, you'll learn the mathematical concepts behind fractals. You don't need to be a mathematician to follow along, however. Everything is presented visually and intuitively. I've included and explained all the basic formulas for making fractals, but those who aren't big on equations can easily skip them and still gain a solid understanding of everything discussed.

For easy reference, I have collected the formulas and algorithms in Appendix B, "Mathematics Review, Formulas, and Algorithms," which also includes some advanced equations not covered elsewhere and a brief review of matrix algebra and complex arithmetic.

To kick off this chapter, I'll unveil how FractalVision software works. Then you'll explore some other kinds of fractals, like the

famous Mandelbrot set and Julia sets. You'll learn how to use FRACTINT to draw these sets in their full splendor and discover more implications and applications of these bizarre pictures. (FRACTINT is a freeware program available on most BBS's, or by sending in the registration form in the back of this book. See the Introduction for more details.)

How to Make a Fractal

In the popular mind, computer-generated images have a mechanistic quality, perhaps due to the fact that popular computer drawing and paint tools come equipped with a repertoire of regular shapes such as lines, circles, and squares. But if the computer artist can supplement those with tools that create fractal shapes, with roughness, texture, branching, and cloudiness, then the mechanistic feel will be replaced by the earthiness of the natural world.
—Timothy Wegner and Mark Peterson, *Fractal Creations,* 1991

To draw fractals, FractalVision uses two basic procedures that you access with the **Draw** and **Paint** commands. These two approaches are closely related mathematically, as you can see from the fact that you can use both with the exact same template. This deep mathematical similarity is hidden in two techniques that seem entirely unrelated on the surface. The meticulous repetition of **Draw** and the random spray of **Paint** hint at the opposite characteristics of their underlying procedures (Figure 5.1).

You Can Do It: Draw versus Paint

Before I explain how **Draw** and **Paint** work, look closely at them in action.

1. **Load** the **Template** called LEAF3 for an example. I've left gaps in this ivy leaf so you can see a fractal pattern inside it.

2. **Paint**, then **Draw**. Notice how different the texture and spirit of the procedures are, and how **Draw** adds many levels of detail that **Paint** missed.

a

b

Figure 5.1. FractalVision's **Draw** (a) and **Paint** (b) commands, applied to the same fractal template (LEAF3).

The Cat Game

In addition to its usefulness for describing the complexities of natural objects, fractal geometry offers a welcome opportunity for the revitalization of mathematics education. The concepts of fractal geometry are visual and intuitive. The forms involved have a great aesthetic appeal and a wide variety of applications. Fractal geometry therefore may help to counter the perception that mathematics is dry and inaccessible and may motivate students to learn about this puzzling and exciting realm of study.

—Hartmut Jurgens, H.O. Peitgen, and Dietmar Saupe, "The Language of Fractals," *Scientific American,* 1990

The best way to understand how the computer does something is to do it yourself. You will learn two games that you can play on paper to "draw" and "paint" fractals by hand. The first game, based on some of the earliest explorations of fractals, I call the *Cat Game.* The second was invented by Michael Barnsley at Georgia Tech and is called the *Chaos Game.* You may want to get a few pieces of paper, a pencil, and a ruler to try them. (I'll warn you that it takes a very precise hand to create a good-looking fractal.)

Here are the rules for the Cat Game:

1. Draw something (a cat, for instance) in the middle of a piece of paper.

2. Draw three half-sized copies of it around it.

3. Draw three copies around each of those, in the same arrangement.

4. Keep going.

In Figure 5.2, as the copies (kittens) get smaller and smaller (shown through the counterclockwise progression of litters), they become just dots. If you are very, very exact with your drawing, those dots form a well-known fractal called *Sierpiński's Triangle.*

You Can Do It: Playing The Cat Game

To play the Cat Game on the computer screen, run FractalVision software and:

1. **Clear** the picture and **Load** the **Template** CATS.

The first cat is the seed, and the three copies are arranged around it.

2. **Draw** to play the game.

FractalVision catches on to the idea and continues the feline procreation procedure automatically.

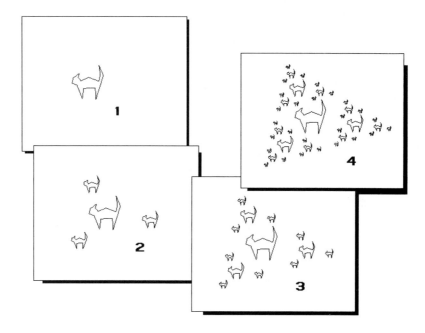

Figure 5.2. The Cat Game. You can draw a fractal by drawing smaller and smaller children around a parent shape (CATS).

The Chaos Game

So, Nat'ralists observe, a Flea
Hath smaller Fleas that on him prey
And these have smaller Fleas to bite 'em
And so proceed ad infinitum

—Jonathan Swift, On Poetry, *A Rhapsody*, 1733

Now you'll play the Chaos Game. Here are the rules:

1. Circle any three points on a piece of paper and make a dot in the middle.

2. Select one of the circled points at random, and make a dot halfway between the last dot you made and that point. (You can roll a die to make the selection truly random if you want.)

3. Repeat step two for a very long time.

   If you measured your halfways with painstaking precision, you would eventually see *Sierpiński's Triangle* again (Figure 5.3).

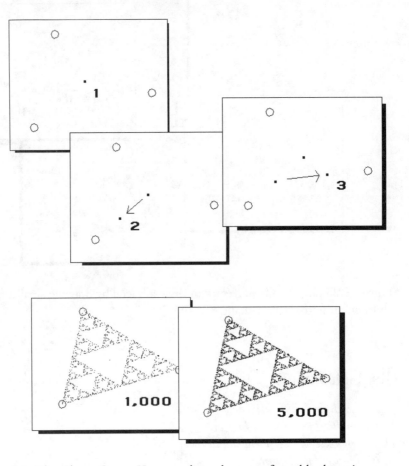

Figure 5.3. The Chaos Game. You can draw the same fractal by hopping randomly, as long as each hop goes halfway to one of three points. The numbers correspond to how many steps (and dots) I've made (SIERPIN).

How does this work? One way to understand it is to notice that the resulting shape consists of three miniature copies of itself. If you took every dot in the entire big shape and moved it halfway to one of the corner points, you'd see one of those three miniatures. So, each random pick proceeds from a dot on the whole to the corresponding dot on one of the parts. Leap around this way (like one of Swift's infinitely small Fleas) on the shape for a long time, and you end up landing on almost all the dots in all three copies.

If you used more than three points, you would get shapes made of more than three copies of themselves. As long as you play by the rule "halfway to the corner point," though, you always get half-sized copies. To see third-sized copies, you could change the rules to "a third of the way to the corner."

You Can Do It: Playing The Chaos Game

What if you wanted to express those rules visually? You could define a rough approximation of the shape (a triangle, perhaps) and then place half-sized copies where the copies of the final shape would appear, halfway toward each corner from the center.

1. **Load** the example **Template** named SIERPIN. This template contains a visual set of rules to play the Chaos Game.

2. **Clear** and **Paint**. The computer generates a sequence of random numbers that it uses to apply the rules and paint a fractal.

The seed shape (red triangle) is a rough approximation of the finished fractal. It doesn't matter how rough this approximation is, because it only defines the relationship "halfway to the corner." In fact, you could use any shape as a seed and still get the same fractal as long as the relationships between the seed and the copies were the same. For example, the CATS template uses a sketch of a cat for the seed. The geometric relationships between the cat and kittens are exactly the same as the relationship between the large and small triangles of SIERPIN: each kitten is "halfway to the corner" from the cat.

3. **Load** the CATS template, **Clear** and **Paint**. You see exactly the same fractal as with SIERPIN.

You see now how you can use the same visual "rules" to play either game. The Cat Game finds the fractal by drawing closer and closer approximations of it. Appropriately enough, this technique is called *successive approximation*. The Chaos Game finds the fractal by hopping randomly between its parts, lighting the fractal up dot-by-dot as it goes. This is called *random iteration*. Both techniques use the geometric relationships between parts to define a fractal.

You can express these relationships in human language (as rules), in mathematical language (as formulas), or in computer language (as a program). With FractalVision software, you can express these relationships in a visual language as a *fractal template*. When you select **Draw** or **Paint**, it uses the relationships you've put on-screen to play the Cat Game or the Chaos Game. These procedures are simply two different ways to distill these relationships into their geometric essence.

Geometric Relationships

A fractal set generally contains infinitely many points whose organization is so complicated that it is not possible to describe the set by specifying directly where each point in it lies. Instead, the set may be defined by "the relation between the pieces." It is rather like describing the solar system by quoting the law of gravitation and stating the initial conditions. Everything follows from that. It appears always to be better to describe in terms of relationships.

—Michael Barnsley, *Fractals Everywhere,* 1988

Usually, when you make a copy of something, you try to get an exact duplicate of the original. Computers are very adept at making exact duplicates of anything that you can express with digital precision, from pictures to novels. In the messy world outside the computer, however, perfect copying is practically impossible. Try photocopying a photocopy of a photocopy, and you'll see what I mean.

Nature's processes seldom include exact duplication—mutations and transformations always creep in somewhere. Therefore, the first thing you need when you set out to model natural systems with a computer is a way to have the computer make *transformed* copies instead of exact clones. Every duplicate you create will be different from the original.

For example, the branch of a tree is not a perfect copy of the trunk. For one thing, its size is different. In other words, a *geometric relationship* exists between the trunk and the branch: the branch is smaller. Another aspect of the geometric relationship might be that the branch is oriented differently in space. You could say that the branch is a shrunken, rotated copy of the trunk.

To use a photocopier, you must learn how to select the right enlargement or reduction lens for the geometric relationship between the original and the copy you want to make. To model natural systems, you need a more extensive set of geometric relationships.

Affine Transformations

Realism is a corruption of reality.

—Wallace Stevens, "Adagia," 1957

Fractal templates provide a visual language to describe geometric relationships between shapes. To obtain a solid understanding of that language, you need to begin with a basic vocabulary. In "Fractalese," the words of the language are geometric relationships called *affine transformations.* You'll find your vocabulary list on the main menu of FractalVision software: **Shrink**, **Grow**, **Spin**, **Skew**, **Squish**, and **Stretch**.

Figure 5.4 demonstrates some of these transformations in action. The top sequence of shapes (Figure 5.4a) shows the result of repeating a *shrink* transformation. Another transformation is being repeated at the same time: a *displacement* or *move.* (The shape moves to the right as it becomes smaller.)

The middle sequence of shapes (Figure 5.4b) employs the *squish* transformation, which is really just a shrinking in one dimension instead of two. The shape gets smaller along the x-axis (horizontal), but remains the same size along the y-axis (vertical). In this example, the squish transformation was added to the shrink and move transformations in the preceding example, so both axes shrink. The x-axis, however, shrinks more than the y-axis.

The bottom sequence (Figure 5.4c) illustrates *stretch,* the opposite of squish. It expands the x-axis rather than shrinks it.

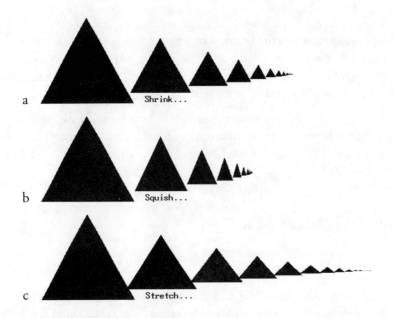

Figure 5.4. Affine transformations in action: shrink (a), squish (b), and stretch (c) (SHRINK, SQUISH, and STRETCH).

You can think of shrink/grow and squish/stretch as variations on a single idea, resizing along one or more axes. Similarly, *spin* (Figure 5.5a) and *skew* (Figures 5.5b and 5.5c) are intimately related. You can spin in either direction (clockwise and counterclockwise), just as you can resize either way (bigger or smaller). Just as squish and stretch resize the x-axis, skew spins the x-axis.

Figures 5.4 and 5.5 illustrate a vocabulary list of affine transformations. *Affine* means that these geometric functions do not alter the basic structure of the shapes they transform. For example, a triangle remains a triangle even when you squish, skew, and move it. Thus, there is a visual and structural "affinity" between the old and new shapes.

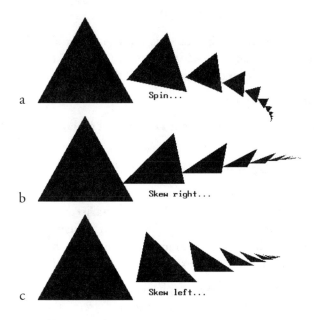

Figure 5.5. More affine transformations in action: spin (a), skew right (b), and skew left (c) (SPIN, SKEW-R, and SKEW-L).

You Can Do It: Affine Transformations

This language is visual, so let's have a look at the "words":

1. **Clear** the picture.

2. **Load** the **Template** named SHRINK.

3. **Draw**.

"Move right" and "shrink" are the visual vocabulary that FractalVision used to draw this picture. To use these "words," you would start with an identical copy of the seed, placed right on top of it. Then you would select **Shrink** and use the right arrow to move the copy. When you **Draw**, you'd see what appears on-screen now.

continues

Every transformation in FractalVision must include **Shrink**age: the *copies* must be smaller than the *seed*. If a copy is larger than the seed, it would grow toward infinite size, and **Paint** would fill the whole screen.

Now for more vocabulary:

4. Don't **Clear** the picture, but **Load** the **Template** named SQUISH and **Draw**.

5. **Load** and **Draw** the STRETCH example, too.

You can distinguish the x- and y-axes of a shape by looking at the handle. The pole (vertical in these examples) is the y-axis, and the crossbar (horizontal in these examples) is the x-axis. When you **Squish** or **Stretch**, only the x-axis changes. When you start to introduce rotation, the x-axis will not always remain horizontal and the y-axis will not always remain vertical.

To **Stretch** with the mouse, simply grab the end of the x-axis and pull straight out from the center. If you want to "stretch the y-axis," simply **Grow** (both axes), then **Shrink** the x-axis back to the size it was before. These same principles apply to **Squish**ing.

6. **Clear** the picture, then **Load** and **Draw** the following **Template**s: SPIN, SKEW-R, and SKEW-L.

As with the previous examples, these transformations are added to the original **Shrink** and displacement, so the shape becomes smaller and moves over as it rotates. **Skew** affects only the x-axis, but you can combine it with **Spin** to change the y-axis.

By grabbing the end of the handle crossbar (x-axis) and moving it up and down, you can **Skew** with the mouse. To skew the y-axis, simply **Spin** both axes (by grabbing and rotating the y-axis pole) and then **Skew** the x-axis back to where it was before.

Numerical Transformations

It is a feature of the artistic imagination that it should be able to reconstitute everything on the basis of very limited data.

—Henry de Montherlant, *The Goddess Cypress,* 1944

You've seen that all affine transformations consist of three basic operations: displacement, resizing, and rotation. Each of these can occur in either of two dimensions (x or y). This means that you can express any affine transformation as six numbers: x displacement, y displacement, x size, y size, x spin, and y spin. The computer actually translates each *copy of the seed* into those six numbers.

When you move a part of the template or choose another transformation from the FractalVision menu, the program simply changes the value of one or more of these variables. For example, selecting **Spin** alters the values of spinx and spiny.

How do these six numbers become a fractal? Simple linear algebra (reviewed in Appendix B, "Mathematics Review, Formulas, and Algorithms," for those who care to brush up on it) provides an easy way to take any point and apply an affine transformation to it. If x,y is the point before the transformation and x_2,y_2 is the point after the transformation, then:

```
x₂ = a * x + b * y + movex
y₂ = c * x + d * y + movey
```

The program already knows movex and movey—they are just the x displacement and y displacement. But where do a, b, c, and d originate? Again, standard linear algebra comes to the rescue and tells us that:

```
a =   sizex * cos(spinx)
b = - sizey * sin(spiny)
c =   sizex * sin(spinx)
d =   sizex * sin(spiny)
```

When you save a template in FractalVision, the sizex, sizey, spinx, spiny, movex, and movey values for each part of the template are actually stored on the disk (along with information about the seed's shape, coloring, and so on).

325

For Programmers Only: Two Ways to Create a Fractal

Listing 5.1 displays a Sierpiński's Triangle using the successive approximation and random iteration algorithms.

Notice the `probsum[]` array, which is used by the `paint()` function to determine the relative probability of choosing any given transformation. This ensures that large parts of the fractal are visited more often than small parts, so the program shades the entire fractal evenly. The probability of visiting a given part is simply the ratio between the area covered by that part and the area covered by all parts combined. Hard-core geometricians tell us that the area covered by an affine transformation is the *determinant* of the transformation matrix, or:

```
t = a * d - b * c
```

Therefore, the probability of visiting a part is the t for that part divided by the sum of t for all parts. For Sierpiński's Triangle, all the parts cover the same area, so it's a moot point. For other fractals, though (a fern, for instance), the bigger parts would take ages to fill without the `probsum[]` array making sure they get the lion's share of the dots.

You might like to use the `loadifs()` and `saveifs()` routines from MUTATE.C (presented in Chapter 4, "The Art of Fractal Modeling") along with `draw()` and `paint()` to display FractalVision IFS codes in your own programs.

Listing 5.1. A program to draw Sierpiński's Triangle two different ways from the same IFS codes.

```
/* IFS.C
 *
 * A program to "draw" and "paint" Sierpinski's Triangle,
 * defined by a seed shape and three transformations.
 */

#include <stdio.h>   /* For getch() */
```

```
#include <math.h>     /* For cos() and sin() */

#define MAIN              /* See Appendix D for compile */
#include "fv.h"          /* instructions and header files */


#define NPOINTS 3         /* Number of points on the seed */
#define NTRANS  3         /* Number of transformations */
#define NLEVELS 6         /* Number of levels to draw */
#define COUNT 10000       /* Number of dots to paint */
#define SEEDX -100,  100,  0  /* The seed corner points*/
#define SEEDY -100, -100, 100


/* Initial values for the transformations */

#define MOVEX -50.0,  50.0,   0.0              /* Displacement */
#define MOVEY -50.0, -50.0,  50.0
#define SIZEX  0.5,   0.5,   0.5               /* Size change */
#define SIZEY  0.5,   0.5,   0.5
#define SPINX  0.0,   0.0,   0.0               /* Rotation */
#define SPINY  0.0,   0.0,   0.0

int seedx[NPOINTS] = {SEEDX},                  /* The seed shape */
    seedy[NPOINTS] = {SEEDY},
    probsum[NTRANS];                    /* Cumulative probability */


          /* The tranformations that define the "children" */

float movex[NTRANS] = {MOVEX},                 /* Displacement */
      movey[NTRANS] = {MOVEY},
    sizex[NTRANS] = {SIZEX},                   /* Size change */
      sizey[NTRANS] = {SIZEY},
    spinx[NTRANS] = {SPINX},                   /* Rotation */
      spiny[NTRANS] = {SPINY},

    /* The transformation matrix itself */

        Ta[NTRANS], Tb[NTRANS], Tc[NTRANS], Td[NTRANS];
```

continues

Listing 5.1. continued

```c
/* Function prototypes */

void draw(float a, float b, float c, float d,
          float mx, float my, int iter);
void paint(int mx, int my);

void main(void)
{   int vidmode, t;                  /* video mode and a counter */
    vidmode = pickmode(detectmode());     /* get video mode */
    if (setvidmode(vidmode, 1) != 1)
    {   printf("\nUnable to set graphics mode.\n");
        exit(0);
    }

/* Compute a,b,c,d from the move, size, and spin variables */

        for (t = 0; t < NTRANS; t++)
        {   Ta[t] =   sizex[t] * cos(spinx[t]);
            Tb[t] = - sizey[t] * sin(spiny[t]);
            Tc[t] =   sizex[t] * sin(spinx[t]);
            Td[t] =   sizey[t] * cos(spiny[t]);
        }

    /* Compute the relative area of each part of the template
       so paint() can use decide how often to visit each part.
       The cumulative probability probsum should add up to
       32768 (the largest possible int) */

    {   float area[NTRANS], areatot;   /* areas, total area */
        int prob, probtot;       /* probability, total prob. */

        for (t = 0; t < NTRANS; t++)
            areatot += (area[t] =
                        fabs(Ta[t] * Td[t] - Tb[t] * Tc[t]));
        if (areatot == 0) areatot = 0.01;
        areatot = 32768.0 / areatot;
        probtot = 0;
```

```
        for (t = 0; t < NTRANS; t++)
        {   if ((prob = area[t] * areatot) == 0) prob = 1;
                probsum[t] = (probtot += prob);
        }
    }

/* Invoke draw with an initial transformation to move
 * the triangle to the center of the screen,
 * unchanged in size or rotation
 */

    setcolor(ncolors - 1);
    draw(1.0, 0.0, 0.0, 1.0,
         (float) scrnx / 2.0,
         (float) scrny / 2.0, NLEVELS);
    moveto(0, scrny - 16);
    outtext("Press any key to paint.");
        getch();
    clearscreen();

/* Invoke paint, telling it the center of the screen */

    paint(scrnx / 2, scrny / 2);
    moveto(0, scrny - 16);
    outtext("Press any key to exit.");
        getch();

        /* Go back to text mode and exit */

    closedown();
    settextmode();
}


/* This recursive routine draws one "parent" polygon,
 * then calls itself to draw the "children" using the
 * transformations defined previously
 */
```

continues

Listing 5.1. continued

```
void draw(float a, float b, float c, float d,
          float mx, float my, int iter)
{   int t;
    iter—;         /* Count one more level of drawing depth */
      {
              /* Use a,b,c,d,mx,my to transform the polygon */

        float x1, y1;                   /* Point on the parent */
        int p, x2[NPOINTS], y2[NPOINTS]; /* Points on child */
                for (p = 0; p < NPOINTS; p++)
                {   x1 = seedx[p];
                        y1 = seedy[p];
                        x2[p] = a * x1 + b * y1 + mx;
                        y2[p] = c * x1 + d * y1 + my;
                }

                /* Now draw the new polygon on-screen */

        moveto(x2[NPOINTS - 1], y2[NPOINTS - 1]);
        for (p = 0; p < NPOINTS; p++) lineto(x2[p], y2[p]);
      }
    if (iter < 0) return; /* at the deepest level, back out */

    /* Do a recursive call for each "child"
     * of the polygon we just drew
     */

        for (t = 0; t < NTRANS; t++)
        {   draw(Ta[t] * a + Tc[t] * b,
                     Tb[t] * a + Td[t] * b,
                     Ta[t] * c + Tc[t] * d,
                     Tb[t] * c + Td[t] * d,
                     movex[t] * a + movey[t] * b + mx,
                     movex[t] * c + movey[t] * d + my,
                     iter);

        }
}
```

```
/* This routine uses random iteration
 * to paint the fractal dot-by-dot.
 * The resulting shape will be the same
 * as if you called draw with a
 * huge value for the number of levels
 */

void paint(int mx, int my)
{   int t, r;
    unsigned long ct = 0;        /* Counter for dots painted */
    float x1 = 0.0, y1 = 0.0, x2, y2;  /* Current, next dot */

    /* Keep going until a key is pressed
     * or we reach the COUNT limit
     */

    while(!kbhit() && (++ct < COUNT))
    {   r = rand();    /* Pick one transformation at random */
        for (t = 0; t < NTRANS - 1; t++)
            if (r < probsum[t]) break;

        /* Then move from a dot on the "whole" to the
         * corresponding dot on some transformed "part"
         */

            x2 = x1 * Ta[t] + y1 * Tb[t] + movex[t];
            y2 = x1 * Tc[t] + y1 * Td[t] + movey[t];
            x1 = x2, y1 = y2;

        /* Skip the first few dots—it takes a while
         * to "find" the fractal
         */

        if (ct > 8)
            putpixel((int) x2 + mx,
                     (int) y2 + my, ncolors - 1);
    }
}
```

IFS Codes

The technical name for a fractal template is *Iterated Function System* (IFS), and the numbers that describe it are called *IFS codes*. For most applications, IFS codes are stored as the six values for a, b, c, d, movex, and movey, and another number to tell the Chaos Game algorithm how often to visit each part of the fractal.

I created Figure 5.6 by designing a template in FractalVision and then exporting the IFS codes to FRACTINT for 3-D projection.

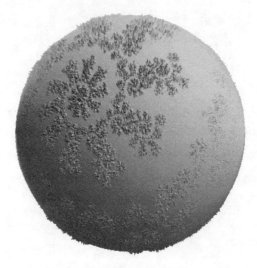

Figure 5.6. You can use IFS files to bring FractalVision templates into FRACTINT for the addition of 3-D effects.

You Can Do It: Exchanging IFS Codes

FractalVision can exchange IFS codes with FRACTINT (see the Introduction for more on FRACTINT) through the **Save IFS Codes** command. You can use this feature to project your favorite fractal template onto a FRACTINT 3-D planet, for example.

1. Run FractalVision and **Load** a favorite template that works well with the **Paint** command (FRACTINT can't **Draw**). Try VSWIRL.

2. **Paint** to get an idea of what the template will look like from within FRACTINT. Keep in mind that you will lose the coloring in the translation.

3. **Save**, then select **IFS Codes** and give the IFS file the same name as the template.

4. **Quit** and press Y to exit FractalVision.

Before you continue, you might want to take a peek at the IFS codes themselves—just out of curiosity.

5. At the DOS prompt, enter TYPE VSWIRL.IFS (or whatever filename you saved the IFS codes under).

   (If that doesn't work, the file was probably saved in the EXAMPLES subdirectory. Try TYPE EXAMPLES\VSWIRL.IFS instead.)

   You should see the name of the file, followed by a row of seven numbers for each part of the template. Don't feel dumb if they don't make any sense to you. No one can intuitively understand the geometry of those numbers without an IFS editing program like FractalVision anyway.

6. Run FRACTINT and choose a high-resolution video mode.

7. Press T and pick the **ifs** fractal type by typing I and pressing Enter.

8. Press the F6 function key to choose a IFS file other than FRACTINT.IFS.

9. Select VSWIRL.IFS (again, you may need to go into the \FRACTAL\EXAMPLES subdirectory to find it).

You should now see the same shape on-screen that you saw in FractalVision.

10. Press the Page Up key repeatedly until the *zoom box* is slightly smaller than the fractal, then use the arrow keys or mouse to move it over the fractal. Press Enter to zoom.

continues

11. Press S to save this picture. Remember the filename that FRACTINT reports.

You can now use any of FRACTINT's 3-D projection features with the picture. For example, you could stamp the pattern onto a sphere.

12. Press 3 to perform a 3-D transform, and select the filename that FRACTINT just reported (probably the last file listed).

13. Press Enter to accept the same video mode.

14. Press the down arrow to go to **Spherical Projection?** on the **3-D Mode Selection** menu, and press Y for Yes.

15. While you're at it, go to **Stereo** and press 2 to turn on red/blue glasses stereovision. Press Enter.

16. Select **light source** for the **3-D Fill Type**, and press Enter.

17. Press Enter once more to accept the default **Funny Glasses Parameters**.

18. On the **Sphere 3-D Parameters** menu, change the **Surface Roughness scaling factor in pct** to 200 and the **Radius scaling factor** to 200 also. Press Enter again.

19. Press Enter one more time to accept the light source default setup.

Something like Figure 5.6 slowly appears. It may take a while unless you have a 486. By going back and trying some of the extra parameters we skipped, like perspective, transparency, rotation, and scaling, you can keep even a fast 486 busy for a while!

For Programmers Only: 3-D IFS Codes

Extending Iterated Function Systems into three dimensions opens many exciting possibilities for realistic modeling, and 3-D IFS codes are relatively easy to display. This program loads any of the 3-D IFS codes provided with this book and enables you to interactively rotate, scale, and move them.

IFS3D will also let you view the fractals in stereo with red/blue glasses. Use the s and S (Shift+s) controls to adjust the spread between red and blue to match your own eyes. You'll know you got it right when the shapes pop out of the screen at you!

Unfortunately, adding one extra dimension complicates everything much more than you might expect. The six codes needed to describe a 2-D IFS become a dozen, the equations to propagate a transformation go from 12 terms to more than 50, and the two axes of rotation available in 2-D expand into six distinct 3-D spatial rotations. A full discussion of the formulas and techniques of interactive 3-D fractal design is more than enough to fill another book.

While you're waiting for me to write that book, you might like to explore further on your own. You can delve into fractal design by modifying IFS3.C so that it changes the transformations in trans[] instead of just viewtrans. You can also vary the parameters passed to spinx(), spiny(), and spinz() for 3-D skewing.

Please also refer to the registration form in the back of this book for information about my complete interactive 3-D fractal CAD system, Fractal Grafics 3-D.

Listing 5.2. A program to display fractals in true 3-D, for viewing with or without red/blue glasses.

```
/* IFS3D.C
 *
 * A program to paint 3D Iterated Function Systems
 * with iteractive rotation, for viewing with red/blue
 * funny glasses.
 */


#include <stdio.h>    /* For getch() */
#include <math.h>     /* For cos() and sin() */

#define MAIN          /* See Appendix D for compile */
```

continues

Listing 5.2. continued

```c
#include "fv.h"          /* instructions and header files */


#define RIGHTCLR 4     /* right eye color */
#define LEFTCLR 1      /* left eye color */
#define OCULARDIST 0.1 /* Ocular distance in radians */
#define OCULARINC 0.01 /* Amount to adjust ocular distance */


#define SPININC 0.2    /* Amount to spin each time */
#define SIZEINC 1.1    /* Amount to grow each time */
#define MOVEINC 10     /* Amount to move each time */
#define NAMELEN 40     /* Maximum length of filename */
#define NPOINTS 64     /* Maximum number of points on seed */
#define NTRANS  20     /* Maximum number of transformations */
#define COUNT 50000    /* Maximum number of dots to paint */


/* addpt adds two 3d points p1 and p2,
 * putting the result into p3.
 * (p3 can be the same variable
 * as p1 or p2 without any problems)
 */


#define addpt(p1, p2, p3) \
        { p3.x = p1.x + p2.x; \
          p3.y = p1.y + p2.y; \
          p3.z = p1.z + p2.z; }


/* mupt multiplies a 3d point p1
 * by a 3x3 transformation matrix m1, putting
 * the result into the 3d point p2.
 * p1 and p2 should NOT be the same variable!
 */


#define mupt(p1, m1, p2) \
   { p2.x = (p1.x * m1.a) + (p1.y * m1.b) + (p1.z * m1.c); \
     p2.y = (p1.x * m1.d) + (p1.y * m1.e) + (p1.z * m1.f); \
     p2.z = (p1.x * m1.g) + (p1.y * m1.h) + (p1.z * m1.i); }
```

```c
struct matrix3x3
{   float a, b, c, d, e, f, g, h, i;
} trans[NTRANS + 1],    /* tranformations define the fractal */
  viewtrans, temat;      /* Viewport rotation, temp. storage */

struct point3d
{   float x, y, z;
} move[NTRANS + 1],     /* translations to define the fractal */
  viewmove, tempt;       /* Viewport translation, temp. storage */

float prob[NTRANS],     /* Probability of each transformation */
      oculardist = OCULARDIST, /* Ocular distance (radians) */
      cosocular, sinocular;  /* Cosine & sine of oculardist */
int probsum[NTRANS],    /* Cumulative probability from prob[] */
    ntrans, drawclr,           /* Number of transformations */
    drawclr;                                /* display color */
    glasses = -1;              /* Red/blue glasses switch */
FILE *diskfile;                /* File handle and filename */
char filename[NAMELEN];

/* Function prototypes */

void paint3d(void);
void load3difs(void);
void save3difs(void);
void spinx(float spiny, float spinz);
void spiny(float spinx, float spinz);
void spinz(float spinx, float spiny);

void main(int nargs, char **arg)
{   int vidmode;                          /* video mode */
    char a;                          /* for keyboard input */
    vidmode = pickmode(detectmode()); /* confirm video mode */
    if (nargs > 1) strcpy(filename, arg[1]);
    else     /* if filename not on command line, ask for it */
    {   printf("\n\nThis program will display a "
            "3D Iterated Function System,\n");
```

continues

337

Listing 5.2. continued

```
        printf("allowing you to interactively spin, "
                "resize and move it.\n\n");
        printf("Controls are:");
        printf("   Xx Yy Zz = Spin\n");
        printf("        * / = Resize\n");
        printf("Arrow keys = Move\n");
        printf("         S s = Adjust spread between eyes\n");
        printf("         G g = Turn red/blue glasses on/off\n");
        printf("         C c = Change color\n");
        printf("          Esc = Quit\n\n");
        printf("Enter the name of the 3D IFS file "
                "to use (try 3DFERN1): ");
        scanf("%s", filename);
    }
    load3difs();                    /* read data from the file */
    if (setvidmode(vidmode, 1) != 1)
    {   printf("\nUnable to set graphics mode.\n");
        exit(0);
    }
    drawclr = ncolors - 1;
    cosocular = cos(OCULARDIST);
    sinocular = sin(OCULARDIST);
    viewtrans.a = 1.0, viewtrans.b = 0.0, viewtrans.c = 0.0;
    viewtrans.d = 0.0, viewtrans.e = 1.0, viewtrans.f = 0.0;
    viewtrans.g = 0.0, viewtrans.h = 0.0, viewtrans.i = 1.0;
    viewmove.x = (float) scrnx / 2.0,
    viewmove.y = (float) scrny / 2.0,
    viewmove.z = 0.0;
    do
    {   clearscreen();
        paint3d();
        switch(a = getch())
        {   case 'x': spinx(SPININC, SPININC);    /* Spin x */
                    break;
            case 'X': spinx(-SPININC, -SPININC);
                    break;
```

```
case 'y': spiny(SPININC, SPININC);      /* Spin y */
          break;
case 'Y': spiny(-SPININC, -SPININC);
          break;
case 'z': spinz(SPININC, SPININC);      /* Spin z */
          break;
case 'Z': spinz(-SPININC, -SPININC);
          break;
case 'C': if (++drawclr == ncolors)
              drawclr = 1;              /* change color */
          glasses = 0;
          break;
case 'c': if (—drawclr == 0)
              drawclr = ncolors - 1;
          glasses = 0;
          break;
case 'S': oculardist += OCULARINC; /* eye spread */
          cosocular = cos(oculardist);
          sinocular = sin(oculardist);
          glasses = -1;
          break;
case 's': oculardist -= OCULARINC;
          cosocular = cos(oculardist);
          sinocular = sin(oculardist);
          glasses = -1;
          break;
case 'G':
case 'g': glasses = !glasses;
          break;
case '*': viewtrans.a *= SIZEINC;       /* Grow */
          viewtrans.c *= SIZEINC;
          viewtrans.d *= SIZEINC;
          viewtrans.e *= SIZEINC;
          viewtrans.f *= SIZEINC;
          viewtrans.g *= SIZEINC;
          viewtrans.h *= SIZEINC;
          viewtrans.i *= SIZEINC;
          break;
```

continues

339

Listing 5.2. continued

```
            case '/': viewtrans.a /= SIZEINC;      /* Shrink */
                      viewtrans.c /= SIZEINC;
                      viewtrans.d /= SIZEINC;
                      viewtrans.e /= SIZEINC;
                      viewtrans.f /= SIZEINC;
                      viewtrans.g /= SIZEINC;
                      viewtrans.h /= SIZEINC;
                      viewtrans.i /= SIZEINC;
                      break;
            case 0:
                switch(a = getch())
                {   case 'H': viewmove.y -= MOVEINC;   /* Up */
                              break;
                    case 'P': viewmove.y += MOVEINC; /* Down */
                              break;
                    case 'K': viewmove.x -= MOVEINC; /* Left */
                              break;
                    case 'M': viewmove.x += MOVEINC; /* Right*/
                              break;
                }
        }
    } while(a != 27);
    closedown();              /* Go back to text mode and exit */
    settextmode();
}

/* This routine uses random iteration
 * to paint the fractal dot-by-dot
 * for viewing with red/blue glasses */

void paint3d(void)
{   int t, r;
    unsigned long ct = 0;  /* number of dots painted so far */
    struct point3d p1, p2;          /* Current and next dot */
    p1.x = 0.0, p1.y = 0.0, p1.z = 0.0;
    while(!kbhit() && (++ct < COUNT))  /* go until keypress */
```

```
    {   r = rand();          /* Pick transformation at random */
        for (t = 0; t < ntrans - 1; t++)
            if (r < probsum[t]) break;
        mupt(p1, trans[t], p2);     /* Do the transformation */
        addpt(p2, move[t], p2);
        p1 = p2;
        mupt(p1, viewtrans, tempt);   /* viewport transform */
        addpt(tempt, viewmove, tempt);
        if (ct > 8)      /* Skip first few dots then display */
        {   if (glasses)
            {   putpixel((int) (tempt.x),
                         (int) (tempt.y), RIGHTCLR);
                putpixel((int) (tempt.x * cosocular +
                              tempt.z * sinocular),
                         (int) (tempt.y), LEFTCLR);
            }
            else
            {   putpixel((int) (tempt.x),
                         (int) (tempt.y), drawclr);
            }
        }
    }
}

/* Load the first set of 3D IFS codes
 * in a FRACTINT compatible IFS file.
 */

void load3difs(void)
{   int i, psum = 0;
    float p;
    char str[NAMELEN + 15];
        strcpy(str, filename);
    strcat(str, ".IFS");
    if ((diskfile = fopen(str, "r")) == NULL)
    {   printf("Can't find a file named %s.", str);
        exit(0);
```

continues

341

Listing 5.2. continued

```
    }
    diskfile = fopen(str, "r");
    while(fgetc(diskfile) != '(');
    if ((fgetc(diskfile) != '3') ||
        (fgetc(diskfile) != 'D') ||
        (fgetc(diskfile) != ')') ||
        (fgetc(diskfile) != ' ') ||
        (fgetc(diskfile) != '{'))
    {   printf("\7The first IFS in the file "
                "is not a valid set of 3D codes.");
        getch();
    }
    else
    {   for (i = 0; i < NTRANS; i++)
        {   if (fscanf(diskfile,
                " %f %f %f %f %f %f %f %f %f %f %f %f %f\n",
                &(trans[i].a), &(trans[i].b), &(trans[i].c),
                &(trans[i].d), &(trans[i].e), &(trans[i].f),
                &(trans[i].g), &(trans[i].h), &(trans[i].i),
                &(move[i].x),  &(move[i].y),  &(move[i].z),
                prob + i) != 13) break;
            move[i].x *= -50.0;
            move[i].y *= -50.0;
            move[i].z *= -50.0;
            probsum[i] = (psum += (int) (prob[i] * 32768.0));
        }
        ntrans = i;
    }
    fclose(diskfile);
}

/* These functions spin the viewport transformation
 * by a specified number of radians.
 * If the two parameters are different, a skew will occur
 */
```

```
void spinx(float spiny, float spinz)  /* Spin around x axis */
{   temat = viewtrans;
    viewtrans.b = temat.b *  cos(spiny) - temat.c * sin(spiny);
    viewtrans.e = temat.e *  cos(spiny) - temat.f * sin(spiny);
    viewtrans.h = temat.h *  cos(spiny) - temat.i * sin(spiny);
    viewtrans.c = temat.b *  sin(spinz) + temat.c * cos(spinz);
    viewtrans.f = temat.e *  sin(spinz) + temat.f * cos(spinz);
    viewtrans.i = temat.h *  sin(spinz) + temat.i * cos(spinz);
}

void spiny(float spinx, float spinz)  /* Spin around y axis */
{   temat = viewtrans;
    viewtrans.a = temat.a *  cos(spinx) + temat.c * sin(spinx);
    viewtrans.d = temat.d *  cos(spinx) + temat.f * sin(spinx);
    viewtrans.g = temat.g *  cos(spinx) + temat.i * sin(spinx);
    viewtrans.c = temat.a * -sin(spinz) + temat.c * cos(spinz);
    viewtrans.f = temat.d * -sin(spinz) + temat.f * cos(spinz);
    viewtrans.i = temat.g * -sin(spinz) + temat.i * cos(spinz);
}

void spinz(float spinx, float spiny)  /* Spin around z axis */
{   temat = viewtrans;
    viewtrans.a = temat.a * cos(spinx) - temat.b * sin(spinx);
    viewtrans.d = temat.d * cos(spinx) - temat.e * sin(spinx);
    viewtrans.g = temat.g * cos(spinx) - temat.h * sin(spinx);
    viewtrans.b = temat.a * sin(spiny) + temat.b * cos(spiny);
    viewtrans.e = temat.d * sin(spiny) + temat.e * cos(spiny);
    viewtrans.h = temat.g * sin(spiny) + temat.h * cos(spiny);
}
```

Orbiting Iterations

The mysterious quality of these pictures comes from the fact that in some sense they exist. These objects have been lurking in abstract geometry and nobody's ever seen them before, but mathematically they exist just as much as a square exists and has identity of its own.
—Alan Norton (quoted by Peter Sorensen, "Fractals," *BYTE*, 1984)

Repetitive procedures that use the results of one step to create the next are called *iterative.*

You can create an iterative system with a hand calculator simply by pressing the same operation over and over again. For example, you might type a number and press the cos (cosine) key repeatedly. If you try this, you'll discover that after a few *iterations,* the number 0.9998477 appears and won't go away. It doesn't matter what number you start with—0.5, 0.1, or even 155.0—all go to 0.9998477 after a few pokes at the cos key.

The number 0.9998477 is called the *attractor* of the cosine function because all numbers are attracted to it when the function iterates. Many iterated functions have attractors. The equation $rp(1-p)$, discussed in Chapter 3, "The Philosophy of Fractals," is attracted to a single number so long as r is between 0 and 3, for instance. Just as the progress of $rp(1-p)$ quickly settles to a straight line when you graph it, cos(y) also settles on a linear attractor (Figure 5.7).

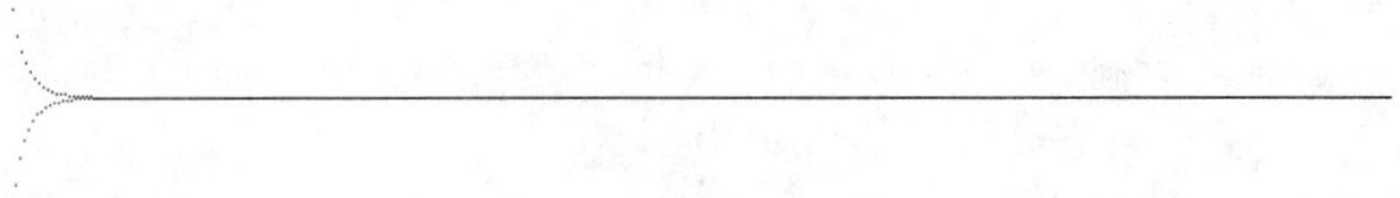

Figure 5.7. The iterated function cos(y) is attracted to a single number (0.9998477).

Functions involving more than one variable often possess more interesting attractors. The Chaos Game and Cat Game are iterative functions with all sorts of fractals as their attractors, depending on the geometric relationships in use as "rules." When you plotted the r in $rp(1-p)$ as an additional variable (along with p) rather than a constant, an intricate bifurcation map resulted as its attractor. If you plot $x\cos(y)$ (x times the cosine of y) on an x verses y graph (Figure 5.8), you will see a similar attractor.

Not only does Figure 5.8 strongly resemble the graphs of May's population equation from Chapter 3, but the points at which it bifurcates fall at exactly the same intervals. In fact, the ratio between successive bifurcation intervals in almost all iterated systems is precisely 4.6692016090. This universal constant, called *Feigenbaum's number,* reveals a rigid hidden order in almost all chaotic attractors, from the simple cosine function to the magnificent Mandelbrot set.

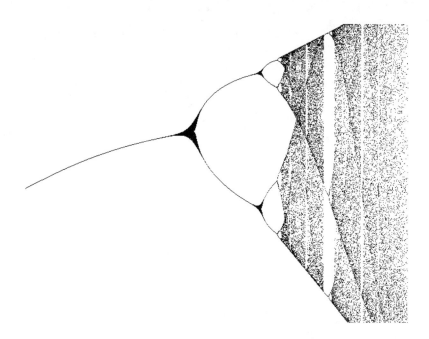

Figure 5.8. Equations with two variables, such as $x\cos(y)$, can possess more complex attractors.

But I'm getting ahead of myself—there are far more attractive attractors coming up soon enough. First, let's step back a bit and examine just how iteration can work with points instead of numbers in the first place.

Iteration on a Plane

Perhaps an angel of the Lord surveyed an endless sea of chaos, then troubled it gently with his finger. In this tiny and temporary swirl of equations, our cosmos took shape.
—Martin Gardner, *Scientific American*

When you carry out iterative procedures on a two-dimensional surface (such as a computer screen), it is called *iteration on a plane*. Almost all fractal images—both those from FractalVision and those from FRACTINT—are products of some kind of iteration on a plane. (The **julibrot** fractal type in FRACTINT is actually the product of iteration in four-dimensional space, but I'll leave that adventure for you to undertake on your own. Be sure to wear your 3-D glasses to lessen the impact of warping into 4-D.)

To understand how you can iterate a single point on a plane, look at an example from Figure 5.4. I created Figure 5.9 using exactly the same spin transformation, but with a point as the seed shape instead of a triangle. You might not think that a single point could rotate, but remember that I am dealing with a relationship between points. Notice how the *relationship* between subsequent points shrinks and spins, not just the points themselves.

Figure 5.9. A single point traveling in a spinning and shrinking orbit (SPIN).

This sequence of points is called an *orbit*. The location of each point on the orbit is computed from the preceding point's location and the predefined transformation. When you use shrinking (or *contractive*) affine transformations, the orbit of any point always converges toward a single location on-screen. This location is called the *fixed point* of the transformation. (Therefore, if you use FractalVision's **Paint** command when you have only one copy of the seed, the infinite level fractal that appears will be only a single fixed point.)

You Can Do It: Going into Orbit

To see the orbital pattern of any fractal template, you can easily turn the seed shape into a point.

1. **Clear** the picture and **Load** any fractal template you like (try SPIN to reproduce Figure 5.9).

2. Select **NextPoint** and **New**.

3. Type 1 and press Enter to make the seed a single point.

4. When you **Draw**, the point repeatedly undergoes a transformation. (If you did this using a fractal template with more than one copy of the seed, the point will split into several orbits.)

What if the transformation isn't contractive? For example, what if you had an affine transformation in which the copy was bigger than the seed? Obviously, the orbits would no longer converge on a fixed point but would diverge outward to infinity.

The points you see on-screen could represent the beginning of an *expansive* orbit, if you imagined that they would appear in the opposite order. Such an orbit's transformation would be the geometric inverse of the one you actually used. It would begin near the fixed point and move outward. When it reached your seed point, it would keep going in larger and larger jumps until it escaped to infinity.

A lone affine transformation creates a somewhat boring orbit. If it's contractive, it quickly settles to the fixed point; if it's expansive, it zooms off to infinity. The orbit of one point will closely resemble the orbits of nearby points. When you use more than one contractive affine transformation to move a point along its orbit (for example, when you **Paint** a template that has more than one copy of the seed), things begin to get interesting. The orbit zips about on a richly detailed fractal attractor.

Escaping IFS

…the attractor lies imbedded in space like a jewel…
—Michael Barnsley, describing the escape time algorithm applied to an IFS,
Fractals Everywhere, 1988

Figure 5.10 shows the contraction of a contractive affine transformation. When you repeat the transformation (Figure 5.11), you'll see a series of nested boxes spiraling into the *fixed point.*

At this point, you may ask, "How would each point on-screen behave on the inverse, *expansive* orbit?" Imagine points in the middle of the shape orbiting outward until they escaped the outside box in Figure 5.10 to fly toward infinity. The outside layer of black points in Figure 5.11 is already outside the escape region. The first region of white points escapes in one iteration, the next stripe of black points escapes in two, the next white ones in three, and so on. So you have the same color pattern as if you had actually used an expansive transformation.

The famous (and upcoming) Mandelbrot and Julia sets utilize the *escape time algorithm,* which colors points according to how quickly their expansive orbits flee a certain region. The dramatic coloring effect this algorithm achieves has wowed millions.

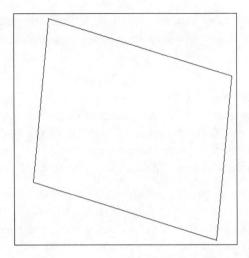

Figure 5.10. A simple contractive affine transformation (ESCAPE).

Figure 5.11. The transformation in Figure 5.10 falls into a fixed point when repeated (ESCAPE).

Theoretically, you can reproduce any picture of an expansive orbit (and a contractive orbit, for that matter) with its inverse. Likewise, you can achieve the famous escape time look with any set of contractive transformations. Figure 5.12 shows a redefined FractalVision template that creates a collapsing field of alternating color around the fractal, just like the colorful sets in FRACTINT.

Figure 5.12. You can bestow any of your fractal models with a colorful aura (FERNZOOM).

You Can Do It: Colorful Contractions

Mesmerizing pictures of escape time fractals have captured the imaginations of the masses, and part of the reason for this has nothing to do with the mathematical structures they reveal. Remove the majestic vortex of alternating colored bands around a Julia set, and the fractal itself loses much of its fascination.

continues

Conversely, adding a vortex of alternating colored bands to everyday images gives them a whole new life. You can use the inverse-escape time technique shown in Figures 5.11 and 5.12 to add hypnotic color fields around any fractal you create with FractalVision. Here's how:

1. **Load** any **Template** that normally uses the **Paint** command. Try FERN1 or FLAKE1 for starters.

2. **Paint**. There it is.

   To make the fractal whirl downward into itself, create a seed shape bigger than the screen without changing the relationships between the parts that define the fractal itself.

3. Select **NextPoint** and **New**, then press 4 and Enter. The seed becomes a square standing on one corner.

4. **Spin** four times to settle the square onto its side.

5. **Grow** until the square is larger than the screen.

6. **Draw**. Outlines or regions of color now collapse inward toward the shape. **Paint** to throw the fractal into their midst.

   Those colors, by the way, could use some work. Use the techniques from Chapter 4 to **Adjust** the color palette to your liking. Here is one possibility:

7. Select **Adjust** and set the **Fill** to 100%, and select **Fill All Parts**. You can do this quickly by pressing the following keys in order: A down-arrow End |.

8. Press H to select **Color** H.

9. Adjust the **Red** and **Blue** settings to 0% and the **Green** to 50%.

10. Select **Color** B, then set the **Red** and **Green** to 0% and the **Blue** to 100%.

11. Select **Color** G, then set the **Red** to 100% and the **Green** and **Blue** to 0%.

12. Select **Blend Colors** and press B to blend from color G to color B.

13. Press the following keys to assign the new colors to the parts and levels of the fractal drawing: 1 B \ 2 C \ 3 D \ 4 E \ 5 F \ 6 G \ 0 H 6.

14. Press Esc to return to the main menu, then **Draw**.

15. Finally, select **Adjust**, press 0 to set the level of detail to zero, press Esc, and **Paint**.

If you'd like to see just the end result of all this, taken to a few more levels of detail, **Load** the FERNZOOM template.

Escape Time

The concern is growing, almost simultaneously in many different fields, that far too little is known about the consequences of nonlinear laws. It came as a surprise even to physicists that there is chaos in their simplest equations. Our pictures express an optimistic attitude in this respect.

Mindboggling at first glance, they also show that the complex is accessible to systematic study, that even the chaos has its rules. The regularities of the Mandelbrot set encourage our hope that more characteristic scenarios will be identified in the nonlinear world. This hope rests on the power of computer experimentation which has so quickly become one of the main sources of insight and inspiration.

—H.O. Peitgen and Peter Richter, *The Beauty of Fractals,* 1986

Don't think that affine transformations are the only possible vocabulary for defining geometric relationships. Many mathematical operations don't preserve the structure of the shapes they transform, and you can iterate them to create magnificent fractals, too. However, the results are very difficult to visualize and control, simply because the entire structure may change with each iteration.

These *nonaffine* transformations can produce chaotic orbits: two points right next to each other may behave in entirely different ways. Some of the most famous examples stem from a seemingly simple transformation: multiplying a point by itself and then adding it to another point. (You say you don't know how to "multiply a point"? Read up on complex numbers in Appendix B, "Mathematics Review,

Formulas, and Algorithms," later, and just trust that it can be done for now.) Some points converge to *basins of attraction,* and others zoom off to infinity. You can use FRACTINT to picture the behavior of these orbits and, in the meantime, produce intricate designs like those shown in Figures 5.13 through 5.20.

The Mandelbrot Set

The Mandelbrot set broods in silent complexity at the center of a vast two-dimensional sheet of numbers called the complex plane. When a certain operation is applied repeatedly to the numbers, the ones outside the set flee to infinity. The numbers inside remain to drift or dance about. Close to the boundary minutely choreographed wanderings mark the onset of instability. Here is an infinite regress of detail that astonishes us with its variety, its complexity and its strange beauty.

—A.K. Dewdney, "Computer Recreations," *Scientific American*

To paint the *Mandelbrot set* (Figure 5.13), each point on a computer display is multiplied by itself repeatedly, adding the original point each time. For those who think in symbols better than in words, the iteration formula for the Mandelbrot set is

$$z_2 = zz + c$$

where z is the current point on the orbit and z_2 is the next point. Because z is a point on the plane (also called a *complex number*), it really consists of two regular numbers, the x and y coordinates of the point. Likewise, c is really two numbers, cx and cy. According to the laws of complex number arithmetic (reviewed in Appendix B, "Mathematics Review, Formulas, and Algorithms"), the following two equations mean exactly the same thing as the preceding one:

$$x_2 = xx - yy + cx$$
$$y_2 = 2xy + cy$$

To draw the Mandelbrot set, a program scans each point on-screen. For each point, the program starts an orbit at $x=0$, $y=0$ and keeps iterating the first equation, feeding in the value of z to return a new z each time around. The value of c stays constant for the whole iteration: it is the point on-screen that is about to be colored.

If z stays within a certain region (between $-2,-2$ and $2,2$, to be exact), it is "part of the set" and takes on a certain color (white in this illustration). If it leaves this region, its color depends on how many steps along its orbit it went before departure. Here, I used alternating black and white.

Figure 5.13. The Mandelbrot set, drawn with FRACTINT software.

(In case you were wondering, the reason we care about staying within the region between –2,–2 and 2,2 specifically is that mathematicians have proven that any point escaping those boundaries will eventually zip off to infinity. It's infinity that matters, not the –2 and 2.)

Julia Sets

Fractal geometry reveals that some of the most austerely formal chapters of mathematics had a hidden face: a world of beauty unsuspected until now.
       —Benoit Mandelbrot, *The Fractal Geometry of Nature,* 1982

Julia sets emerge from picking a certain point and multiplying every other point by it repeatedly, then adding the original point each time. Therefore, each point on the plane has its own Julia set. A few Julia sets are shown in Figure 5.14.

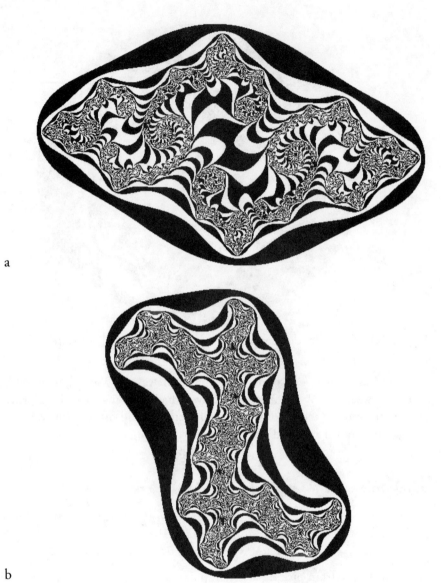

a

b

c

d

Figure 5.14. Julia sets, drawn with FRACTINT.

The iteration equation for Julia sets is exactly the same as that for the Mandelbrot set. The only difference is the meaning of c and the starting point of the orbit. When computing a Julia set, you use a constant c value for all points on-screen, and the orbit starts at the point on-screen that will be colored instead of at the origin (0,0). The next **For Programmers Only** box demonstrates all this in good, clean C.

The Mandelbrot and Julia sets obviously bear close relation to one another. In fact, if you zoom in on a point in the Mandelbrot set (Figure 5.15), the Mandelbrot image around that point resembles its Julia set (Figure 5.16) the closer you look.

a

b

c

d

continues

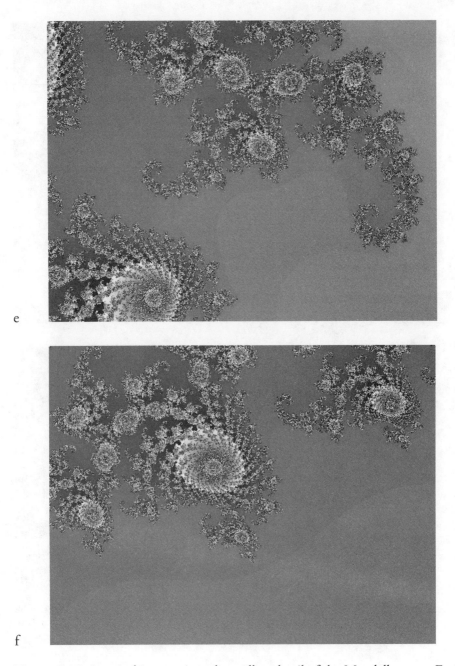

e

f

Figure 5.15. A typical journey into the endless detail of the Mandelbrot set. Each picture is a 20x magnification of the very center of the one before it.

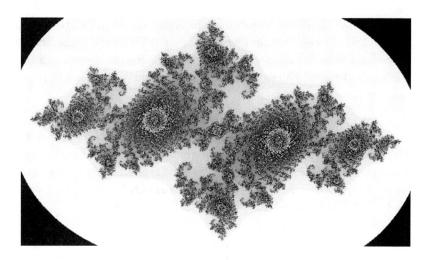

Figure 5.16. The Julia set associated with the center point of the Mandelbrot set images in Figure 5.15.

Despite the simplicity of the formula that gives birth to the Mandelbrot set, the mathematicians who discovered it have donned it "the most complicated object in mathematics." (Mandelbrot did not discover the Mandelbrot set, by the way. It was described by at least four other mathematicians—Pierre Fatou in 1906, Robert Brooks and J. Peter Matelski in 1978, and John Hubbard in 1979—before Mandelbrot brought it into the public eye in 1980.) If you try to explore the Mandelbrot set with the short JANDELIA program listed in the **For Programmers Only** box that follows, you will discover endless magnificent landscapes of intricacy and beauty. You will also discover that these intricate and beautiful images can take an unbearably long time to appear on your screen. It certainly would be nice if someone could figure out a way to make them appear, say, a hundred times faster...

Luckily, somebody did. Bert Tyler originally created FRACTINT software to display the Mandelbrot set in a tolerable amount of time on PCs. He was soon joined by a loosely coordinated team of volunteer fractaliers, including Mark Peterson, Tim Wegner, and Pieter Branderhorst. This ever-expanding electronic allegiance communicates via the COMART forum on CompuServe and calls itself the "Stone Soup Group." (Stone soup is water and a rock, with a little bit of meat and veggies contributed by whoever happens by. If enough people happen by, stone soup can be quite a feast!)

By now, I hope you've taken my incessant advice and gotten yourself a copy of FRACTINT through CompuServe, another BBS, or the registration form in the back of this book. If you're still procrastinating, why not download a copy or send in the form right now? You won't want to miss seeing the next few illustrations grow in color on your own screen.

You can apply the escape time algorithm (used to generate the Mandelbrot, Julia, and Newton sets) to any equation that takes one 2-D point and transforms it into another. FRACTINT offers more than 50 escape time fractal types—many of which you explored in previous chapters—and even enables you to create your own by typing a formula. (The next **For Programmers Only** box will get you started with FRACTINT's custom formula interpreter.)

You Can Do It: The Mandelbrot and Julia Sets

FRACTINT has expanded to display oodles of fractals, but Mandelbrot and Julia sets are still what it does best.

1. Run FRACTINT, press the Delete key, and pick the 320x200 video mode with 256 colors. If you have a fast 386 or 486, select the 640x480 256 color mode instead. (Don't have Super VGA? Pick the best video mode your system can muster, then pry a couple hundred bucks out of your pocket and get a real video card.)

2. Press T and select the **mandel** fractal type.

3. Press Enter to accept the default parameters.

4. The famous almond shape of the Mandelbrot set appears—and darn fast, too.

5. Press the left mouse button and move up until the *zoom box* is less than an inch wide. (What, you have no mouse? Use the Page Up key, then pry another hundred bucks out of your pocket.)

6. Release the left button and move the box over the V-shaped trench between the circular blue "head" and the big blue "body."

7. Double-click the left button.

8. Press the plus key. Be impressed. Press Enter a few times.

9. Press Esc and zoom in again. Find a particularly interesting region, and explore. Notice that you can zoom back out after positioning the zoom box by double-clicking the right button instead of the left.

   As you delve deeper into the Mandelbrot set, you may find that the outlines of the set smooth out. This is an illusion. ("The problem is not with your set...") To fix it:

10. Press X and change the **Maximum Iterations** to a larger value—1000, for example. This tells FRACTINT to perform a thousand iterations (instead of the default 150) before deciding to bail out and call a pixel part of the set. Fortunately, FRACTINT uses a trick called *periodicity checking* to detect repeating patterns in orbits—usually in the first few iterations. Therefore, you will probably experience only a minor slow-down due to the increased **Maximum Iteration** setting.

    You can think of the Mandelbrot set as a map of all possible Julia sets. When you find an area in the Mandelbrot set that looks intriguing, you can view an entire Julia set landscape based on the point in the center of the screen simply by pressing the Spacebar.

11. Press the Spacebar. See?

    If you zoom into the Julia set, you'll find endless detail there as well.

12. Press the Spacebar again to return to the Mandelbrot set.

    Entire research teams, newsletters, books, and secret societies are dedicated to exploring the Mandelbrot and Julia sets. (I haven't actually heard of any secret societies, but if I had, they wouldn't be secret, would they?) Unless you are entirely immune to the beauty of mathematics, you will end up spending quite some time adventuring in this spectacular abstract universe yourself.

    Press F1 from anywhere within FRACTINT to unlock the 500-page hypertext online help system, which will instruct you in the finer details of fractal spelunking.

For Programmers Only: JANDELIA

The endless variety of visually complex images that this program can produce is out of proportion to its modest size. In fact, most of this short program dedicates itself to asking the user what region of which set to display.

Quite frankly, I only included this program to show you how simple the code is that creates the Mandelbrot and Julia sets. Even if you want to try your own formulas to construct similar fractals, you would be better off using FRACTINT's built-in formula interpreter than modifying this program. Here's how to access a complete description of FRACTINT's powerful programming-without-programming features:

1. Run FRACTINT and select any video mode.

2. Press T and type formula. Don't press Enter yet, but press F2 instead for online help specific to the **formula** fractal type.

Listing 5.3. A simple program to display the Mandelbrot and Julia sets.

```
/* JANDELIA.C
 *
 * A program to display Mandelbrot and Julia Sets.
 */

#include <stdio.h>        /* standard input/output */
#include <conio.h>

#define MAIN              /* See Appendix D for compile */
#include "fv.h"           /* instructions and header files */

#define drawclr 15        /* color for outline box */

int niter,                /* maximum number of iterations */
    px, py,               /* current pixel */
    nx, ny,               /* number of pixels */
    nc,                   /* number of colors to use */
    i, j,                 /* counters for miscellaneous use */
```

```
        keepon,              /* 1 = keep going, 0 = abort */
        jul,                 /* 1 = Julia Set,  0 = Mandelbrot */
        scrnx, scrny;        /* resolution of screen */

float x, y,                  /* last point on orbit */
      xx, yy,                /* next point on orbit */
      xsquared, ysquared,    /* used to speed up computations */
      dx, dy,                /* theoretical size of pixels */
      cx, cy,                /* number to add each iteration */
      x0, y0,                /* starting x,y */
      xI, yI;                /* ending x,y */

void getparms(void);

void main(void)
{   int vidmode;                            /* video mode */
    vidmode = pickmode(detectmode());    /* get video mode */
    if (setvidmode(vidmode, 1) != 1)
    {   printf("\nUnable to set graphics mode.\n");
        exit(0);
    }
    settextmode();       /* go back to text mode momentarily */
    getparms();       /* ask the user what they'd like to see */
    setvidmode(0, 0);        /* then set graphics mode again */
    keepon = 1;             /* keepon tells when to abort */
    setcolor(drawclr);   /* rectangle around drawing region */
    drawrect(0, 0, nx - 1, ny - 1);
    dx = (xI - x0) / nx;            /* compute size of pixels */
    dy = (yI - y0) / ny;
    for (px = 0; (px < nx) && (keepon); px++)  /* main loop */
        for (py = 0; (py < ny) && (keepon); py++)
        {   x = x0 + px * dx,    /* start julia set on pixel */
            y = y0 + py * dy;
            if (jul == 0)     /* start mandelbrot set on 0,0 */
                cx = x, cy = y,
                x = 0.0, y = 0.0;     /* and use pixel for c */

/* main iteration loop; go until the distance to the origin is
```

continues

Listing 5.3. continued

```
* greater than 2 (i.e. square of the distance > 4), or we hit
* the maximum number of iterations */
          xsquared = 0, ysquared = 0;
          for (i = 0; (i < niter) &&
                       (xsquared + ysquared < 4.0); i++)
          {   xsquared = x * x;
              ysquared = y * y;
              xx = xsquared - ysquared + cx;
              yy = x * y * 2.0 + cy;
              x = xx, y = yy;
          }
          if (i == niter) i = 0;    /* hit limit, color 0 */
          else i = (i % nc);      /* color determined by i */
          putpixel(px, py, i);        /* lite up the pixel */
          if (kbhit() && (getch() == 27))
              keepon = 0;             /* stop if user hit Esc */
      }
   printf("\7");                        /* beep when done */
   getch();                         /* wait for a keypress */
   settextmode();         /* close down graphics and quit */
   closedown();
}

/* Ask the user which set and region they want to display */

void getparms(void)
{   float ox, oy, ax, ay;
   printf("\n\n");
   printf("This program displays pictures of "
          "the Julia and Mandelbrot Sets.\n");
   printf("You will be asked for information "
          "needed to create a picture.\n");
   printf("To quit the program, press ctrl+C during "
          "input or Esc during display.");
      while(1)
   {   printf("\n\n");
       printf("Enter 0 now for the Mandelbrot Set, "
```

```
            "or 1 for a Julia Set: ");
scanf("%d", &jul);
if (jul)
{   printf("\n\n");
    printf("Each point between -2,-2 and 2,2 "
           "has its own Julia Set.\n");
    printf("Compute a Julia Set for the point: x = ");
    scanf("%f", &cx);
    printf("                               y = ");
    scanf("%f", &cy);
    printf("\nThe Julia Set spans "
           "from -1.5, -1.5 to 1.5, 1.5.");
}
else
{   printf("\n\nThe Mandelbrot Set spans "
           "from -2.25, -1.5 to 0.75, 1.5.");
    }
printf("\nThe minimum (top left) point to view: x = ");
scanf("%f", &xO);
printf("                               y = ");
scanf("%f", &yO);
printf("\nMaximum (bottom right) point to view: x = ");
scanf("%f", &xI);
printf("                               y = ");
scanf("%f", &yI);
printf("\n\nThe whole screen is %d by %d pixels.",
        scrnx, scrny);
printf("\nThe size of the image in pixels: x = ");
scanf("%d", &nx);
if (nx > scrnx) nx = scrnx;
printf("                               y = ");
scanf("%d", &ny);
if (ny > scrny) ny = scrny;
printf("\n\nMore iterations show more detail, "
        "but take longer.");
printf("\nThe number of iterations = ");
scanf("%d", &niter);
```

continues

Listing 5.3. continued

```
        if (ncolors > 2)
        {   printf("\n\nYou can use any number "
                    "of colors from 2 to %d", ncolors);
            printf("\nThe number of colors to use = ");
            scanf("%d", &nc);
                }
            else nc = 2;
        if (nc > ncolors) nc = ncolors;
        printf("\n\nWould you like to change "
                "any of the above? (Y or N)");
        switch(getch())
        {   case 'n':
            case 'N': return;
                }
        }
    }
```

Nature Revisited

Mathematicians are inexorably drawn to nature, not just describing what is to be found there, but in creating echoes of natural laws.

—Roger Lewin (quoted by Clifford Pickover in *Computers, Pattern, Chaos and Beauty*, 1990)

"So, ahem, what ever happened to that book I was reading about real-world fractals?"

Good question. You obviously can use fractal templates based on affine transformations to model nature. But all this Julia set business seems about as far from nature as you can get. Chaotic, nonlinear transformations such as z squared plus c can produce pretty pictures, but they don't seem to have any connection with the physical world at all.

You could think of the Mandelbrot set as a mathematical exercise—a purely intellectual diversion, just to prove that mankind is more inventive than nature.

Doesn't that sound a bit familiar? Didn't some mathematicians—way back in the old days of Chapter 1—try inventing weird, unnatural shapes to outsmart Nature? Sierpiński's Triangle, Peano's Space-Filling Curve, Cantor's Dust—they called them "monsters." In this book, I've shown you how to use the same geometry to create realistic models of trees, ferns, clouds, and galaxies.

You could call the Mandelbrot set a mathematical monster. Mandelbrot himself called it "The Geometry of Nature."

The Secret Life of the Mandelbrot Set

Life is an offensive, directed against the repetitious mechanism of the Universe.
—Alfred Whitehead, *Adventures of Ideas,* 1933

Figure 5.17, a close-up of a piece of the Mandelbrot set, shows the same polychotomous branching found in natural phenomena from lightning to soot crystals to plant growth.

Figure 5.17. Patterns in the Mandelbrot set resemble plant growth, electrical discharge, liquid diffusion, and many other natural phenomena.

Spiral forms such as the Mandelbrot set snapshot in Figure 5.18 are abundant in nature's creations, from seashells to sunflowers.

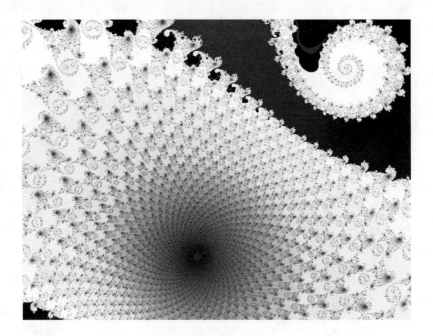

Figure 5.18 The Mandelbrot set's spiraling forms are as common in nature as in mathematics.

Figure 5.19 uses a slight variation on the standard escape time procedure that gives the Julia sets a more biological appearance. Clifford Pickover discovered this technique quite serendipitously, when a programming bug in his Julia set generator started generating bugs—the kind with little cilia and antennae—on his screen. Pickover named these cell-like critters *biomorphs.*

Figure 5.20 shows part of the Mandelbrot set as it develops through successively higher iteration counts, with biomorph coloring added. This monopodial branching pattern could easily serve as a model for the shoot (or, upside down, the root) of a tropical plant.

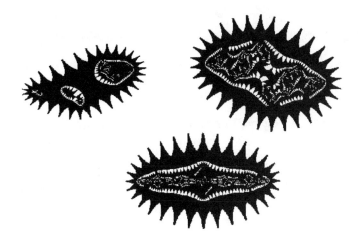

Figure 5.19. When you turn on FRACTINT's biomorph coloring scheme for Julia sets, the output resembles single-celled organisms.

You Can Do It: Biomorphs

You can turn any FRACTINT fractal into a Pickover biomorph.

1. Start FRACTINT, and select any video mode (16 colors are just as good as 256 for many biomorphs).

2. Press T and select the **mandel** fractal type. Press Enter again to accept the default parameters.

3. Press X, use the down arrow to go down to **Biomorph Color**, and change it to 2. (You can try other colorings, but most settings for this parameter produce similar results.)

4. Press Enter. It's a Mandelbug!

5. Zoom in using Page Up or the mouse, and explore. Can you find plant shapes? (Hint: Look closely in the bottom of the Mandelbug's belly for branching intestinal cilia like Figure 5.20.)

continues

When you find interesting forms, you can watch them grow:

6. Press X and set the **Maximum iterations** to a lower number—50, for example. (If a blank screen appears, the iteration count is too low. Press X again and try bigger numbers until the beginnings of the shoots start to appear.)

7. To make a sequence of pictures like Figure 5.20, set the **Maximum iterations** to higher and higher values, pressing S to save the picture each time.

8. Be sure to press the Spacebar to explore a Julia set or two, as well. Many biomorph Mandelbrot and Julia set images bear a strong resemblance to plants, jellyfish, or single-celled animals.

a

b

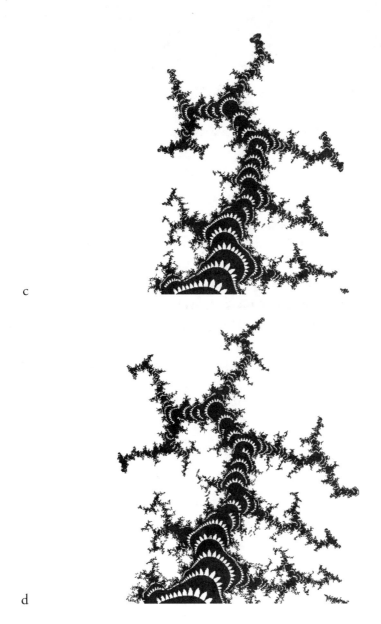

c

d

Figure 5.20. A plant grows in the mathematical soil of the Mandelbrot set as the iteration count increases.

Fractal Vision

Fractals turned out to be a mathematical curiosity that science was just waiting for.
—D.E. Thomsen, *"Fractals: Magical Fun or Revolutionary Science?", Science News,*
1987

No one is certain how the spirals and branches in the Mandelbrot and Julia sets arise from simple nonlinear equations, let alone why they follow the archetypical patterns of nature so closely. These topics are at the forefront of current mathematical and scientific research.

As you will discover when you explore FRACTINT's many fractal types, these natural forms are not specific to any one set of equations. Mathematics itself seems to delight in a naturalistic visual poetry, when left to its own rambling iterations.

Since ancient times, the clean orderliness of mathematics has stood in cool opposition to nature's reckless chaos. Yet mathematicians have always marveled at and mimicked natural patterns. In this century, the profound and often mysterious connection between these two realms seems to have grown suddenly stronger.

Scientists are caught in the midst of this interplay between intellect and observation. From it, they have gained powerful new tools for modeling almost all natural phenomena. They also face the challenge of assimilating a new view of the universe, and the obsolescence of many cherished patterns of thought.

Welcome to the world of fractals. With FractalVision and its accompanying software, you stand on the edge of a vast continent, the unexplored frontiers of which are literally infinite. But the territory isn't inside your computer. It's all around and deep within you. All it takes to see a new world is a new kind of vision.

Epilogue

Life in a Box

If a line is true, a corner clean, and a rectangle honest, many of us now live in a nearly perfect world. We drive our cars between lines straight enough to inspire religious awe in a sixteenth century priest, past buildings beyond the wildest modular dreams of Descartes himself, and then retire to white-box living rooms with corners and walls more precise than the most grand cathedral. Billions of urbanites see only a scattered few nonlinear forms in their daily lives: some struggling trees, each other's faces, perhaps a swirl of dust in the street.

Still, we thirst for linearity more than ever. We breed vegetables to grow straight and round; we straighten and pave twisting paths. Even the night sky—once a familiar speckled disarray—is reduced by electric light and smog

to a flat haze. At the same time, our reverence for the straight and true has all but disappeared. We've become linear junkies: the mystical high has worn off, but our craving for larger and larger doses of linearity rages on.

Once familiar and comforting, the nonlinear organic world has become threatening and alien. From the swirling, living cosmos of ages past, we have retreated into a universe of boxes. We eat from boxes, live in boxes, travel in boxes, talk into boxes, and seek our entertainment from boxes.

The boxiest box of them all is the computer. Within the physical box lies a world of conceptual boxes, from the perfectly rectangular pixels that compose the display to the evenly measured ticks of the clock that controls all the computer's actions. Compared to the unerringly digital world of the computer, our boxed-up society is richly irregular. Even a line-addicted urbanite can easily feel overwhelmed by the experience of entering the machine's reality.

Only the most recent generations, those brought up in the blinding straight-forward motion of their parents' cars and raised within the confines of a television screen, can feel truly at ease with "computing." We computer whiz kids may be incapable of sitting still for more than a few seconds outdoors, and we may not even hear background noise (like wind and bird songs), but the flip-flop of microscopic electronic bits, unnoticed and incomprehensible to many of our elders, can keep us entranced for days.

Measured by a linear ruler, the experience of computing is a virtual paradise (in both the old and new senses of the word "virtual"). This electronic Eden, however, is as far from the primeval garden as we can get. The only direction left to go is back.

Benoit Mandelbrot coined the term "fractal" from the Latin "fractus," meaning an irregular fragment. He also called it "the geometry of nature," because its forms so closely resemble those of the untamed world. Why does Mother Nature's work show a different geometry than our own? Aren't we nature, too? Indeed, the difference lies not so much in whose hand does the work, but in the swiftness of that hand. Linearity is the geometry of motion, of cutting, of separation. The faster the saw blade, the smoother the cut. Nature, too, has her arcs and lines: the speeding orbits of the planets, the streaming trail of a light ray, the zip of a bee to the hive. Fractal geometry, on the other hand, grows from stillness, from layer upon layer of repeated joining. When humans slow down, we create lacework, Persian rugs, Baroque furniture, and Gothic palaces. That richly woven artifacts have all but disappeared from our culture is above all a reflection of its velocity. Who has time to weave?

We have rushed to encase ourselves in the geometry of haste, and now the geometry itself feeds our hurry. No longer distracted by "petty details," we can safely speed from box to box, keeping physically still only when pacified by the visual frenzy behind a TV screen or windshield. Whatever may be said for the aesthetic value of modern architecture and industrial artifacts, their beauty is certainly not the kind that demands lengthy contemplation. Mankind has "wasted" centuries simply staring in appreciation and wonder at the elements of his world: an ear of corn, a carved window frame. Few are stilled into reverence by their box of corn flakes or aluminum storm door.

Yet our very existence depends on things that can only arise from stillness—and not just intangibles like peace of mind. Clean air is still a product of 60-year-old trees, and nutritious food still demands rain clouds and humus (despite our best efforts). In our haste to consume and dismantle fractal forms into linear ones, some question whether we will leave Mother Nature herself time enough to weave our continuing livelihood.

Nevertheless, fractal geometry is above all a "geometry of Man." Fractals arose in the minds and computers of a scientific, industrial civilization, and have revolutionized our analytical understanding of almost every department of knowledge. It is not our environmentalists and mystics who are so fascinated by the dancing shapes, but our mathematicians and scientists, our idea-slicers. From the dualistic, abstract mode of thought has come a universe of shapes that challenge its most basic tenets and stir the primitive emotions it has sought to deny.

Once, we carved linearity out of the rich organic world we found around us. Now, we are beginning to sculpt rich organic forms from the linear world we've built around ourselves. Surprisingly enough, the intuitive feeling of it is much the same. A deep satisfaction accompanies the working of jagged, digital bits into sweeping, richly symmetrical figures—a sense very much akin to that of a woodcarver working natural roughness into smooth curves and edges.

The taking of a life so that it could be cut up and made to fit the purposes (and geometry) of humankind was once a sacrament. Watching these fractals grow, I find a very similar feeling of sacredness emerging in myself. I sense that this is the completion of a cycle—that a profound, aesthetic justice exists in allowing the faces of Nature to coalesce on an electronic screen.

Sacrifice of nature to the knife belongs to another time. To what new god do we sacrifice the knife itself?

FractalVision Software Quick Reference

Refer to this appendix as you get ac-
quainted with FractalVision software. It
contains a brief description of each menu
action and control key, along with a summary
of mouse operations.

The Main Menu

Use the Spacebar and Backspace to pick an
action, and Enter to perform it. Press Esc to
hide the menu and bring it back.

General Commands

Action	Key	Use this to...
Help	H	Get online help
Quit	Q	Exit FractalVision
Load	L	Access **Load menu**: load a file from disk
Save	S	Access **Save menu**: save a file to disk
View	V	View the picture and captions without the menu or template

Drawing Commands

Action	Key	Use this to...
Draw	D R	Draw successive approximations of the fractal defined by the template (D draws level by level, R draws rapidly)
Paint	P I	Paint the fractal defined by the template (P is timed, I goes until Esc is pressed)
Adjust	A	Access **Adjust panel**: level of detail and coloring
Extras	E	Access **Extras menu**: randomness and handle size, numerical definition of template, fractal dimension estimate, and captions
Clear	Page Up	Clear the picture (leaves captions)
Restore	Page Down	Restore the picture and captions (as last **Draw**n or **Paint**ed)

Template Control Commands

Use the arrow keys to move a part or point.

Action	Key	Use this to...
Next Part	Tab	Place the handle on the next part (Shift+Tab for the previous part)
NextPoint	' ~	Place the handle on next corner point of the seed shape (~ for previous point)
New	0	Create new parts or points from scratch (place with the mouse or type a number to be arranged automatically around the seed)
Insert	Ins	Insert a new part (identical to current part) or point (between the current point and the next point)
Delete	Del	Delete the current part or point
Precision	End	Select large or small movements

When the handle is on...	The following control moves...
The seed	The whole template
Any other part	That part only
A point on the seed	The seed shape

Action	Key	Use this to...
Grow	*	Get bigger
Shrink	/	Get smaller
Spin	+ -	Rotate clockwise (- to spin counterclockwise)
Skew	; '	Rotate one axis only (' to skew counterclockwise)
Squish	[	Shrink one axis only

continues

Action	Key	Use this to...
Stretch	]	Grow one axis only
Center	Home	Move the seed to the center of the screen

The Adjust Panel

Use the Spacebar and Backspace or the up and down arrows to pick an action or item. Press Enter to do it.

Action	Key	Use this to...
Next Part	Tab	Move the handle to the next part of the template (Shift+Tab moves to the previous part)
Color All Levels	=	Apply the current color to one part at all levels (When the handle is on seed, this colors the entire template)
Color All Parts	\	Apply the current color to all parts at one level only
Fill All Parts	¦	Apply the current fill level to all parts, including the seed
Blend Colors	.	Create a gradual blend from the current color to any other color
Accept	Esc	Return to the main menu

Use + and - or the right and left arrows to adjust the following settings. The Home key jumps to the lowest setting, and the End key jumps to the highest.

Action	Use this to...
Level	Adjust the current level of detail and view colors for the current part (Shortcut: type the level number)
Fill	Adjust the shading of the current part (at all levels)
Colors	Select the color for the current part and level from the palette (Shortcut: type the color letter)
Red	Adjust the amount of red,
Green	green, and
Blue	blue light in the current color

The Extras Menu

You can also access these functions directly from the main menu by pressing the appropriate action keys.

Randomness Control

Action	Key	Use this to...
More Random	!	Increase the random variation added during **Draw** or **Paint**
Less Random	@	Decrease the random variation
(Now = XX%)		See the current amount of randomness, from 0 to 100 percent

Handle Size Control

Action	Key	Use this to...
Grow Handle	^	Increase the handle size without changing the template
Shrink Handle	%	Decrease the handle size without changing the template

Special Functions

Action	Key	Use this to...
Show Numbers	N	Display the spin, size, and movement for each part of the template, and the location of each seed point
Fractal Dim.	F	Estimate the fractal dimension (roughness) of the current picture
Captions	C	Access the **Caption menu**: add a text overlay to the template
Main menu	Esc	Return to the main menu

The Caption Menu

> **NOTE**
>
> Because the Spacebar and Backspace keys are used to type, they do not pick items from this menu. You must use the action keys or the mouse.

Action	Key	Use this to...
Text	Type!	Type text to appear at the cursor (function keys make lines and boxes, ' makes a vertical line)
Move	Arrows	Move the blinking cursor
ClearText	Page Up	Clear captions (leaves the picture)
Restore	Page Down	Restore the picture and captions
Imprint	Tab	Imprint the caption onto the picture (Normally, the caption is only saved with the template. After **Imprint**ing, the caption is also part of picture)
Beg Line	Home	Move the cursor to the beginning of the line
End Line	End	Move the cursor to the end of the line
Backsp	Backspace	Delete the character to the left of the cursor (does not move any text)
Insert	Ins	Insert a space under the cursor, and move the existing text to right
Delete	Del	Delete the character under the cursor, and move the remaining text to the left
Color	\ ¦	Change the text to the next color (¦ for the last color)
No Menu	Esc	Hide (or retrieve) the caption menu
Accept	Enter	Return to the main menu

The Load and Save Menus

Use the Spacebar and Backspace or the up and down arrows to pick an action, and press Enter to do it. Type the filename, then press Enter to load or save the file.

Action	Key	Use this to...
Picture	P	Load or save a PCX picture file (with palette)
Template	T	Load or save a fractal template (FRT) file (with coloring, shading, location, captions, and palette)
Both	B	Load or save both picture and template (separate files with the same name)
IFS Codes	I	Load or save the text file of numbers that define the basic pattern of the template (IFS files are FRACTINT compatible)
Vector DXF	V	Save the polygons made by **Draw** to an AutoCAD drawing exchange file (cannot Load DXF files)
Vector DAT	A	Save the polygons made by **Draw** in a scientific notation ASCII file (cannot Load DAT files)
DOS	D	Enter DOS temporarily
Cancel	Esc	Return to the main menu

Some Handy DOS Commands

These standard commands are here for your reference when entering DOS within FractalVision. See your DOS manual for more details.

Command	What it does	Example
DIR	Lists files in a current directory	DIR DIR *.FRT

Command	What it does	Example
MD	Makes a new directory	MD PLANTS
RD	Removes a directory	RD PLANTS
CD	Changes the current directory (or prints the current directory name)	CD PLANTS CD
DEL	Deletes files	DEL OLDPIC.PCX
REN	Renames files	REN OLD.* NEW.*
COPY	Copies files	COPY T.FRT I.FRT

Using the Mouse

If you have a mouse, you can carry out many FractalVision operations without using the keyboard at all.

What you want to do	How to do it with the mouse
Select a menu action	Point and click with the left button
Pick a "reverse" menu action (for items with two action keys)	Point and click with the right button
Hide (and return to) the menu or to exit a submenu	Click with the right button (pointing to nothing)
Answer a question	Click the left button for the default (Yes), or click the right button to cancel (No)
Control the adjust panel	Click an action or setting with any button
Position the cursor when captioning	Click with the left button at the desired location

continues

What you want to do	How to do it with the mouse
Manipulate the template	Drag with left button:

Grab here to resize and spin

Grab here (or the other side) to skew, squish, and stretch

Grab here to move

Sketch a new template from scratch	Select **NextPoint** and **New**, then place the points with the left button. When finished, click the right button. Select **Next Part** and **New** to place copies of the seed
Attach a handle to a part of the template	Click with the left button in the center of the part
Move a point on the seed	Drag with the left button (handle shape turns into a +)
Resize, spin, skew, squish, or stretch the seed shape	Use the menu while the handle is attached to a point on the seed
To resize the handle for easier grabbing	Select **Grow Handle** and **Shrink Handle** on the **Extras** menu (^ and % keys)

FractalVision Software Reference

T his appendix explains how to install and run the FractalVision software, which is bundled with this book. It also includes instructions for exchanging files with other software and recommendations for utilities that work well with FractalVision.

At the end of this appendix, you'll find an alphabetical list of sample files with short descriptions and references to the figures that illustrate them.

What is FractalVision Software?

FractalVision is a drawing program and educational tool. As with any drawing program, you use the mouse and keyboard to create pictures

on your PC screen from dots and lines, with full control over coloring and shading. The images you design are limited only by your artistic skill and imagination.

FractalVision provides you with a new, powerful drawing tool called a "fractal template." You use the template to create complex shapes with rich detail and to assemble these shapes into eye-catching, colorful images. With practice, you can make pictures more realistic than anything you've ever created on a computer (or, more than likely, on paper). Many of the most difficult things to draw with other programs (like plants, landscapes, and other flowing natural forms) you can draw with great detail in seconds with a single "imprint" of a fractal template.

But realism is only half the story. Even before you build your drawing skills enough to mimic the real world, you'll embark on a breathtaking journey into the fantastic world of fractal geometry. The easiest shapes to create are spiraling vortexes, otherworldly plants, enchanting galaxies of color, and dazzling portraits of infinity.

FractalVision is designed as an intuitive and easy-to-use tool for anyone. You don't need to know any mathematics or be any good at art—though you'll find plenty of chances to use both skills if you have them. The mission of FractalVision is to let you get creative with the geometry that has revitalized both science and art, from the prediction of earthquakes to state-of-the-art motion picture special effects.

Backing Up the Disk

Before you run FractalVision for the first time, be sure to back up the FractalVision disk. Use the backup copy from now on, and put the original in a safe place. If you're not sure how to back up a disk, here's how:

1. Insert the FractalVision floppy disk in drive A. (You may use drive B if necessary—simply type B: instead of A: in the following command.)

2. Type DISKCOPY A: A: and press Enter.

3. Follow the computer's instructions for inserting disks during the copy. The "SOURCE diskette" is the FractalVision disk, and the "TARGET diskette" is the blank disk.

4. Label the copy and stash the original.

Installing the Software

1. Insert the backup copy of the FractalVision disk in drive A, type A: (the letter A and a colon), and press the Enter key. (The DOS prompt should now read A>.)

   (If, for some reason, you can't use drive A, just type the letter of the drive you will be using, followed by a colon, and press Enter. For example, to use drive B, type B:.)

2. Type INSTALL C: FRACTAL and press Enter.

   (If you want to install to a different hard disk drive than C, or to a different directory than FRACTAL, use the drive letter and directory name of your choice in place of C: and FRACTAL.)

   Notice that FRACTINT software is not included on the FractalVision disk, but is available free from several sources. See the registration form in the back of this book for information on obtaining FRACTINT. All other programs and sample files discussed in the book are included on the disk and will be installed automatically along with FractalVision.

   The installation procedure also displays the contents of the README.TXT file on-screen. This contains last minute details about the program that aren't covered anywhere else.

   The next section gives instructions for starting FractalVision once you've successfully copied it to your hard drive.

Running the Program

Once you've installed FractalVision, you can run it by entering FV from the directory where the program resides. For example, to run from the default hard drive directory, type the following (pressing the Enter key after each line):

```
C:
CD \FRACTAL
FV
```

To run from another directory (if you specified one during installation):

```
(drive letter):
CD \(directory name)
FV
```

Mouse Users Take Note

If you want to use your Microsoft-compatible mouse with FractalVision, you must be sure to install your mouse driver before running the program. In many cases, the driver is installed automatically when you start the computer. See your mouse manual for more instructions.

When you run the program, a list of video modes appears. If you plan to follow along with the on-line tutorial or the examples in this book, I recommend pressing V for 640x480, 16-color VGA. If you don't have a VGA adapter or would like to try a higher resolution Super VGA mode, simply press the letter for the mode you want. An arrow will suggest the highest resolution mode that FractalVision finds available on your system.

(You can bypass the video mode selection list by specifying your adapter on the command line or in a batch file. For example, you could type FV/V to start Fractal-Vision in VGA mode.)

The words Fractal Vision will appear at the top of the screen after a pause, along with the message "Press H for Help, or any other key to begin." Unless you press H (in which case you will get the online Help index), a white menu with the words ACTION and KEY at the top should appear on the right side of the screen when you press a key. If you don't see this, turn to the section on **Troubleshooting** for more help.

For a quick tour of FractalVision software, turn to the **You Can Do It: Introducing FractalVision Software** box in the Introduction to this book. Also, a quick reference to the FractalVision menu system is printed on the inside of the front cover.

The next section explains an advanced trick for running FractalVision. You don't need to read it until you've used the program for a while.

Startup Files

Whenever you run FractalVision, it automatically loads a picture file named STARTUP.PCX and a template file named STARTUP.FRT if they exist in the current directory. You can save any picture and/or template under the name STARTUP, and it will appear every time you start the program.

However, if you start in a black-and-white mode (such as CGA hi-res mode /C or monochrome VGA mode /M or Hercules mode /H), the program will automatically load the files STARTBW.PCX and STARTBW.FRT instead.

You can specify another startup filename on the command line. For example, to start FractalVision in 320x200 mode and bring up a picture and template named CGASTART, enter:

```
FV CGASTART /L
```

To start up without loading any files, either rename the files named STARTUP and STARTBW (located in the EXAMPLES subdirectory) or specify a nonexistent name (example: FV NOFILE). In this case, the picture comes up blank and a simple triangular template is centered on-screen.

Exchanging Images and Data with Other Software

FractalVision supports several industry standard file formats, enabling you to exchange pictures and geometry with almost all graphics and CAD software. FractalVision does not print hard copy on its own, but you probably already own software that will print at least one of the file formats it can output. (See the **Recommended Utilities** section that follows for some inexpensive programs that print PCX files.)

PCX Files

When you **Save** a **Picture**, FractalVision stores the image as a PCX file, a standard bitmapped format originally designed by Zsoft for PC Paintbrush software. This format is supported by every major paint program, including Pictor, PC Paint,

Windows Paintbrush, DeluxePaint, ColorRIX, Photostyler, and many others. It is also supported by most scanners, so you can scan an image and **Load** the **Picture** into FractalVision to add fractal effects.

DXF Files

With FractalVision, you can also **Save Vector DXF**—or drawing exchange file—files, the format designed by Autodesk for its AutoCAD line of products. *Vector DXF files* contain a numerical description of the polygons in a model, rather than a fixed-resolution bitmap. Therefore, you can rescale and rotate them without loss of clarity. Every major CAD package, and most draw programs (such as CorelDRAW, Arts & Letters, and Micrografx Designer) can import DXF files.

If you use 3-D rendering software (3D Studio, Topas, BigD, etc.), you can use fractal PCX files for surface texture maps or bring DXF files from FractalVision into the "lofter" part of the program and extend it into three dimensions. (You may also be interested in Fractal Grafics 3D, a version of FractalVision that creates true three-dimensional models as 3-D DXF files. See the registration form in the back of this book for ordering information.)

DAT Files

If you work with scientific software or do your own programming, you may want to **Save** a **Vector DAT** file, which is an ASCII list of corner points in standard floating-point format. This format is directly compatible with Digistar Planetarium .DAT files, and you can easily import and manipulate it by most numerical and geometric software written in FORTRAN, BASIC, Pascal, LISP, or C.

IFS Files

As discussed in Chapter 5, "The Math Behind the Magic," you can also exchange IFS codes directly with FRACTINT using the **Save** and **Load IFS Codes** commands. Notice that FRACTINT versions 15 and lower use a different format for IFS codes. (To convert to the older format, simply delete the first and last lines of a FractalVision

IFS file.) Also notice that FRACTINT versions 16 and above save more than one set of IFS codes in a single file. FractalVision reads only the first set in the file and outputs only one set of codes per file.

You can also exchange 3-D IFS codes between FRACTINT and the IFS3D program presented in Chapter 5. Again, IFS3D reads only the first set of codes in the file.

Important

The IFS files with names that begin with 3D are three-dimensional IFS codes, and all others are regular two-dimensional IFS codes. Do not try to read 3-D IFS codes with any program besides IFS3D and FRACTINT, and do not try to read regular 2-D IFS codes with IFS3D. Error checking is very limited, and doing so could cause your system to crash.

Recommended Utilities

If you find that you would like to exchange images or data with a program that doesn't support the PCX, DXF, DAT, or IFS file formats, several excellent conversion programs are available. I especially recommend Graphics Workshop by Steve Rimmer of Alchemy Mindworks, which can convert PCX files to and from almost every format imaginable. It also rotates, scales, crops, dithers, and prints PCX files on most printers. (The program is available for $40 from Alchemy Mindworks; PO Box 500; Beeton, Ontario, L0G 1A0, Canada, or you can order it from Cedar Software when you send in the registration/order form in the back of this book.)

Several other commercial software packages specialize in file conversion and printing. The best is Hijaak from Inset Systems, 1-800-374-6738.

I also must mention Dave Parker's ACROSPIN, a nifty little $30 program which allows you to rotate, scale, and move 2-D or 3-D vector models and point clouds in real time on your screen. You have to see it to believe it. (Call 1-800-ACROBITS for more information or to obtain a copy.)

Troubleshooting

FractalVision has been extensively tested on many brands of IBM-compatible PCs and has been checked for conflicts with a wide variety of software, including Windows 2.1 through 3.1, Quarterdeck products, alternative operating systems such as 4DOS and DR-DOS, and many different Terminate-and-Stay-Resident (TSR) programs.

Unfortunately, the structure of PC-compatibles makes it possible for unexpected interactions between software, even when each program works fine by itself. Should you find that you can't run FractalVision, load files, or use your mouse, this section will help you locate the source of the conflict and eliminate the problem.

First, make sure your distribution disks are not damaged (insert the disk in drive A and type CHKDSK A: or use a more thorough surface scanning tool such as one found in the Norton Utilities and other disk management software).

Second, check to make sure that you have at least 384K of available conventional memory. If you find that the program will not run on a system with at least this much RAM, try unloading any TSRs as previously described.

You can tell how much memory is available in your computer by typing CHKDSK C: (or CHKDSK A: if you don't have a hard disk) at the DOS prompt. The last number displayed is the "Bytes free." (Divide by 1,024 to obtain the number of K you have available.)

FractalVision will use extended *XMS memory* and expanded *EMS memory*, but only if not enough conventional memory is available to store the picture. If not enough XMS, EMS, or conventional memory exists, the hard disk will automatically be used as *virtual memory*. If you have MS-DOS Version 5.0 or later, you can find out the total memory configuration of your system by typing MEM at the DOS prompt.

If you have trouble running in Super VGA or VGA, try running in EGA mode by typing FV /E, or in CGA mode by typing FV /C. The lower resolution modes require less memory.

A Note for Tandy Users

Tandy systems lie to you about how much free memory they have. You may need 512K to run in EGA or VGA mode on a Tandy machine. Also note that older 16-color Tandy computers like the Tandy 1000 are not EGA compatible, so you'll need to run in CGA mode by typing FV /C.

If the program files are intact and you have enough free memory, you are probably encountering a conflict with a TSR program. Try starting your computer without any TSRs. (You can do this by copying your AUTOEXEC.BAT and CONFIG.SYS files and then deleting all the commands that load TSRs and rebooting your computer with the new AUTOEXEC.BAT and CONFIG.SYS files. Once you're done testing, you can copy the old AUTOEXEC.BAT and CONFIG.SYS back again.) If FractalVision works without the TSRs loaded, try installing them one at a time until you find the one that caused the conflict. The documentation for that TSR program may explain how to change the way it uses memory and/or interrupts to eliminate such conflicts.

Finally, some programs that support older versions of the PCX image file format may not be completely compatible with the latest ZSoft approved standard. (FractalVision strictly adheres to this standard through the use of Genus Microprogramming's PCX Programmer's Toolkit.) If you run into compatibility problems, it may help to load a file into ZSoft's PC Paintbrush (preferably an older version) and then resave it.

Listing of Example Files

Figure numbers beginning with a P refer to color plates. All files have the FRT extension.

This book also includes four PCX picture files: AVGTEMP.PCX (Figure 2.23), HERON.PCX (Figure 4.56), and MAINE.PCX, and UK.PCX (discussed in Chapter 1 in the **Fractal Dimension** section).

The FV.PAR file is a FRACTINT parameter file. See the Introduction for details on accessing the examples in it.

Template Filename	Figure	Description
APPLE	4.8, 4.9	An apple tree
ARC	3.13, 3.14	A predictable linear arc
ARCHY	4.48	Infinite Greek columns and an arch
ARCHY2		Similar to ARCHY—or is it?
ARMS	3.40	Human arms reflected in the whole
ARROW	1.17	Mandelbrot's Arrowhead
AURA	P31	BODY with colors around it
AVGTEMP1	2.24	An average temperature graph
AVGTEMP2	2.25	A better forgery of AVGTEMP.PCX
BARNSLEY	1.30	Barnsley's Black Spleenwort Fern
BEND	3.39	Human bending to show joints
BIGFISH	4.39-4.42	Big fish that eat little fish
BODY	3.37, 3.38	The structure of the human body
BORDER		A decorative border
BORDER2		A picture frame
CANTOR	1.8	Cantor's "Dust"
CARPET	1.6	Sierpiński's Carpet
CARTOON1	4.55, P33	Mr. Cartoon's ears
CARTOON2	4.55, P33	Mr. Cartoon's face
CARTOON3		A fancy design around CARTOON
CASCADE	1.18	Mandelbrot's "Koch Cascade"
CATS	5.2	A feline Sierpiński's Triangle

Template Filename	Figure	Description
CESARO	1.19	Cesaro's Triangle Sweep
CHAOS	P25	The word chaos
CHERRY	P1, P6	A cherry tree in bloom
CIRRUS	2.3, P1, P9	A wispy cirrus cloud
CITY1	P34	A skyscraper skyline extending to the right
CITY2	P34	A skyscraper skyline extending to the left
CITYBIRD	P34	A flock of birds
COLLAGE	4.16	An illustration of complex tiling
COMB	4.54, P38	A comb for HEN, goes with NEST
CREEPY	3.42	A human face with a sinister grin
CUMULUS	2.2, P9	A sunny day's cumulus cloud
DAVIS		Davis's Dragon cellular automata
DRAGON		Fire breath and all
ESCAPE	5.10, 5.11	Escape time algorithm coloring
F-1	4.28	The first 2 copies on a letter F
F-2	4.29	The first 4 copies on a letter F
F-3	4.30, 4.31	A simple letter F
F-AXES	4.37	A crossbones style letter F
F-FANCY	4.35	F-3 with the top extended
F-FILL	4.34	F-3 with the Fill adjusted
F-FIX	4.32, 4.33	F-3 with better shading
F-FORKED	4.37	A snake-tongue style letter F

continues

Template Filename	Figure	Description
F-GOOFY	4.37	A "Flintstones" style letter F
F-POW	4.38	The letter F exploding
F-RACTAL	3.1, P26	A fractal-looking letter F
F-ROMAN	4.36	A Roman style letter F
F-SPARK	4.38	The letter F sparkling
F-STRUTS	4.37	An engineering style letter F
F-SWISH	4.38	The letter F swishing like a broom
F-ZOOM	4.38	The letter F zooming forward
FACE1	3.41	Human body reflected in the head
FACE2	3.41	Body stretched to fill the head
FACE3	3.41	A bird-face with a torso as a nose
FACE4	3.41	A clown-face with a torso as a tongue
FACE5	3.41	Structure of a human face
FERN1	2.11, P1, P4	A fern made by tiling
FERN2	2.10, P1, P4	A fern made from stems
FERNZOOM	5.12, P30	The BARNSLEY fern surrounded by colors
FIRAL	4.53, P37	A zooming spiral of fire
FIRE		A cozy campfire
FIREWORD		The word FIRE
FLAKE1	2.4, 2.6, P10	A 6-pointed snowflake
FLAKE2	2.5, P10	Another 6-pointed snowflake
FLAKE3	2.5, P10	An 8-pointed snowflake
FLEX-IN	3.39	A human flexing his arms and muscles

Template Filename	Figure	Description
FLEX-OUT	3.39	A human flexing her arms and muscles
FLOWER	1.13, P22	A Lindenmayer Plant Automata
FLOWER1		Flowers,
FLOWER2		Flowers,
FLOWER3		Flowers,
FLOWER4		And more
FLOWER5		Flowers!
FOURNIER	1.9	Fournier's Universe Dust
FR	3.1, P26	R to go with F-RACTAL
FRA	3.1, P26	A
FRAC	3.1, P26	C
FRACT	3.1, P26	T
FRACTA	3.1, P26	A
FRACTAL	3.1, P26	L
FRACTALS		S
GALAXY	P12	A spiral galaxy
GALAXY1	2.13	A nonrandom spiral galaxy
GALAXY2	4.22, 2.14	The Milky Way
GALAXY2A	4.23, 4.24	A rough sketch of a four-arm galaxy
GALAXY2B	4.25, 4.26	A closer approximation of a galaxy
GEM	4.49	A colorful subdivided triangle
GOSPER1	1.23	Gosper's Island south coast
GOSPER2	1.23	Gosper's Island east coast

continues

Template Filename	Figure	Description
GOSPER3	1.23	Gosper's Island north coast
GOSPER4	1.23	Gosper's Island west coast
GOUL	4.45, 4.46	Scary faces within faces
GRASS	P3	Grass going to seed
GRID	4.27	A caption for lining up designs
GROWSQ	4.18	Grow applied to part of a square
HALVES		A line with half-sized copies
HEAD	3.40	A human head reflected in the whole
HEIGH-C		Colorful Heighway's Dragon
HEIGHWAY	1.14, P23	Heighway's Dragon Curve
HEN	4.54, P38	A hen, goes with COMB and NEST
HERON	4.57, 4.58	A fractal heron head from HERON.PCX
HIVE	4.52	A hexagonal spiral design
HORTER	P23	Horter-Heighway Dragon
HOUSES		Pebbly pueblos
HUMP		A simple cosine shaped graph
ISLAND	1.25	Mandelbrot's Island Generator
ISLANDS	1.26	Mandelbrot's Island and Lakes
JULIA		A faked Julia Set
KNUTH		A famous cellular automaton
KOCH	1.10	Koch's original Coastline
KOCH2	1.11	An alternate Koch Coastline
KOCHPLUS		Koch never saw this one

Template Filename	Figure	Description
LACEWORK		An intricate doily pattern
LEAF1	2.8, P2	A maple leaf made from stems
LEAF2	2.9	A maple leaf made by tiling
LEAF3	4.43, 5.1	A leaf design with bright colors
LEGS	3.40	Human legs reflected in the whole
LINDEN	1.12	Lindenmayer's Plant Automata
LINE2	3.11, 3.12	A line created by dividing space
LINEAR1	3.2	A Force vs. Distance line graph
LINEAR2	3.3	A line graph with a changing slope
LINEAR3	3.4	A graph of a linear curve
LITES1	P34	Lights for the skyscrapers in CITY1
LITES2	P34	Lights for the skyscrapers in CITY2
LOBSTER		A creative crayfish
LUNGS	2.39	Two-dimensional bronchial passages
LUNGS2		Wider bronchial passages
MANDALA		Middle-Eastern circle pattern
MANDEL1		Faked Mandelbrot Set
MANDEL2		Part of Mandelbrot Set faked
MAPLE	2.8, 2.12, P2	A maple tree
MOHAWK		A fractal haircut
MONKEY	1.22	Mandelbrot's Monkeys' Tree
MONKSTAR		Monkeys' Tree colored in
MOUNT2	2.16, P1, P7	A more realistic MOUNTAIN horizon

continues

Template Filename	Figure	Description
MOUNTAIN	2.15	An outline of a mountain & lake
NEST	4.54, P38	A nest for HEN with COMB
NEWLUNGS		A mutant of LUNGS made with MUTATE
NONLIN1	3.5, 3.6	A graph of a nonlinear curve
NONLIN2	3.7, 3.8	A smooth nonlinear curve graph
OAK	4.1-4.7	An oak tree
OAK2	4.4	OAK with a broad canopy
OAK3	4.5	OAK with a tilted top
PAISLEY		Painted paisley
PALMLEAF		Jungle geometry
PEANO	1.7	Peano's Space-Filling Curve
PINE	2.8, P1, P2	A pine tree
PLANT1	P5	A plant blossom
PLANT2	P5	A plant shoot
PLANT3	P5	Plant roots
POT	4.10, 4.11	Starting point to make GRASS
POTGRASS	4.12	Dried grass growing from POT
PYRAMID	4.47, P40	An abstract pyramid design
QUADRAT	1.24	Mandelbrot's Quadratic Koch Islands
QUAKE	2.21, 2.22	A graph of an earthquake
QUARTERS		A line with fourth-sized copies
QUILT	4.44	A colorful old-fashioned quilt
RAINBOWS	P35	Rainbow colored hexagon stars

Template Filename	Figure	Description
RANDY	1.16, P1, P7, P19	A pseudorandom SINE wave
REACH	3.36	An abstract tree/explosion
RIVER	2.1, P1, P8	A twisting river
SEAHORSE		If it's not a seahorse, what is it?
SERPENT		DRAGON's little brother
SEVEN	1.21	Mandelbrot's Seven-Intervals
SHELL	4.51	An abstract shell-like vortex
SHRINK	5.4	An illustration of the Shrink transformation
SHRINKSQ	4.17	Shrink applied to part of a square
SIERPIN	1.4, 5.3	Sierpiński's Triangle
SIERPIN2	1.5	Sierpiński's Triangle holes
SIERPIN3		Fancy Sierpiński's Triangle
SIERPIN4	P18	Equilateral Sierpiński's Triangle
SINE	1.15, P41	Fractalized "sine wave"
SKEW-L	5.5	An illustration of Skew-to-left
SKEW-R	5.5	An illustration of Skew-to-right
SKEWSQ	4.21	Skew applied to part of a square
SPECIAL		The word SPECIAL
SPIN	5.5	An illustration of the Spin transformation
SPINSQ	4.19	Spin applied to part of a square
SQUARE	4.13, 4.14	A square tiled with 4 copies

continues

Template Filename	Figure	Description
SQUISH	5.4	An illustration of the Squish transformation
STAIRS	1.20	The Devil's Staircase
STARS	P12	Close up of GALAXY
STARTBW		This loads when starting in B&W modes
STARTUP		This loads when a program starts in color
STRATUS	2.3, P9	A hazy stratus cloud
STRETCHQ	5.4	An illustration of the Stretch transformation
STRETCHSQ	4.20	Stretch applied to part of a square
TARTAN		A Scottish plaid woven patch
THIRDS		A line with third-sized copies
THUNDER		A towering thunder cloud
TILT	3.39	A human tilting his head and joints
TORSO	3.40	A human torso reflected in the whole
TREE	2.7	An abstract fir tree
TREEGRID	3.15, 3.16	This plants a grid of trees
TREELINE	3.9, 3.10	This plants a straight row of trees
TRI1		A variation on TRIANGLE
TRI2		Another variation on TRIANGLE
TRI3		Still another variation on TRIANGLE
TRIANGLE	4.15	Triangle tiled with 4 copies

Template Filename	Figure	Description
TWINSKIN		Mandelbrot's Twin Dragon Skin
VORTEX	3.36	An abstract spiraling vortex
VSWIRL	P39	Another spiraling vortex
WEBS	4.50	Abstract sinewy webs in space
WEEPY	3.42	A human face with a glum expression
WREATH		Happy holidays!
X-GRID	3.17-3.19	This marks a grid pattern of X's
YES!		YESYESYESYESYESYESYES
YESCLR		YES in lots of colors
ZOOMBIRD	3.36, P36	My favorite

Additional example template files may be documented in the README.TXT file on the disk.

The following sample programs are also illustrated and/or discussed in the book. For a brief description of each, type MENU at the DOS prompt.

Example Program	Data file	Figure (or chapter where discussed)
BIF		3.21-3.32
BOXCOUNT		(Chapter 1)
FORGERY		2.17
JANDELIA		(Chapter 5)
IFS	(IFS files)	(Chapter 5)
IFS3D	(3-D IFS files)	(Chapter 5)
INTERPO	SAMPLE.FIP	2.26

continues

Example Program	Data file	Figure (or chapter where discussed)
	AVG50.FIP	2.27
	AVG100.FIP	2.28
LAND		2.18
LORENZ		2.31
MOIRE		3.20
MUTATE	FERN.IFS	4.59
	NEWFERN.IFS	4.61
	MAPLE.IFS	4.62
	NEWMAPLE.IFS	4.64
TEXTLIFE		(Chapter 1)

Mathematics Review, Formulas, and Algorithms

To bring these fractals to life, your two-dimensional computer screen must become a window to the abstract two-dimensional world called the *complex plane*. Coordinates in the complex plane that correspond to the horizontal axis on your screen are called the *real numbers*, and coordinates that correspond to the vertical axis are called *imaginary numbers*. (The vertical axis is obviously no more imaginary than the horizontal axis. These terms are holdovers from a time in the history of mathematics when no one yet realized that the two sets of numbers corresponded to perpendicular axes on a two-dimensional surface.)

What follows is a brief review of the geometry of two-dimensional numbers and transformations. This type of geometry is part of a larger field called *linear algebra*, or *matrix algebra*. If you want a more comprehensive introduction to the concepts presented here, refer to any college-level text on these subjects.

Complex Arithmetic

A complex number, z, consists of two ordinary numbers, x and y, corresponding to the horizontal and vertical coordinates. By convention, multiplying a horizontal (real) number by the square root of -1, called i, produces a vertical number of the same magnitude. Therefore, you can express a complex number as two real numbers, one of which is multiplied by i. Thus:

$$z = x + iy$$

(Notice that the square of any real number will never produce -1, so the $\sqrt{-1}$ must be *imaginary*. If you are a one-dimensional critter, the second dimension is a figment of your imagination. For us three-dimensional folk, however, multiplying by i simply means rotating 90 degrees.)

To add two complex numbers, z_1 and z_2, simply add their *components*. Therefore, another way to write

$$z_3 = z_1 + z_2$$

is

$$x_3 = x_1 + x_2$$
$$y_3 = y_1 + y_2$$

Geometrically, adding two numbers simply moves a point over and up by the amount of the second point.

Multiplication is a bit more involved. You know that:

$$z_3 = z_1 z_2$$

can also be written

$$(x_3 + iy_3) = (x_1 + iy_1)(x_2 + iy_2)$$

Remember that $i = \sqrt{-1}$, so $i^2 = -1$. Multiplying this out and solving for x_3 and y_3, you find

$$x_3 = x_1 x_2 - y_1 y_2$$
$$y_3 = x_1 y_2 + y_1 x_2$$

What does this mean geometrically? This operation multiplies the magnitude (distance from the origin, also called the *modulus*) of the two points and adds their rotations so that the angle between z_3 and the horizontal is equal to the angles of z_1 and z_2 combined.

Fractal computations seldom multiply one point by another point, but the Mandelbrot and Julia sets originate by multiplying a point by itself. This simplifies the previous equation to:

$$(x_2 + iy_2) = (x_1 + iy_1)(x_1 + iy_1)$$

or

$$x_2 = x_1 x_1 - y_1 \, y_1$$
$$y_2 = 2 x_1 y_1$$

In Chapter 5, "The Math Behind the Magic," I presented the iteration formula for the Mandelbrot and Julia sets as:

$$z_2 = z_1 z_1 + c$$

If the components of c are a and b, then this equation becomes

$$x_2 = x_1 x_1 - y_1 y_1 + a$$
$$y_2 = 2 x_1 y_1 + b$$

which is the formula used in the JANDELIA.C program.

Affine Transformations

As another way to write x and y as the two components of a complex number z, use a matrix z, with two elements, x and y:

$$\vec{z} = \begin{bmatrix} x \\ y \end{bmatrix}$$

In Chapter 5, you learned that an *affine transformation* is the combination of a rotation and a scaling, or a resizing. You can rotate and scale the x and y components independently, so you begin with four numbers:

p = rotation on the x component
q = rotation on the y component
r = scale on the x component
s = scale on the y component

Matrix algebra provides a quick and easy way to multiply a 2 by 2 matrix (four numbers) by a 1 by 2 matrix (a point, which is made up of two numbers). For reasons that I'm not going to fully explain, you cannot simply plug and chug the four numbers (p, q, r, and s) into a 2 by 2 matrix. First, you need to convert them to four different numbers: a, b, c, and d. To do this, use the following formula:

$a = r \cos p$
$b = -s \sin q$
$c = r \sin p$
$d = s \cos q$

You can then put a, b, c, and d in a matrix:

$$A = \begin{bmatrix} a & b \\ c & d \end{bmatrix}$$

and use standard matrix multiplication to apply the affine transformation to the point z

$$\vec{z_2} = A\vec{z_1}$$

Without going into the general form of matrix multiplication, the formula you need here is

$x_2 = ax_1 + by_1$
$y_2 = cx_1 + dy_1$

This takes care of rotation and scaling. An affine transformation can also include a plain movement, or *displacement*. Adding the displacement m, where the components of m are

e = translation in x direction
f = translation in y direction

the result is

$$x_2 = ax_1 + by_1 + e$$
$$y_2 = cx_1 + dy_1 + f$$

These equations appear in INTERPO.C, MUTATE.C, and IFS.C and are the crux of FractalVision's **Draw** and **Paint** commands. The six numbers a, b, c, d, e, and f are the *IFS Codes* that define a single affine transformation. By applying this transformation to each corner point on a polygon, you can rotate, resize, and move the whole shape.

To apply the random iteration algorithm discussed in Chapter 5, you needed to investigate how an affine transformation affected the area covered by a shape. The change in area caused by an affine transformation is proportional to the *determinant* of the 2 by 2 matrix. The determinant, t, is simply:

$$t = ad - bc$$

Therefore, the area covered by a shape is multiplied by the absolute value of t when you apply the transformation.

The IFS.C program compared the total area yield for a set of affine transformations to the area yield for a single member of the set. The formula used was

$$\frac{t_i}{\sum_{k=1}^{n} t_k} = \frac{a_i d_i - b_i c_i}{\sum_{k=1}^{n} |a_k d_k - b_k c_k|}$$

Fractal Interpolation

In Chapter 3, "The Philosophy of Fractals," the INTERPO.C program automatically found affine transformations to fit a shape. These affine transformations did not include y rotation, so the previous formulas become:

$$a = r \cos p$$
$$b = -s \sin 0 = 0$$
$$c = r \sin p$$
$$d = s \cos 0 = s$$

Notice that the b drops out (because sin 0 = 0) and that d is simply the vertical scaling factor (because cos 0 = 1). So you have five numbers that define an affine transformation between two points z_i and z_{i-1}. The Ai transformation must map the endpoints of the entire data set (z_0 and z_N) onto z_i and z_{i-1}. In other words, the transformation must satisfy these equations:

$$a_i x_0 + e_i = x_{i-1}$$
$$a_i x_N + e_i = x_i$$
$$c_i x_0 + d_i y_0 + f_i = y_{i-1}$$
$$c_i x_N + d_i y_N + f_i = y_i$$

where N is the total number of data points.

Because you have four equations and five unknowns, you can remove a variable and still solve the equations for the remaining four. Controlling the vertical scaling factor d independently of the fractal would be handy, so solve for a, c, e, and f:

$$a_i = \frac{(x_i - x_{i-1})}{(x_N - x_0)}$$

$$c_i = \frac{(y_i - y_{i-1})}{(x_N - x_0)} - \frac{d_i(y_N - y_0)}{(x_N - x_0)}$$

$$e_i = \frac{(x_N x_{i-1} - x_0 x_i)}{(x_N - x_0)}$$

$$f_i = \frac{(x_N y_{i-1} - x_0 y_i)}{(x_N - x_0)} - \frac{d_i(x_N y_0 - x_0 y_N)}{(x_N - x_0)}$$

By adjusting the vertical scaling factors for the transformations, you can change individual transformations. You can also control the *fractal dimension D* of the whole fractal by ensuring that:

$$\sum_{i=1}^{n} |d_i| = N^{D-1}$$

Strictly speaking, this relation only holds true when the x values fall in equal increments. In practice, however, the x coordinate intervals may vary somewhat, and the value of D will still be approximately correct.

Advanced Formulas

To reverse an affine transformation where:

$$A' = \frac{1}{A}$$

and

$$x_1 = A'(x_2 - m)$$

if the inverse transformation is

$$A' = \begin{bmatrix} a' & b' \\ c' & d' \end{bmatrix}$$

and the determinant t of A is

$$t = ad - bc$$

then

$$a' = \frac{d}{t} \qquad b' = \frac{-b}{t}$$

$$c' = \frac{-c}{t} \qquad d' = \frac{a}{t}$$

To combine two affine transformations A and A_2:

$$A_2 = \begin{bmatrix} a_2 & b_2 \\ c_2 & d_2 \end{bmatrix}, \quad A_3 = A_2 A = \begin{bmatrix} a_3 & b_3 \\ c_3 & d_3 \end{bmatrix}$$

$$\vec{m_2} = \begin{bmatrix} e_2 \\ f_2 \end{bmatrix}, \quad \vec{m_3} = A_2 \vec{m} + \vec{m_2} = \begin{bmatrix} e_3 \\ f_3 \end{bmatrix}$$

therefore:

$$z_3 = A_2 z_2 + m_2 = A_2(Az + m) + m_2$$
$$= A_2 A z + A_2 m + m_2 = A_3 z + m_3$$

and you find:

$$a_3 = a_2a + b_2c \qquad\qquad b_3 = a_2b + b_2d$$
$$c_3 = c_2a + d_2c \qquad\qquad d_3 = c_2b + d_2d$$
$$e_3 = a_2e + b_2f + e_2 \qquad f_3 = c_2e + d_2f + f_2$$

The successive approximation algorithm (**Draw** command) uses this set of equations to propagate the affine transformations.

Algorithms

I've provided these pseudo code algorithms for those of you who don't know C and would like to create fractal programs in another language. With these algorithms, you can also glance over the procedures without wading through implementation details such as clearing the screen and asking for user input.

The Random Iteration (Chaos Game) Algorithm

Notes:

This procedure paints a fractal image when given two or more affine transformations.

Line 1: Initialize starting point and counter.

Lines 2–18: Main loop, each iteration moves one step on the orbit and makes one dot on the screen.

Lines 3–6: Choose which part to visit next.

Lines 7–9: Compute the next point on the orbit.

Lines 10–18: Color a point on-screen. At each iteration, choose a level at random from all the levels you will color. Then find the color for that level based on which part was "visited" that many cycles ago. How does this work? Each iteration of the orbit proceeds from a point on the "whole" to a point on a "part." Therefore, if you were in part #3 one iteration ago, you would now be in a level 1 reflection of part #3 within the current part. If you were in part #5 two cycles ago, you would now be drawing a point within a level 2 reflection of part #5, and so on.

Givens:

`x0, y0`	Starting point of orbit
`niters`	Number of iterations to perform
`nparts`	Number of parts
`area[]`	Relative area of each part
`clr[][]`	Color for each part at each level
`nlevs`	Number of coloring levels
`a[], b[], c[],`	Affine transformation for each part
`d[], e[], f[]`	

Variables:

`x1, y1`	Current point on orbit
`x2, y2`	Next point on orbit
`i, j, k, l`	Integer counters
`cc`	Color counter
`ci[]`	Color index

Functions:

`rand(x)`	Random number between 0 and x
`setcolor(x)`	Set current color
`setpixel(x,y)`	Give pixel at x,y the current color

Procedure:

```
paint(x0, y0, niters, nparts, nlevs)
 1: x1 = x0, y1 = y0, cc = 1
 2: for i = 1 to niters
 3: j = rand(1)
```

```
 4: for k = 1 to nparts
 5:     if j > area[i] then j = k, k = nparts
 6: next k
 7: x2 = x1 * a[j] + y1 * b[j] + e[i]
 8: y2 = x1 * c[j] + y1 * d[i] + f[i]
 9: x1 = x2, y1 = y2
10: ci[cc] = j
11: k = rand(nlevs - 1) + 1
12: l = cc - k
13: if l < 0 then l = l + level
14: cc = cc + 1
15: if  cc > nlevs then cc = 1
16: setcolor( clr[ci[k]] [l] )
17: setpixel(x1,y1)
18: next i
19: return
```

The Successive Approximation (Cat Game) Algorithm

Notes:

This recursive procedure draws one copy of the seed shape and then calls itself to draw each reflection of that shape on the next level. The first time it is called, it should receive an initial transformation and the total number of levels to draw as arguments.

Line 1:   Count down one level.

Lines 2–3:   Compute the first point on the shape.

Line 4:   Move to the first point on the shape without drawing anything yet.

Lines 5–9:   Outline the shape on-screen by drawing connecting lines between the points.

Line 10:   Finish the shape with a connecting line back to the first point.

Line 11:   If you just drew the last level, return to the most recent recursive call of the draw function (does not return to the main program yet).

Lines 12–22:   Main loop to draw the next level of shapes, one for each part.

Line 13:   Select a color for the next part to draw, according to the current level.

Lines 14–19:   Add the current transformation to the transformation for the next part to draw.

Line 20:   Recursive call to draw the next part and its successive levels.

Line 22:   When all parts are drawn down to the level specified, return to the main program.

Givens:

a0, b0, c0, d0, e0, f0	Current transformation
nparts	Number of parts
a[], b[], c[], d[], e[], f[]	Affine transformation for each part
clr[][]	Color for each part at each level
nlevs	Total number of levels
npts	Number of points on the seed shape
x[], y[]	Location of each point on the seed

Variables:

x0, y0, px, py	First point, current point on shape
a1, b1, c1, d1, e1, f1	Next transformation
i, level	Integer counters

Functions:

setcolor(x)	Set current color
moveto(x,y)	Set current location to x,y
lineto(x,y)	Draw line from current location to x,y

Procedure:

```
draw(a0, b0, c0, d0, e0, f0, level)
 1: level = level - 1
 2: x0 = x[1] * a0 + y[1] * b0 + e0
 3: y0 = x[1] * c0 + y[1] * d0 + f0
 4: moveto(x0, y0)
 5: for i = 2 to npts
 6: px = x[i] * a0 + y[i] * b0 + e0
 7: py = x[i] * c0 + y[i] * d0 + f0
 8: lineto(px, py)
 9: next i
10: lineto(x0, y0)
11: if level < 0 then return
12: for i = 1 to nparts
13: setcolor( clr[i] [nlevs - level] )
14: a1 = a[i] * a0 + c[i] * b0
15: b1 = b[i] * a0 + d[i] * b0
16: c1 = a[i] * c0 + c[i] * d0
17: d1 = b[i] * c0 + d[i] * d0
18: e1 = e[i] * a0 + f[i] * b0 + e0
19: f1 = e[i] * c0 + f[i] * d0 + f0
20: draw(a1, b1, c1, d1, e1, f1, level)
21: next i
22: return
```

The Julia Set Algorithm

Notes:

The julia() function draws a Julia Set for the point cx,cy. To make blowups of a region, use a different x0,y0 and x1,y1. For example, try:

```
x0 = -1, y0 = -1, x1 = -0.5, and y1 = -0.5
```

Lines 1–2: Set maximum and minimum values for the points to be computed.

Lines 3–4: Compute the change in x and y between the pixels on-screen.

Lines 5–6: Loop through every pixel on-screen.

Lines 7–8: Compute the x,y to start iterating.

Line 9: Set the number of iterations at zero.

Lines 10–12: Compute the next point on the orbit.

Line 13: Count one more iteration.

Line 14: If the point has escaped, color it according to the number of iterations so far.

Line 15: If the point has not yet escaped and you haven't reached the maximum number of iterations, return and continue the orbit.

Line 16: If you've reached the maximum number of iterations, color the point black.

Lines 17–20: Color the pixel on-screen, and continue to the next pixel.

Givens:

`cx, cy`	Point that defines Julia Set
`x0, y0, x1, y1`	Maximum and minimum x,y to compute
`m`	Minimum "escaped" value
`niter`	Number of iterations
`nx, ny`	Screen contains nx by ny pixels
`black`	Constant indicating the color black

Variables:

`x, y`	Current point to compute
`xx, yy`	Temporary storage for x,y
`px, py`	Current pixel location
`dx, dy`	Change in x,y for each new pixel
`i`	Integer counter for iterations

Functions:

`setcolor(x)`	Set current color to x
`setpixel(x,y)`	Color pixel at x,y current color

419

Procedure:

```
julia(cx, cy, niter)
 1:  m = 100, x0 = -1.5, y0 = -1.5
 2:  x1 = 1.5, y1 = 1.5
 3:  dx = (x1 - x0)/(nx - 1)
 4:  dy = (y1 - y0)/(ny - 1)
 5:  for px = 0 to nx - 1
 6:  for py = 0 to py - 1
 7:      x = x0 + px * dx
 8:      y = y0 + py * dy
 9:      i = 0
10:      xx = x * x - y * y + cx
11:      yy = 2 * x * y + cy
12:      x = xx, y = yy
13:      i = i + 1
14:      if (x * x + y * y) > m then goto 16
15:      if i < niter then goto 9
16       if i = niter then i = black
17:      setcolor(i)
18:      setpixel(px,py)
19:  next py
20:  next px
```

The Mandelbrot Set Algorithm

Notes:

This function, which draws the Mandelbrot Set, is very similar to julia(). Refer back for line-by-line notes and givens. If you want to compare the two functions, the only differences are in lines 1, 2, 7, 8, 10, and 11. You could place other iterative functions in lines 10 and 11.

As with the Julia Set algorithm, you can zoom in to the set by specifying different x0,y0 and x1,y1 in lines 1 and 2.

Procedure:

```
mandelbrot(niter)
 1:   m = 4, x0 = -2.25, y0 = -1.5
 2:   x1 = 0.75, y1 = 1.5
 3:   dx = (x1 - x0)/(nx - 1)
 4:   dy = (y1 - y0)/(ny - 1)
 5:   for px = 0 to nx - 1
 6:     for py = 0 to py - 1
 7:       cx = x0 + px * dx, x = 0
 8:       cy = y0 + py * dy, y = 0
 9:       i = 0
10:        xx = x * x - y * y + cx
11:        yy = 2 * x * y + cy
12:        x = xx, y = yy
13:        i = i + 1
14:        if (x * x + y * y) > m then goto 16
15:        if i < niter then goto 9
16:       if i = niter then i = black
17:       setcolor(i)
18:       setpixel(px,py)
19:     next py
20:     next px
```

Annotated Bibliography

Hopefully, the rest of this book has stimulated your interest in fractals and in the science of chaos that lies behind them. This appendix will guide you to further fractal adventures, and give you some advice on using FractalVision as a companion to other books.

The list of books, software, and other resources is quite extensive, but I've had to necessarily leave many references out. You can find many more references from the mail-order houses listed in the next section, and the books and articles contain their own bibliographies that will help you locate more that interests you. Of course, new and exciting work is being published continually. *BYTE*, *Scientific American*, and *Science News* are a few of the magazines to watch.

I've tried to give an impression of the general scope and technical level of each book, and I've limited the book references to those that most nonmathematicians could enjoy. If you are comfortable with calculus, you'll find almost everything listed readable. If not, I recommend sticking with the more general expositions.

Where should you begin? Benoit Mandelbrot's original, *The Fractal Geometry of Nature*, remains the best introduction. But be warned that the text does not travel in a straight line and becomes as tangled, at times, as the shapes themselves. James Gleick's *Chaos* is a great place for the general reader to start learning about the applications and implications of the modern nonlinear revolution in science. Scientists who want a more technical introduction will enjoy *Exploring Complexity* by Grégoire Nicolis and Ilya Prigogine. For those who want a complete course in the geometry that drives FractalVision software, there is no better exposition than Michael Barnsley's *Fractals Everywhere*. If you want help exploring the many fractal types and advanced features of FRACTINT software, I recommend *Fractal Creations* by Tim Wegner and Mark Peterson, two of the program's primary authors.

Fractal Mail-Order Catalogs

Almost everything listed in the rest of this bibliography is available from these excellent mail-order houses. Ask for their free catalogs.

Media Magic; PO Box 598; Nicasio, CA 94946
Phone: (415) 662-2426
FAX: (415) 662-2225

This 88-page catalog offers books, videos, software, and "what-not" about fractals, chaos, artificial life, computer animation, virtual reality, and so on. Media Magic carries almost everything listed in this Appendix, plus oodles of amazing videotapes. This is the best catalog you'll find (until they put out next year's). Get one.

Art Matrix; PO Box 880; Ithaca, NY 14851-0880
Phone: (800) PAX-DUTY or (607) 277-0959

This catalog features supercomputer-generated slide sets of many mathematical fractals, along with the computer programs used to create them. You can also get great fractal videotapes, postcards, and T-shirts.

Strange Attractions; 204 Kensington Park Road; London W11 1NR, U.K.
Phone: 071-229-9646

If you're in Europe, this is your best source for information and products relating to fractals and chaos. Ring them up!

Fractal Generation; 2895 Biscayne Blvd #285; Miami, FL 33137
Phone: (305) 445-4955 or (305) 447-7710

Fractal Generation offers fractal fine art poster prints (18" x 24") for $13 apiece and the best selection of fractal T-shirts.

Books on Fractals

Mandelbrot, Benoit. *The Fractal Geometry of Nature.* New York: W.H. Freeman, 1982

The original "casebook and manifesto" on fractals. This book is always fascinating and often frustrating.

Peitgen, Heinz-Otto and Richter, Peter H. *The Beauty of Fractals: Images of Complex Dynamical Systems.* New York: Springer-Verlag, 1986

Flashy pictures and deep commentary on fractals as art and science.

The Science of Fractal Images. Edited by Heinz-Otto Peitgen and Deitmar Saupe. New York: Springer-Verlag, 1988

Essays and pictures provide insight on how to make fractals on a computer and why.

Barnsley, Michael. *Fractals Everywhere.* San Diego: Academic Press, 1988

The best-selling academic book on fractals. If your calculus is rusty, read it anyway and dodge the formulas.

Wegner, Timothy and Peterson, Mark. *Fractal Creations.* Mill Valley, California: Waite Group Press, 1991

A friendly romp through the world-famous FRACTINT software, including all the technical details of how it does what it does so well.

Pickover, Clifford. *Computers, Pattern, Chaos and Beauty.* New York: St. Martin's Press, 1990

Pictures and algorithms for hundreds of graphics techniques, from fractal biomorphs to computer-generated facial expressions.

Devany, Robert. *Chaos, Fractals, and Dynamics: Experiments in Modern Mathematics.* New York: Addison-Wesley, 1989

Introduces chaos and fractals through hands-on computer projects.

Falconer, K. J. *Fractal Geometry: Mathematical Foundations and Applications.* New York: Wiley and Sons, 1990

An up-to-date treatment of the mathematical nitty-gritty of fractals.

Stevens, Roger T. *Fractal Programming in C*; *Fractal Programming in Pascal*; *Advanced Fractal Programming in C*; and *Fractal Programming and Ray Tracing with C++*. Redwood City, California: M&T Books, 1989 and 1990

Charmingly nerdish programming ditties for creating lots of different kinds of fractals, including a simple almost–PCX-compatible file saver.

Prusinkiewicz, P. and Lindenmayer, A. *The Algorithmic Beauty of Plants.* New York: Springer-Verlag, 1990

The authoritative reference on modeling plants with L-systems, including several algorithms and highly realistic illustrations.

You Can Do It: Explore While You Read

Here are some specific hints for using FractalVision software with other books and programs:

The Fractal Geometry of Nature and several other books use a single line segment repeatedly divided into smaller line segments (HEIGHWAY is an example). To produce fractals of this type:

1. Use a line as your seed. Select **NextPoint** and **New**, then press 2 and Enter.

2. Line up copies (created with **Insert** or **Next Part/New**) end-to-end to form the indicated "generator," as Mandelbrot calls it. The first and last copies should meet the ends of the seed.

3. When Mandelbrot provides an "initiator," make several **Draw**ings of your shape, arranged in that pattern (GOSPER1, GOSPER2, GOSPER3, and GOSPER4 are "initiated" on a square, for example).

Usually, you'll want to make everything invisible except the deepest **Level** you **Draw**:

4. Select **Adjust**, then use **Next Part** to place the handle on the seed.

5. Select **Color A** and **Color All Levels**.

6. Set the **Level** and **Color** you want and select **Color All Parts**.

7. Select **Color A** for the seed, **Accept**, and **Draw**.

The HALVES, THIRDS, and QUARTERS templates contain premeasured copies you can use in designing line segment type fractals. GRID is also handy for evening up designs or use **New** to arrange points and pieces around a circle like many traditional fractals.

Michael Barnsley uses a different approach in his book, *Fractals Everywhere,* and its companion software, *The Desktop Fractal Design System.* He defines transformations within a viewing window by showing small copies of the window itself. You can use the BARNSLEY template as a starting point for this approach.

If you have numerical IFS codes, you can type them into an ASCII file (with any text editor or word processor) and then import them into FractalVision with the **Load IFS Codes** command. **Save** some **IFS Codes** and then load the .IFS file into your favorite text editor to have a look at the format you need to use.

Note: IFS Code files saved by FractalVision are directly compatible with FRACTINT. They are not directly compatible with *The Desktop Fractal Design System* or other IFS programs, but you can easily edit them using a text editor. Consult the documentation for the IFS program you have for the specifics of their format.

Books on Chaos

Gleick, James. *Chaos, Making a New Science.* New York: Viking Penguin, 1987

> Nonlinear Thinking Revolutionizes Science: Read all about it!

Nicolis, Grégoire and Prigogine, Ilya. *Exploring Complexity.* New York: W.H. Freeman, 1989

> The playful study of chaos has matured into a serious science of complexity. A rare mixture of technical depth and readability.

Berge, P., Pomeau, Y., and Vidal, C. *Order Within Chaos: Towards a Deterministic Approach to Turbulence.* New York: Wiley and Sons, 1987

> An introduction to dissipative dynamical systems for scientists, by scientists.

Moon, Francis. *Chaotic Vibrations.* New York: Wiley, 1987

> The subtitle: *An Introduction for Applied Scientists and Engineers.*

Glass, Leon and Mackey, Michael. *From Clocks to Chaos: The Rhythms of Life.* Princeton, New Jersey: Princeton University Press, 1988

> All about biological rhythms from a modern dynamical perspective.

Briggs, John and Peat, E. David. *Turbulent Mirror.* New York: Harper & Row, 1989

> The subtitle: *An Illustrated Guide to Chaos Theory and the Science of Wholeness.*

Peters, Edgar E. *Chaos and Order in the Capital Markets.* New York: Wiley and Sons, 1990

> Peters makes a fascinating case for a radical new view of economics and presents fractal techniques for market analysis and forecasting. Not for economists only.

Articles and Other References

Turn to the *Scientific American* articles, especially A.K. Dewdney's "Computer Recreations," for the best balance of depth and friendliness. The *BYTE* articles offer the juiciest tidbits of algorithms and code for true technophiles.

Sorensen, Peter. "Fractals, Exploring the Rough Edges Between Dimensions." *BYTE* (September 1984): 157.

Kenner, Hugh. "In Darkest Self-Similarity." *BYTE* (June 1990): 382.

McWorter, William. "Creating Fractals." *BYTE* (August 1987): 124.

Barnsley, Michael and Sloan, Alan. "A Better Way to Compress Images." *BYTE* (January 1988): 215.

Schroeder, Peter B. "Plotting the Mandelbrot Set." *BYTE* (December 1986): 207.

Dyson, Freeman. "Characterizing Irregularity." *Science* (May 12, 1978): 677.

Thomsen, D.E. "Fractals: Magical Fun or Revolutionary Science?" *Science News* (vol 131, 1987): 184.

Dawkins, Richard. *The Blind Watchmaker*. New York: W.W. Norton, 1986.

Aiken, Conrad. "The Room," *Collected Poems*. New York: Oxford University Press. 1953.

Rosenberg, Harold. *Discovering the Present: Three Decades in Art, Culture and Politics*. Chicago: University of Chicago Press, 1973.

Swaine, Michael. "Programming Paradigms. " *Doctor Dobb's Journal* (September 1990): 199.

Lancaster, Don. "Hardware Hacker." (January 1990): 69.

Garder, Martin. "Order and Surprise." *The Philosophy of Science* (vol 17): 109.

Krynicki, Victor. "Market Prediction Through Fractal Geometry." *Technical Analysis of Stocks and Commodities* (March 1992): 4.

Richardson, Lewis F. *Weather Prediction through Numerical Methods*. Cambridge: Cambridge University Press, 1922.

Hoffman, Paul. "The Man Who Loves Only Numbers." *The Atlantic* (November 1987): 60.

Carson, Rachel. *Silent Spring.* New York: Haughton Mifflin. 1962.

Alexander, Christopher. "The Nature of Order." Unpublished. 1986.

Sessions, George and Duval, Bill. *Deep Ecology.* Salt Lake City, Utah: Peregrine Smith Books, 1987.

Ruelle, David. "Strange Attractors." *Mathematical Intelligencer* (vol 2, 1980): 137.

Stevens, Wallace. "Adagia." *Opus Posthumus.* New York: Alfred A. Knopf, 1957.

Norton, Alan. *SIGGRAPH Proceedings* (July 1982).

Wolfram, Stephen. "Computer Software in Science and Mathematics." *Scientific American* (September 1984): 188.

Jurgens, Hartmut, Peitgen, H.O., and Saupe, Dietmar. "The Language of Fractals." *Scientific American* (August 1990): 67.

Dewdney, A.K. "Computer Recreations." *Scientific American* (August 1985): 16. (December 1986): 14. (August 1985): 16. (July 1987): 108. (November 1987): 140. (December 1988): 116. (February 1989): 108. (May 1990): 126.

Newsletters

True fractal fanatics will want to subscribe to all of the following newsletters. For those with a broader interest in all things fun and programmable, I recommend only ALGORITHM. There is, as of yet, no newsletter dedicated to real-world applications of fractals and chaos. (Anyone out there want to start one?)

AMYGDALA, Newsletter of Fractals and the Mandelbrot Set
c/o Rollo Silver; Box 5279; Taos, NM 87571
Phone: (505) 586-0197

ALGORITHM, The Personal Programming Newsletter
c/o A.K. Dewdney; PO Box 29237 Westmount Postal Outlet;
785 Wonderland Rd South; London, ON, Canada N6K 1M6
Phone: (519) 432-8042

Recreational and Educational Computing
(devoted to the playful interaction of computers and "mathemagic")
c/o Dr. Michael Ecker; 909 Violet Terrace; Clarks Summit, PA 18411
Phone: (717) 586-2784

Fractal Report (editorials, announcements, reviews, and articles on all types of fractals)
c/o John de Rivaz; Reeves Telecommunications Laboratorise Ltd.; West Towan House, Porthtowan, Truro; Cornwall TR4 8AX United Kingdom

Computer Software for PC-Compatibles

Mandelbrot Set Programs

These programs generate images of the Mandelbrot/Julia Sets. Most are much slower but slightly more user-friendly than FRACTINT.

FracTOOLS, $69, and *FracZOOMS*, $59.
Bourbaki, Inc.
PO Box 2867; Boise, ID 83701

Mandelbrot 3, $25.
Midnight Beach
1805A Felt St; Santa Cruz, CA 95062

FractalMagic, $35.
Sintar Software
1001 4th Ave, Suite 3200; Seattle, WA 98154

Fractal Explorer, $30, and *Fractal FX,* $40.
Andromeda Research
6441 Enterprise Ln; Madison, WI 53719

SUPERMAND, $20.
c/o Guy Cox
Box 206, Wentworth Bldg; University of Sydney; NSW 2006, Australia

Mandelbrot Magic, $15, *Recursive Realm*, $20, and *Mandle*, $35.
Available as Shareware ($5/disk) from:
Public Brand Software
PO Box 51315; Indianapolis, IN 46251

The Desktop Fractal Design System, $40.
Michael Barnsley, 1988
Academic Press; Orlando, FL 32887-0510

The disappointing companion to *Fractals Everywhere* (see **Books on Fractals**).

Chaos in the Classroom, $75.
Dynamical Systems, 1988
PO Box 35421; Tucson, AZ 85710

Educational software to teach the mathematics of nonlinear systems. (They also sell software to process nonlinear dynamical information.)

Cellular Automata Lab, $60.
Autodesk, Inc., 1989
2320 Marinship Way; Sausilito, CA 94965

Lets you experiment with a wide variety of cellular automata.

CHAOS: The Software, $60.
Autodesk, Inc. (address above), 1990

A basic introduction to fractals, attractors, and cellular automata. Includes a unique chaotic pendulum simulation.

FRACTEDT, $70.
Tardis Systems Inc, 1989
945 San Ildefonso #15; Los Alamos, NM 87544

Creates fractal simulations of planets, plants, and so on.

EXPLOR-I, $45.
Turing Omnibus Inc., 1988
PO Box 1456; London, ON Canada N6A 5M2

A collection of small programs to create fractals, cellular automata, etc.

Many of these, plus a variety of Apple Macintosh and Commodore Amiga software, are available from Media Magic (see Catalogs section). For Apple II and IIe software, contact EduTech; 1927 Culver Rd; Rochester, NY 14609.

Graphics Library Support

To compile one of the C programs with your particular compiler and graphics library, use one of the following batch files.

The .EXE files supplied on the disk have been compiled with GX graphics, which supports faster operations and higher resolution Super VGA modes than most native graphics libraries. Therefore, you should copy the originals to another directory for safekeeping before you recompile any of them.

The full C source code for FV.EXE is not included with this book, but it is available directly from Cedar Software. See the registration form in the back of the book for details.

The header files define constants, variables, macros, and functions to handle all video access. These are then used in the rest of the source code files (see the Introduction to this book for compile instructions).

Compiler/Graphics Library	Header	Batch file for compile
Microsoft/Microsoft Graphics	FVMS.H	CMS.BAT or CMS2.BAT
Borland/Turbo C/BGI	FVTC.H	CTC.BAT
Zortech/Flash Graphics	FVZT.H	CZT.BAT
Power C/MIX Graphics	FVPC.H	CPC.BAT
Microsoft C/GX Graphics	FVGX.H	CMSGX.BAT
Borland/Turbo C/BGI	FVGX.H	CTCGX.BAT

Microsoft users: If you combined GRAPHICS.LIB into your main libraries when you installed the Microsoft C compiler, use CMS2.BAT instead of CMS.BAT because CMS.BAT assumes that you have a separate GRAPHICS.LIB. If you're not sure what all that means, just look in the LIB compiler subdirectory for GRAPHICS.LIB. If it's there, use CMS.BAT. If not, use CMS2.BAT.

Borland users: When you run a program compiled to use the Borland Graphics Interface (the graphics library that came with your compiler), you must make sure that EGAVGA.BGI, or another valid BGI driver file, is in the subdirectory where the program resides, on your PATH.

For example, to compile changes you had made in the LAND.C program from Chapter 2 with Borland Turbo C or Borland C/C++, you would enter

```
CTC LAND
```

You can use the graphics macros and functions in these header files for much more than just compiling these programs. In fact, several operations are defined in the header files that are not used in any of the C programs (`fillellipse`, for example). With these header files, you can write software that is portable to any C graphics library.

Some C purists will object to the inclusion of functions in header files. This does go against standard practice, but it remains within standard C syntax, and eliminates the need for half a dozen extra .c files cluttering up your disk.

You must #define the MAIN constant before you #include FV.H. If you expand a program and split it into more than one source code file, the main module should #include FV.H with MAIN defined, and all other modules should #include FV.H with MAIN undefined. (You probably won't expand any of these programs to get that big. The capability to do so is included primarily to maintain compatibility with the full source code of FractalVision in case you decide to order it.)

Also, the *videomode* variable name is reserved for internal use by the graphics functions and should not be used in your programs.

Constants

NMODES   Number of possible video-modes

Variables

int	scrnx	Horizontal resolution of the screen in pixels
	scrny	Vertical resolution of the screen in pixels
	charx	Width of one text character in pixels
	chary	Height of one text character in pixels
	ncolors	Number of colors in the palette
char	modecode[NMODES + 1]	Array of command line switches for each video-mode
	modedesc[NMODES+1][32]	Array of text descriptions of each video-mode

Macros

settextmode()	Exit the graphics-mode and return to the text-mode
putscreen()	Display the picture buffer to the screen
getscreen()	Store the screen image in the picture buffer
setclipregion(x1,y1, x2,y2)	Set the clipping region for all drawing operations

`getclipregion(x1,y1, x2,y2)`	Get the current clipping region
`clearscreen()`	Clear the screen
`setcolor(c)`	Set the current text and drawing color
`getcolor()`	Get the current text and drawing color
`getpixel(x1, y1)`	Get the color of the screen pixel at x1,y1
`putpixel(x1, y1, c)`	Set the screen pixel at x1,y1 to color c
`drawline(x1, y1, x2, y2)`	Draw a line
`drawrect(x1, y1, x2, y2)`	Draw the outline of a rectangle
`fillrect(x1, y1, x2, y2)`	Fill a rectangle with the current color
`eraserect(x1, y1, x2, y2)`	Erase a rectangular region (fill with background color)
`drawpoly(poly, n)`	Draw a polygon array with n vertices
`fillpoly(poly, n)`	Fill a polygon with the current color
`drawellipse(x1, y1, x2, y2)`	Draw an outline of an ellipse
`fillellipse(x1, y1, x2, y2)`	Fill an ellipse with the current color
`moveto(x, y)`	Set the current text and drawing position
`lineto(x, y)`	Draw a line from current position to x,y
`outttext(str)`	Output one line of text at the current position

Functions

`int setvidmode(short vmode, int mal)`	Set the video-mode indexed in the `modecode` and `modedesc` arrays by `vmode`, and allocate memory for the picture buffer if `mal` is a nonzero number

| int detectmode(void) | Detect a default video-mode automatically |
| void closedown(void) | Close all graphics and mouse stuff and free any memory allocated for the picture buffer |

Sample Header File

I've listed FVMS.H, the Microsoft C header file, in case you want to create a similar header file to use with a graphics library or compiler not supported on the disk. You should also examine the other header files to find the one that comes closest to the syntax of the compiler you'd like to support.

Even if your graphics library is supported, you may want to modify the header file to support additional video-modes (such as the 256 color modes) or graphics operations (such as flood fill or XOR rasterops).

Remember that FVMS.H is only one of several header files on the disk. The others are not listed here.

Listing D.1. FVMS.H, the Microsoft C graphics support header file.

```
/* FVMS.H
 *
 * FractalVision Microsoft Graphics Library support header file
 * See the file GRAPHICS.TXT for more information.
 */

#include <graph.h>              /* for graphics */
#include <malloc.h>             /* for memory allocation */

#define NMODES 7  /* Number of video modes */
#define NPTS   64  /* Maximum number of polygon points */

#ifdef MAIN
/* If in the main program module, set up graphics variables
 * scrn will hold a copy of the current picture.
```

continues

Listing D.1. continued

```
 * scrnsize is the number of bytes needed for scrn.
 * videoconfig is a video configuration structure
 */

char huge *scrn;
long scrnsize;
struct videoconfig vc;

/* scrnx, scrny are the resolution of the screen in pixels
 * charx, chary are the width and height of a text character
 * ncolors is the number of colors in the palette
 * clip is the corners of the clipping region
 */

int scrnx, scrny, charx, chary, ncolors,
    clipx1, clipy1, clipx2, clipy2, videomode;

/* msvmode[] is the Microsoft C video mode codes
 * modecode[] is the command line switches
 * modedesc[] is the descriptions of available video modes.
 */

int msvmode[] = {0, _MRES4COLOR, _HRESBW, _HERCMONO,
            _ERESCOLOR, _VRES2COLOR, _VRES16COLOR};
char modecode[NMODES + 1] =
                {' ', 'L', 'C', 'H', 'E', 'M', 'V'},
    modedesc[NMODES + 1][32] = {"NONE",
                    "Low-res CGA   320x200 4-color",
                    "CGA hi-res    640x200 2-color",
                    "Hercules      720x348 2-color",
                    "EGA hi-res    640x350 16-color",
                    "Mono VGA      640x480 2-color",
                    "VGA standard 640x480 16-color"};

int setvidmode(short vmode, int mal);
int detectmode(void);
void closedown(void);
#endif

#ifndef MAIN
```

```
/* If not in the main program module,
   reference the variables as external */

extern char huge *scrn;
extern long scrnsize;
extern struct videoconfig vc;
extern int scrnx, scrny, charx, chary,
          ncolors, clipx1, clipy1, clipx2, clipy2;
extern int videomode, msvmode[NMODES + 1];
extern char modecode[NMODES + 1], modedesc[NMODES + 1][32];

extern int setvidmode(short vmode, int mal);
extern int detectmode(void);
extern void closedown(void);
#endif

/* graphics macros */

/* go back to text mode */

#define settextmode() _setvideomode(_DEFAULTMODE)

/* display the picture from the buffer to the screen */

#define putscreen() _putimage(0, 0, scrn, _GPSET)

/* store the screen into the picture buffer */

#define getscreen() _getimage(0, 0, scrnx - 1, scrny - 1, scrn)

/* set and get the clipping region corners */

#define setclipregion(x1, y1, x2, y2) \
        {_setcliprgn(x1, y1, x2, y2); \
         clipx1 = x1, clipy1 = y1, \
         clipx2 = x2, clipy2 = y2;}
#define getclipregion(x1, y1, x2, y2) \
        {*x1 = clipx1, *y1 = clipy1, \
         *x2 = clipx2, *y2 = clipy2;}
```

continues

439

Listing D.1. continued

```
/* clear the screen */

#define clearscreen() _clearscreen(_GCLEARSCREEN)

/* set the current color */

#define setcolor(x) {_setcolor(x); _settextcolor(x);}

/* return the current color */

#define getcolor()   _getcolor()

/* get and put color of a pixel */

#define getpixel(x1, y1)    _getpixel(x1, y1)
#define putpixel(x1, y1, c) {int tempc; \
                             tempc = _getcolor(); \
                             _setcolor(c); \
                             _setpixel(x1, y1); \
                             _setcolor(tempc);}
/* draw a line */

#define drawline(x1, y1, x2, y2)    _moveto(x1, y1), \
                                    _lineto(x2, y2)


/* draw outlined rectangle */

#define drawrect(x1, y1, x2, y2) \
   _rectangle(_GBORDER, x1, y1, x2, y2)

/* draw a filled rectangle in background color */

#define eraserect(x1, y1, x2, y2) \
      {int tempc;  tempc = _getcolor(); \
       _setcolor(0); \
       _rectangle(_GFILLINTERIOR, x1, y1, x2, y2);\
       _setcolor(tempc);}

/* output one line of text to current position */
```

```
#define outtext(x) _outtext(x)

/* move current drawing and text cursor position */

#define moveto(x1, y1) \
   {_moveto(x1, y1); \
      _settextposition(y1/chary+1, x1/charx+1);}

/* draw a line from the current position to a new position */

#define lineto(x1, y1)           _lineto(x1, y1)

/* draw a filled polygon */

#define fillpoly(poly, n) \
        {int i; struct xycoord op[NPTS]; \
         for (i = 0; i < n; i++)  \
         op[i].xcoord = poly[i][0], \
         op[i].ycoord = poly[i][1]; \
         _polygon(_GFILLINTERIOR, op, n);}

/* draw a polygon outline */

#define drawpoly(poly, n); \
   {int i; \
      if (n > 2) \
      for(i = 0; i < n - 1; i++) \
      drawline(poly[i][0], poly[i][1], \
      poly[i + 1][0], poly[i + 1][1]); \
      drawline(poly[0][0], poly[0][1], \
      poly[n - 1][0], poly[n - 1][1]);}

/* draw a filled ellipse */

#define fillellipse(x1, y1, x2, y2) \
      _ellipse(_GFILLINTERIOR, x1, y1, x2, y2)

/* draw an outlined ellipse */
```

continues

Listing D.1. continued

```
#define drawellipse(x1, y1, x2, y2) \
      _ellipse(_GBORDER, x1, y1, x2, y2)

/* fill a rectangle, or outline if bkgd color */

#define fillrect(x1, y1, x2, y2, c); \
    {int max, oc; \
     oc = _getcolor(); \
     if (c > 0) max = _GFILLINTERIOR, \
     _setcolor(c); \
     else max = _GBORDER, \
     _setcolor(ncolors - 1);\
     _rectangle(max, x1, y1, x2, y2); \
     _setcolor(oc);}

#ifdef MAIN
/* This sets the video mode and gets the
   video configuration information. If mal
   is nonzero (meaning this is the first time
   it's been called), it tries to allocate the
   memory for picture storage as well.
*/

int setvidmode(short vmode, int mal)
{   int i;
    if (vmode != 0) /* vmode=0 means reset current mode */
        videomode = msvmode[vmode];
    else videomode = vc.mode;    /* reset current mode */
    if (_setvideomode(videomode) == NULL) return(NULL);
    _getvideoconfig(&vc); /* get video configuration data */
    scrnx = vc.numxpixels, scrny = vc.numypixels;
    ncolors = vc.numcolors;
    _wrapon(_GWRAPOFF); /* turn text line wrapping off */
    charx = vc.numxpixels / vc.numtextcols;  /* char width */
    chary = vc.numypixels / vc.numtextrows;  /* and height */
    if (mal)   /* allocate memory to store the picture */
    {   scrnsize = _imagesize(0, 0, vc.numxpixels - 1,
                                    vc.numypixels - 1);
```

```
        if ((scrn = (char huge *)
             halloc(scrnsize, sizeof(char)))
             == (char huge *) NULL)
        {   _setvideomode(_DEFAULTMODE);
             return(NULL);
        }
    }
    _setcliprgn(0, 0, scrnx - 1, scrny - 1);
    return(1);
}

int detectmode(void)  /* detect best video mode */
{   int i;
    struct videoconfig vi;
    _getvideoconfig(&vi);
    switch(vi.adapter)
    {   case _MDPA: i = 0;
                    break;
        case _CGA:
        case _MCGA: i = 2;
                    break;
        case _HGC:  i = 3;
                    break;
        case _EGA:  i = 4;
                    break;
        case _VGA:  i = 6;
                    break;
    }
    return i;
}

/* Ask user to pick a video mode */

int pickmode(int trythis)
{   int i, a;
    settextmode();
    printf("\nPlease choose a video mode, "
           "or press Q to quit.\n\n");
```

continues

443

Listing D.1. continued

```c
    for (i = 1; i <= NMODES; i++)
    {   if (i == trythis) printf("\nTRY THIS ONE —>");
        else printf("\n                 ");
        printf(" %c    %s", modecode[i], modedesc[i]);
    }
    printf("\n\nYour choice: ");
    while(1)
    {   a = toupper(getch());
        if ((a == 'Q') || (a == 27))
        {   printf("Quit\n\n");
            exit(0);
        }
        for (i = 1; i <= NMODES; i++)
        {   if (modecode[i] == a)
            {   printf("%c", a);
                return(i);
            }
        }
    }
}


/* shut down MS Graphics and free up the buffers it used */

void closedown(void)
{   _setvideomode(_DEFAULTMODE);   /* go back to text mode */
    hfree((void huge *) scrn);     /* free up picture memory */
}
```

Glossary

3-D IFS code   A numerical description of a three-dimensional fractal. (See also: **Iterated Function Systems**.)

3-D point   Three numbers describing a location in three-dimensional space.

3-D space   A mathematical or physical space with three dimensions. We live in 3-D space.

3-D transform   A geometric relationship between two points or objects in 3-D space.

Ad infinitum   Latin for *to infinity*, usually used to indicate that a pattern continues forever. Fractaliers love to use this phrase!

Affine transformation   A geometric relationship that preserves the basic form and integrity of a shape. An affine transformation can consist of rotation (spin), scaling (size), and translation (movement). By spinning or scaling along one axis (direction) more than another, affine transformations can also skew or stretch the shape of an object. Affine transformations are linear (a

small change in the transformation always produces a small change in the way it alters an object), but they can produce nonlinear fractal shapes when several transformations are iterated.

Aggregation   The repeated joining together of small particles to form a larger mass. (See also: **Diffusion limited aggregation**.)

Algorithm   A description of procedures; a specific technique for carrying out a task. Algorithms usually refer to the general process expressed in a computer program.

Altocumulus   High, broken patches of puffy clouds.

ASCII   The American Standard Code for Information Interchange; the standard coding system used for text storage on computers.

Attractor   When a mathematical function is iterated (the results of one procedure are repeatedly fed back into the same procedure), it may converge to a certain value or set of values, no matter what number you use at the beginning. This value or set of values is called an attractor, because all other values move toward it when the function iterates. If a function works on two numbers at once, you can plot those numbers on a two-dimensional screen or page to see the shape of the attractor. (Likewise, functions of three variables can have three-dimensional attractors.) Because most fractals are drawn by iterating a function and plotting the values it converges toward, fractal shapes are pictures of attractors.

Auto-arrange feature   The feature of FractalVision software that automatically arranges parts or points in a circle when you select **New** and press a number.

Basin of attraction   A mathematical function may converge to an attractor when certain values are input, while other values zoom off to infinity when the function is iterated. For two-dimensional functions, a region of points with attractors is called a basin of attraction. The Mandelbrot set is the most well-known basin of attraction. (See also: **Attractor**.)

Bénard heat convection cells   Small alternating regions of rotation that form when a liquid is heated under certain conditions.

Bifurcation   The process of splitting in two. Many mathematical functions have attractors that start as a single value, then split into two, four, eight, and more as one of the variables changes. This is also called Period doubling. (See also: **Feigenbaum's number**.)

Big Bang   The theory that the universe started from a single point that exploded and formed space as we know it.

Biomorph   A term used by several authors to refer to anything that resembles biological organisms. Most commonly, Clifford Pickover's variations on the Mandelbrot and Julia sets that give them a biological appearance.

Bitmap   Computers often store images by recording the average color value for each small square of a grid. The size of the grid (the resolution) determines the quality of the picture, and a picture stored in one resolution cannot easily be increased to a higher resolution. (See also: **Vector**.)

Black spleenwort fern   A highly self-similar species of fern. Michael Barnsley used fractal reproductions of this fern to demonstrate that you can produce visually complex realistic models from a few simple mathematical codes.

Box counting   A technique for estimating the irregularity, or fractal dimension, of a shape. The area where the shape resides is divided into successively larger square boxes, and the number of boxes that contain part of the shape are counted. The ratio of the logarithms of the counts is an estimate of the irregularity of the shape. For fractals, this estimate is the same over a large range of box sizes. (See also: **Fractal dimension**.)

Breeding   The process of selecting only offspring that meet certain criteria to produce future generations. Because you can describe fractals with a few codes, you can breed fractals by randomly mutating those codes and choosing the most satisfactory mutations.

Bronchial branching   The diverging, tree-like pattern of bronchial tubes in the lungs.

Butterfly Effect   The idea that a small change in initial conditions, such as a butterfly flapping its wings, can create a large difference in final conditions, such as tomorrow's weather. Technically, this is called *sensitive dependence on initial conditions.*

C compiler   A computer program that translates instructions written by humans in the C programming language into the native language of a specific computer so that the computer can carry out the instructions.

C program   A set of instructions for computers, written in the C programming language. C is currently the most popular language for writing microcomputer programs.

Carrying capacity   The maximum population of a species sustainable in a given environment or ecosystem.

Cartesian   Relating to René Descartes. Usually used in reference to Cartesian coordinates, a set of numbers that locate a point by describing its distance from a central point in two or more straight-line dimensions.

Cat Game   My silly name for the successive approximation algorithm, based on the idea that cats have kittens and before you know it, kittens have kittens, too. This also sounds vaguely like the Chaos Game, Michael Barnsley's silly name for another algorithm.

Cell   A single unit, usually among many nearly identical units. (See also: **Benard heat convection cells** and **Cellular automata**.)

Cellular automaton   A computer-simulated universe where many nearly identical artificial cells reproduce according to logical or geometric rules. Conway's Game of Life is the best known cellular automaton. FractalVision templates are also cellular automata; copies of the seed shape are the cells, and the geometric relationships between them are the rules of propagation.

CGA   Color Graphics Adapter, the first color graphics card available for IBM PC compatibles.

Chance   A name given to any phenomena with causes that we cannot easily explain; randomness. Interestingly enough, nearly all such phenomena seem to follow similar patterns, or probability distributions. The new science of chaos is turning up new clues as to why this is so.

Chaos   In general usage, anything threateningly uncontrollable and messy. The word has also taken on a specific technical meaning: sensitive dependence on initial conditions. In other words, a small difference in the initial state of a chaotic system can quickly lead to a large difference in the state of the system as measured at a later time—even though the state of the system is completely dependent on those initial conditions. (See also: **Butterfly Effect**.)

Chaos Game   Michael Barnsley's pet name for the random iteration algorithm. This is actually a misnomer because the algorithm does not demonstrate chaotic behavior in the technical sense. Barnsley is using the word *chaos* to mean randomness.

Chaos science   The cross-disciplinary study of chaotic systems.

Chaotic symmetry   Statistical self-similarity, usually over a broad range of scales. Instead of containing exact copies of itself, a shape with chaotic symmetry usually contains copies with a nonlinear geometric relationship to the whole. Often, no two copies are quite the same. In order to officially earn the name "chaotic," adjacent points—even those infinitely close to one another—must sometimes show entirely different behavior. Most iterated nonlinear systems (such as the Mandelbrot and Julia sets) show chaotic symmetry.

Chaotic system   See **Chaos**.

Child   In fractal geometry, a transformed copy of a shape is sometimes called its child. (See also: **Parent**.)

Cirrocumulus   High, patterned clouds that often appear in the evening in the Eastern U.S.; a "Mackerel Sky."

Cirrus   Wispy clouds in the upper atmosphere, caused by abrupt changes in pressure and by strong winds.

Clear   In this book, when I tell you to "**Clear**," I mean to select the **Clear** command from the FractalVision main menu. This erases the picture, but leaves the template intact.

Code   (1) Instructions written in computer language; source code. (2) A compact way of representing information. (See also: **IFS Code**, **Genetic code**, and **Geometric genetic code**.)

Collage   A method of finding a fractal that approximates a given shape; the shape is tiled with copies of itself.

Color cycle   To shift, or rotate, the palette of colors displayed on the computer screen, creating wild motion effects. To color cycle from within FRACTINT software, press the + key or - key.

Compiler   A computer program that translates a human-readable language (such as C or FORTRAN) into machine-readable language (such as 8086 machine code).

Complex   (1) Complicated, intricately detailed. (See also: **Complexity**.) (2) Having two numerical components rather than one. (See also: **Complex number** and **Complex plane**.)

Complex number   A set of two numbers (sometimes denoted x and y) that define a point on a flat surface. In order to distinguish the two numbers, one of them is multiplied by the square root of 1 (usually denoted *i* or *j*). This produces the convenient mathematical result of making the multiplication of two complex numbers behave as if the two points were rotated in a consistent way around the point 0,0. There are more esoteric definitions of a complex number, but don't worry about them unless you are trying for a PhD in mathematics.

Complex plane   A two-dimensional mathematical flat surface, used both to model real surfaces and to visualize abstract functions on a two-dimensional computer screen.

Complexity   The science of chaos is maturing into a science of complexity as we develop tools for understanding the nature of complex systems. (Foremost among those tools is computer graphics, which can help us see patterns hidden in a vast quantity of detailed information by displaying it visually.) A distinction is made between algorithmic complexity (the size of the minimum set of instructions needed to reproduce a set of data) and visual or structural complexity (the minimum size of a description of the data set in its raw form, as observed).

Component   One of two numerical parts that compose a complex number. (See also: **Complex number.**)

Conservative system   A system that does not lose or gain a significant amount of energy over time. Conservative systems are easy to work with mathematically, but are relatively rare outside the laboratory and classroom. (See also: **Dissipative system.**)

Constant   A value that remains unchanged over the course of a computer program's execution or throughout an algorithm.

Continuous   A curve is continuous if every point is adjacent to one other point on each side of it. For continuous curves, you can always find a line that approximates the slope, or direction, of the curve at any given point. Fractal curves may sometimes appear continuous, but you cannot find approximations of the slope. (See also: **Tangent lines** and **Differentiation.**)

Contractive   A geometric transformation is contractive if it causes objects to shrink. FractalVision uses contractive affine transformations to define fractals. (See also: **Affine transformation.**)

Control   (1) The ability to determine the initial state of a system. (2) The ability to intentionally create a reproducible sequence of system states over a period of time.

Most nonlinear systems are controllable in the first sense, but not in the second because the ability to control the initial state is always less than perfectly accurate and a small difference in the initial state can lead to a completely different sequence of system states over time.

Controlled variable   A measurable property that humans can control.

Conway's Game of Life   A popular cellular automaton in which the local population density in a grid of artificial cells determines which cells live and die during each generation.

Coordinate   A number that describes a location in space or on a plane (on a computer screen, for example).

Copy   Throughout the book, I use this term to mean transformations of a shape rather than exact duplicates.

Copy of the seed   FractalVision software uses a seed shape, or parent, and transformed copies of the seed, or children, to define fractals. The seed shape and its copies are called "parts" of the template, and the corner points that define the seed shape itself are called "points."

cos   The cosine function, which returns the horizontal location of a point given a distance around the perimeter of a circle. When iterated, this function produces a bifurcating attractor with cycles of all possible lengths, including completely chaotic regions.

Critical point   A point in time or a particular value of a variable at which a sudden radical change in the behavior of a system occurs.

Cumulus   Low, fluffy white clouds.

Curve   A one-dimensional geometric shape with a slope, or direction of motion, that is always changing from point to point; as opposed to a line, which has a constant slope throughout. Fractals are curves with a slope that changes at an infinitely rapid pace; they are therefore the only curves with slopes that cannot be approximated at any particular point.

Curvilinear   A term used to lump lines and curves together under one heading.

Cyclic   (1) Repeating; periodic. (2) Containing nearly periodic variation, without actually ever repeating. Fractals are usually cyclic in the second sense, but not in the first.

DAT File   A file containing the corner points of polygons that approximate a fractal, output by FractalVision for use with scientific software and custom applications.

Dendrite   A squiggly branch, often used in reference to nerve cells or aggregates. (See also: **Diffusion limited aggregation**.)

Dependent variable   A measurable property of a system that cannot be controlled directly but is dependent on variables that can be controlled. Dependent variables become predictable only when you find a mathematical function that relates them to controlled variables.

Determinant   A property of a matrix in linear algebra, which corresponds geometrically to the area covered by the transformation that the matrix defines.

Differential   See **Differential calculus**.

Differential calculus   The mathematics that deals with finding the slope, or rate of change, of curves. This slope is also called the differential, or tangent line.

Differentiation   The mathematical process of finding the slope of a curve at a given point. (See also: **Differential calculus**.)

Diffusion limited aggregation   A computer simulation technique that models many different natural phenomena, such as electrical discharge, diffusion of gases in fluids, and the deposition of chemicals. Small particles are released on the perimeter of a circle and allowed to wander at random until they stick to a growing mass of particles at the center of the circle.

Dimensions   (1) Perpendicular lines used to locate points on a flat surface (which requires two dimensions) or in space (three dimensions). The location where the lines meet is called the origin. (2) The variables in a system that do not depend on one another. A system with two independent variables is called a two-dimensional system and can be visualized by locating points as in the first definition.

Discontinuous   Curves that contain breaks or sudden changes in direction are called discontinuous. Because each point in a fractal contains all the directions of motion in the whole, the direction is said to change infinitely fast and fractals are said to be infinitely discontinuous. This is the opposite of **Continuous**.

Disorder   A general term encompassing several scary kinds of messiness; sometimes used more specifically to mean entropy.

Displacement   Movement without rotation or change in size; also called translation.

Dissipative system   A system that loses energy over time; the opposite of a conservative system. A dissipative system is said to be time irreversible because it tends toward the same state (called homogeneity, or "heat death"), no matter what the initial conditions were.

Dragon curve   Any fractal that (even vaguely) resembles a dragon.

DXF File   An AutoCAD drawing exchange file; a standard vector format that FractalVision supports.

Dynamical disease   Any ailment that arises when fractal rhythms in the human body fall out of sync.

Dynamical system   A system with a state that at one moment can be determined from its state at the previous moment and a set of equations that model how the system iterates. (See also: **Iterative system.**)

e   A constant with an infinite nonrepeating decimal equal to 2.71828… used as the base for the system of natural logarithms. Universal constants such as *e*, pi, the square root of two, and Fiegenbaum's number seem to pop up in all sorts of unexpected places.

EGA   Enhanced Graphics Adapter; an older graphics card still supported by most programs, including FractalVision.

Element   One of the numbers that compose a matrix. (See also: **Matrix algebra.**)

EMS memory   Expanded memory; an old, slow type of memory for PCs that is still supported by some programs, including FractalVision. XMS, or extended memory (also supported by FractalVision), is faster, and you can often choose which type your system offers.

Entropy   The mathematical property of a system that makes an observer unable to tell the parts of the system from one another—a measure of randomness (ΔS).

Equilibrium   A stable state in which the amount of energy coming into a system is approximately equal to the amount of energy leaving the system. Most systems studied in chaos science are far from equilibrium.

Escape time algorithm   A technique for displaying maps of iterated functions; points are colored according to how quickly they escape a region when the function is iterated.

Escape to infinity   With certain mathematical functions, such as the one used to draw the Mandelbrot set, if a point escapes a certain region when the function is iterated, mathematicians can prove that it will eventually run off to infinity. Therefore, the point is said to have escaped to infinity as soon as it leaves the region. (See also: **Escape time algorithm.**)

453

Euclidian Following the geometric rules described by Euclid, a 300 B.C. Greek mathematician. Euclidian systems generally involve only straight-line dimensions that are directly perpendicular to one another. (See also: **Cartesian**.)

Evolution The generation of increasingly complex and efficient forms through natural selection. Modern theories of evolution recognize that more is going on here than just "survival of the fittest," and chaos theory may offer some help in understanding sudden leaps and irregular cyclic patterns in evolution.

Execute See **Run**. (See Dick. See Jane. See Dick run after Jane. See Jane execute Dick. See Spot.)

Executable file The file that contains instructions in machine code for a computer program to run. Executable files usually contain the file extension .EXE.

Expansive A geometric transformation is expansive when it makes objects larger or causes points to move farther apart.

Extension The three letters at the end of a filename that indicate the type of file.

Extrapolation The practice of projecting a behavior of a system into a time or space that has not actually been measured, based on a mathematical model.

Feigenbaum's number Many nonlinear iterated systems bifurcate at regular intervals. The ratio between those intervals is almost always 4.6692016090..., which is called Feigenbaum's number after mathematician Mitchell Feigenbaum. Examples of functions with splits obeying this ratio are the Mandelbrot set, Robert May's population equation, and the cosine function.

File extension See **Extension**.

Fill (1) The shading control on FractalVision software's Adjust panel, as in "Set the Fill to 100 percent." (2) The infinite twisting of a one-dimensional shape to occupy a two-dimensional area, as in "Peano's curve fills part of the plane." (See also: **Space-filling**.)

Fixed point The point where a transformation will end when iterated. Every contractive affine transformation has a fixed point.

Fractal Technically, this term has several meanings—the original being a shape where the Hausdorff/Besicovitch (fractal) dimension exceeds its topological (ordinary) dimension. More commonly, a fractal is any shape where the parts, when magnified, reveal as much detail as the whole. To add confusion, some mathematicians (such as Robert Devany) use *fractal* to mean shapes that are strictly self-similar rather than statistically self-similar. (By this definition, the Mandelbrot set is not a fractal!)

Fractal dimension   A measure of the irregularity, or roughness, of a shape; the degree to which the shape "fills space." No one has yet found a consistent definition of fractal dimension, let alone a universal formula for computing it. Generally, however, it is estimated by taking the logarithmic ratios of some measurable property on varying scales. (See also: **Box counting**.)

Fractal interpolation   A technique for finding a fractal curve that passes through a given set of data points. Unlike linear interpolation, fractal interpolation can always find a curve to precisely fit any set of data. Because fractal curves are so flexible, they are better for producing detailed, realistic models than for supplying the constraints necessary for prediction and control. (See also: **Interpolation**.)

Fractal template   A geometric definition of a fractal, consisting of a seed shape (parent) and copies of the seed (children). This term is in general usage and also refers specifically to the visual models created with FractalVision software.

Fractalier   Someone who is nuts about fractals.

FractalVision   (1) This book. (2) The software that comes with this book. (3) A new, improved outlook on reality.

FractalVision template   See **Fractal template**.

FRACTINT   A freeware program written by the Stone Soup Group, a volunteer collaboration headed by Bert Tyler. See the registration form in the back of this book for information on obtaining a copy of FRACTINT software.

Fractional dimension   See **Fractal dimension**.

Function   Any mathematical operation or computer procedure that takes a number or set of numbers and changes them in some way to produce another number or set of numbers.

Generator   Benoit Mandelbrot's word for a fractal template.

Genetic code   The information encoded in DNA and RNA molecules that controls the development of living organisms.

Geometric genetic code   Coded visual rules for the development of geometric shapes. A geometric code can produce shapes similar to real genetic codes.

Geometric relationship   The difference between two geometric shapes; the description of an operation (such as spin or shrink) that maps one shape onto another.

Graph   A visual representation of abstract data, often made by plotting one variable on the horizontal axis and another variable on the vertical axis.

Graphics library   A collection of computer program functions that handle the display of lines, points, and other graphics operations.

Grow   (1) To develop, as in "a tree grows on your screen." (2) To become larger. (3) The **Grow** command on the FractalVision main menu that makes a part of the template larger.

Growth rate   The rate at which a population reproduces; the ratio between parents and children for each generation.

Handle   The T-shape that FractalVision uses to show the current part of the template or point on the seed.

Header file   A computer language file that can be included at the beginning of other files. The header file FV.H is included in all the C programs in this book, for example.

Hercules adapter   A popular monochrome (black & white) graphics card for IBM PC compatibles (supported by FractalVision software).

Homogeneous   Unchanging, the same all over.

Horizontal   Parallel to the ground (or bottom of a page or computer display).

i   A constant equal to the square root of 1. (See also: **Complex number.**)

IFS code   See **Iterated Function System.**

IFS file   A file that contains Iterated Function System codes in ASCII format, used by FractalVision and FRACTINT software. Some other programs generate IFS files that are similar to but not directly compatible with FRACTINT and FractalVision IFS files.

Image compression   The manipulation of electronically stored images in order to make them fit in less space on a storage device (such as a computer disk). Fractal image compression techniques have achieved compression ratios far beyond other approaches.

Imaginary number   The part of a complex number that represents the vertical; the component of a complex number that is multiplied by *i*. The term "imaginary" remains from days of old and has no relevance anymore. (See also: *i* and **Complex number.**)

Increment   To increase by a certain amount, usually one.

Infinite level   You can approximate fractals by drawing successively more intricate levels of detail. The fractal itself is an abstraction that exists at the most intricate imaginable level of detail, the infinite level.

Infinitesimal   A vanishingly small number, used by Leibnitz to understand how differential calculus works. Turns out it doesn't really work that way after all, so no one talks about infinitesimals much anymore.

Initial state   All measurable properties of a system at the moment when observation of the system begins.

Initiator   Mandelbrot placed his fractal templates (*generators*) around regular polygons, called "initiators," in his book, *The Fractal Geometry of Nature.*

Insert   The FractalVision **Insert** command. When I tell you to "**Insert** a part," I mean to select **Insert** from the menu (or press the Insert key on the keyboard, which does the same thing).

Instructions   A list of how to do something. This book discusses verbal instructions, computer language instructions, visual instructions (such as fractal templates), and mathematical instructions (functions).

Integer math   A type of computer arithmetic used by FractalVision and FRACTINT to speed up operations. A scaling factor is used to store nonintegers as if they were integers.

Integers   Counting numbers with no fractional part. One, two, three...

Integration   The inverse of differentiation; given a slope, or rate of change, one must integrate to find the original function to which the slope belongs. Mathematically, this is (sort of) the same as finding the area under a curve. (See also: **Differential calculus**.)

Interference pattern   The pattern that arises when two or more phenomena overlap in the same space. The MOIRE program displays interference patterns between small concentric circles and the grid that makes up your computer display.

Interpolation   Estimation of unmeasured data that falls between measured data points. (See also: **Fractal interpolation**.)

Irregularity   Roughness, which can be quantified as fractal dimension.

Iterated   See **Iteration**.

Iterated Function System (IFS) (1) Any system that employs iteration. (2) Specifically, a system that iterates a set of contractive affine transformations using the techniques pioneered by Michael Barnsley, *et al.* These systems can be expressed as a small set of IFS codes. FractalVision templates are Barnsley-type Iterated Function Systems.

Iteration The process of repeatedly taking the results of a function and feeding them back into the same function.

Iteration on a plane Iteration of functions with input and output that are points on a two-dimensional surface (such as a computer screen).

Iterative Involving iteration.

Julia set (1) Any set containing only points that remain stable during iteration of a function. (2) Specifically, a Julia set associated with the function $z = z \cdot z + c$, where c is an arbitrary constant. (See also: **Mandelbrot set**.)

Koch Coastline (1) The fractal produced by raising a bump with the measurements of an equilateral triangle on the middle third of a line segment and repeating the process to make smaller bumps on each resulting line segment. (2) Any fractal curve made by repeatedly replacing line segments with a greater number of smaller line segments in a different arrangement.

L-System See **Lindenmayer system**.

Level See **Level of detail**.

Level of detail You can approximate fractals by drawing successively more intricate levels of detail. In FractalVision, the seed shape is the first level of detail (Level 0), and the rest of the template is the next level of detail (Level 1). When you select **Draw**, successive levels of detail appear. You control how many levels appear with the **Level** setting on the **Adjust** menu.

Levels of scale Different size perspectives, as in "the macroscopic level of scale versus the microscopic level of scale."

Life (1) See Conways's **Game of Life**. (2) Get away from your computer once in a while.

Limit Mathematically, the value that a function approaches as one of the variables becomes infinitely large or small.

Lindenmayer System   A cellular automaton that uses strings of characters to represent geometric patterns. Aristid Lindenmayer invented these to model the branching patterns of plants.

Linear   (1) Consisting of or approximated by lines or line segments. (2) Concerning vectors or matrices that can be interpreted to represent coefficients in differentiable equations. (The second meaning is seldom used in this book, but is the basis of the terms "Linear algebra" and "Linear equation." Technically, this comes to mean about the same thing as the first definition when you work through the math.)

Linear algebra   For all practical purposes, synonymous with matrix algebra. The connection to "linear" is that matrices can be interpreted as arrays of coefficients of linear equations (an interpretation into which this book does not delve.)

Linear equation   An equation or group of equations that can be differentiated (more rigorous mathematical criteria exist, but I won't get into them here). Linear equations don't just describe lines! (See also: **Linear**.)

Linearity   The characteristic of being linear, as defined in the previous definition.

Load   To read from a disk into the computer's memory. You must **Load** a fractal template, for example, in order to use it within the FractalVision program.

Lossy technique   Image-compression technique that sacrifices some image quality for more compact storage.

Macro   A definition of terms used in a computer program that is automatically expanded to its full meaning by the compiler. You can choose a header file, for example, which defines graphics macros for a particular variation of the C language.

Mandelbrot Set   (1) The set of points that do not escape to infinity when the function $z \cdot z + c$ is iterated, where c is the point itself and z starts at the origin (0,0) (2) More generally, any set of points that do not escape to infinity when a function including the point itself as a constant is iterated. A Mandelbrot set is always a map of an infinite number of related Julia sets.

Matrix   (Plural: matrices) A rectangular array of numbers that can be interpreted as a point, a geometric transformation, or a set of linear equations, depending on the context.

Matrix algebra   The mathematics dealing with matrices. FractalVision software uses matrix algebra to carry out arithmetic on complex numbers and affine transformations.

Memory   (1) The stuff you buy for your computer so it can store more information without having to access the hard drive. (2) A synonym for **Persistence**.

Milky Way   The galaxy in which we live.

Mode locking   The tendency of a system to spontaneously coordinate its behavior into fixed rhythms, despite external perturbations. Mode locking is often cued by very weak rhythmic signals from outside the system, such as another rhythmic system of the same type. (For example, two or more pendulums on a slightly unsteady table will tend to synchronize under certain conditions.)

Model   A simplified copy of something. Often, the model consists of mathematical equations or computer programs, and the subjects being modeled are physical natural phenomena.

Modulus   The distance from a point to the origin, the square root of the sum of the coordinates squared.

Moiré   Interference patterns caused when two screens or pieces of woven fabric overlap. *Moiré* is a french word for "water," not a person's name.

Monopodial branching   A branching pattern where a single member splits into two or more parts, none of which continue in the same direction as the original.

Mouse   (1) A pointing device used for interactive computer graphics applications such as FractalVision software. (2) The grey scoundrel that raided the fresh raspberries I left on the kitchen counter last night.

Move   In this book, a "move" implies a motion without rotation, skew, or resizing—a simple displacement. It is occasionally also used in a more general sense, as in "How can I make this shape move toward the shape I'm after."

Mutation   A random change to a genetic code. In Chapter 4, "The Art of Fractal Models," IFS codes also undergo mutation.

Natural selection   The process by which beneficial mutations survive and reproduce while disadvantageous mutations die off.

Newton's Method   A method of solving an equation that uses iteration.

Nonaffine transformation   A geometric transformation that does not preserve the structure of shapes. (See also: **Affine transformation**.)

Nonlinear   Any curve, system, or set of equations that cannot be differentiated; that is, for which lines cannot be found to approximate the rate of change of the system at any given point. Not linear.

One-dimensional Capable of being expressed with one variable only. A line and a smooth curve are one-dimensional because the location of any point can be expressed as a single number representing the distance along the line or curve.

Orbit The trajectory of a point or object, either through physical space (such as the path of an electron or a planet) or through mathematical space (such as the complex plane).

Order (1) Generally, anything predictable and controllable. (2) Specifically, the lack of entropy or randomness.

Origin The point where all coordinates are zero (0,0).

Paint (1) A command in FractalVision software that employs the random iteration algorithm. (2) Programs that use bitmaps to store and produce images are called paint programs. (3) Messy goop used by old-fashioned artists.

Parameters The values given to a function or computer program procedure. FRACTINT software calls everything you can control a parameter and files containing predefined fractals parameter files.

Parent Fractal geometricians like to use the analogy of parents and children to describe iteration. You can imagine that the seed shape in FractalVision software is a single sexless parent who gives birth to copies of itself. (See also: **Child**.)

Part In FractalVision software, copies of the seed shape are called parts. The seed itself is also called a part. All operations can be done on a part or a point. (See also: **Point**.)

PCX Files Bitmapped image files based on ZSoft's PC Paintbrush format. An industry standard supported by FractalVision software.

Period (1) The number of distinct states that an iterative system cycles through. (2) The amount of time a repeating event takes to repeat.

Period doubling See **Bifurcation**.

Periodicity checking A trick that FRACTINT uses to find repeating cycles in the orbits of fractals, speeding up the display of a fractal. When a cycle is found, FRACTINT figures out that the orbit isn't ever going to escape to infinity and stops waiting for it to do so.

Persistence Traditional theories of phenomena from physics to economics assume that systems have no memory of past perturbations—that their behavior is determined only by the state at the previous moment. Evidence now indicates that many of these systems do show memory, or persistence, because they show fractal cycles within cycles spanning both short and long time periods.

Perturbation   An outside influence that temporarily or permanently changes the behavior of a system.

pi (π)   The number 3.14159.... The ratio of the circumference and diameter of a circle.

Point   (1) A particular location on a line, on a two-dimensional plane, or in 3-D space. Also, the numbers that describe that location. (2) In FractalVision software, a corner point on the seed shape.

Polychotomous branching   A branching pattern where the branches sprout from a single main member that continues along past them without changing direction significantly.

Prediction   The ability to tell what's going to happen before it does. Prediction should be easy when you have control over the situation, but chaos theory teaches us otherwise.

Procedure   (1) A course of action, an algorithm. (2) Specifically, the main part of an algorithm, as opposed to subsidiary parts that are usually referred to as functions. In some computer languages, procedure means a function that returns no values.

Pseudocode   Abbreviated language used by humans to exchange algorithms. No machine would touch the stuff because the syntax is not strictly defined.

Pushed pendulum   A pendulum that gets occasional, usually rhythmic, pushes. Pushed pendulums can exhibit all sorts of weird behavior (don't invite one to a party unless you hide the lamp shades).

Random iteration algorithm   The procedure used by FractalVision's **Paint** command and Barnsley's Chaos Game to generate fractals. A point chooses one affine transformation at random at each stage of its orbit, from several transformations defined ahead of time.

Randomness   (1) In FractalVision, the percentage of random variation added to a fractal when it's drawn or painted. (2) See **Chance**.

Rate of change   The amount a curve alters its direction at a given point. Synonymous with slope, tangent line, and differential.

Real number (1) The horizontal part of a complex number. (2) A number that may contain a fractional part, as opposed to an integer or whole number.

Reflection Another name for a transformed copy of a shape. When transformed copies of a whole shape appear in its parts, we say that "the shape of the whole is reflected throughout its parts." This is a more liberal use of the word than the common meaning of "mirror image."

Regular (1) Having some kind of orderliness. (2) "Regular fractals," such as those which FractalVision creates when no randomness is added, are strictly self-similar. Fractals that are only statistically self-similar, such as the Mandelbrot set, are not deemed "regular."

Relationship (1) See **Geometric relationship**. (2) Be nice to your spouse.

Reproductive rate (1) See **Growth rate**. (2) Be nice to your spouse.

Resolution The number of pixels on a computer screen or in a bitmapped image, usually expressed as the horizontal and vertical resolution (for example, 640x480).

Rotation See **Spin**.

Rules of propagation The rules that determine how a cellular automaton evolves.

Run (1) To make a computer program or a cellular automaton do its thing. (2) Something (reportedly healthy) that people used to do to pass the time before they bought computers.

Scalable Identical on any level of scale. Most regular fractals are scalable.

Scale invariance The property of being scalable.

Scaling See **Scalable**.

Scaling factor A number that determines the size of a shape in one or more dimensions.

Science of complexity See **Complexity**.

Second Law of Thermodynamics The scientific law stating, "All natural processes tend toward increased entropy, or disorder." Many chaotic dynamical systems seem to break this law by transforming energy into order.

Seed shape The polygon in a fractal template that serves as the parent for all other parts of the template.

Seeyalader   Larrydocker.

Self-organizing   Able to spontaneously create order, or decrease entropy. Self-organizing behavior is not a free lunch; self-organizing systems are almost always sucking up a lot of energy from somewhere. Therefore, they are sometimes said to be transforming energy into order.

Self-reflective   Containing parts that resemble the whole; self-similar.

Self-similarity   The property of being self-similar, or self-reflective.

Sensitive dependence on initial conditions   See **Chaos**.

Sierpiński's Triangle   A famous fractal that looks like a triangle with its middle punched out, leaving three triangular regions in the corners. These three regions have their middles punched out and so on. Sometimes called Sierpiński's Gasket.

Simplicity   The opposite of complexity!

Simulation   An artificial working model of something, usually on a computer.

sin   The sine function, which returns the height of a point at a given distance around the perimeter of a circle.

Sine wave   A graphical representation of the sine function, the archetype of smooth oscillation. A "fractal sine wave" would have oscillations within oscillations.

Singularity   A zero-dimensional system, or a point in a multidimensional system where distances between points collapse to zero, and other strange stuff happens. The Big Bang Theory suggests that our universe was once a singularity (and no one is really very sure what that might mean).

Skew   A spin of one axis without spinning the other axis; also called shear. When you skew a square, it becomes a parallelogram.

Slope   See **Rate of change**.

Space-filling   A one-dimensional curve that is infinitely twisty and convoluted and can actually fill a region of two-dimensional or three-dimensional space.

Spin   (1) The same thing it means with everyday physical objects. (2) The **Spin** command on the FractalVision menu, which rotates a part of the template around the handle.

Squish   Used in FractalVision software to mean a shrinking of the x-axis only.

Stem-and-branches technique   The process of modeling a plant by approximating the stem or trunk with a seed shape and then adding copies of the seed as the first level of branches.

Stone Soup Group   (1) All the people who have contributed to FRACTINT, a freeware program developed through collaboration on the CompuServe's COMART (computer art) forum, section 15 (fractals). (2) The four main developers of FRACTINT: Bert Tyler, Tim Wegner, Mark Peterson, and Peiter Branderhorst.

Strange attractor   A mathematical model and graphical representation of a chaotic nonlinear dynamical system, such as Lorenz' model of fluid convection or Henon's model of celestial orbits.

Stratus   Hazy overcast clouds.

Stretch   Used in FractalVision software to mean an expansion (Grow) of the x-axis only.

Successive approximation algorithm   The process of drawing increasingly accurate approximations of a fractal, implemented in the FractalVision **Draw** command.

Super VGA   (1) Any graphics adapter that supports standard VGA modes and also supports extended modes with higher resolution or more colors. (2) Specifically, the Video Electronics Standards Association (VESA) 800x600 16-color or 640x480 256-color video modes.

System   (1) Anything under observation. To call it a system, you just need to decide what will count as "part of the system" and what will count as "outside the system." (2) A set of mathematical equations relating several variables to one another.

Tangent line   A line that touches a point on a curve and has the same slope as the curve at that point. (See also: **Rate of change** and **Differential calculus**.)

Template   See **Fractal template**.

Text file   Any file containing ASCII test characters, usually readable with any text editor or word processor.

Thermodynamics   The study of heat, temperature, entropy, and organization.

Three-dimensional   Describable with three variables. The physical space we live in is three-dimensional because we can locate any point in space using height, latitude, and longitude.

Tiling   The act of covering a shape exactly with copies of itself. See **Collage**.

Time irreversible   A system where you can't determine its past or future by measuring its current state, or a system for which this will be true at some time or another.

Time reversible   A system where you can always determine its past and future by measuring its current state.

Trace-and-tile technique   The process of approximating a shape by tracing a rough outline of it for a seed shape and tiling that shape with copies of itself to fill in details that the rough outline missed. See **Collage**.

Transformation matrix   A set of numbers that describes a geometric relationship. (See also: **Matrix** and **Affine transformation**.)

Transformed copies   Variations on a shape made by spinning, shrinking, moving, or otherwise transforming it.

Translation   See **Displacement**.

Two-dimensional   Describable with two variables. A flat surface, or plane, is two-dimensional because any point on it can be located with x- and y-coordinates.

Variable   A changing quantity, or a storage place in a computer representing a quantity.

Vector   (1) A point on a plane or the shortest path from the origin to that point. (2) Of or relating to lines or linear curves. Specifically, a drawing stored as a collection of geometric shapes rather than a bitmap is called "vector data." (3) A matrix.

Vector DAT file   See **DAT file**.

Vector DXF file   See **DXF file**.

VGA   Video Graphics Array, the current low-end standard in graphics adapters for IBM PC compatibles.

Virtual memory   Hard disk space that a program uses as if it were internal memory chips.

Visual instructions   Directions expressed nonverbally or graphically (as opposed to a written language). Fractal templates are visual instructions because the visual relationships between shapes on-screen instruct FractalVision how to continue the pattern.

x   Often used to refer to the horizontal, or real, part of a complex number.

XMS memory   Extended Memory Specification; a faster alternative to the older, expanded memory standard. Both are work-arounds for the shortsighted decision to limit the Intel 8088 processors to a memory space of 640K.

y   Often used to refer to the vertical, or imaginary, part of a complex number.

z   Often used to denote a complex number, or the third dimension in three-dimensional space.

Zoom box   A rectangle displayed by FRACTINT, which enables you to specify which part of a fractal to zoom in on.

Zoom in   A much more fun way to say "magnify."

Index

Symbols

3-D
  IFS codes, 334-343, 445
  mountains, 109-111
  point, 445
  space, 445
  transform, 445

A

Accept command, 380, 383
Ad infinitum, 445
Adjust command, 378
Adjust Panel, 380-381
adjusting level of detail, 21-22
affine transformations, 321-325,
  409-414, 445
    orbital iterations, 345-351
    shrink transformation, 321-324

Q-R

S

YES! Name: _____

Address: _____ Phone: _____

City: _____ State: _____ ZIP: _____

____ **Register me as a licensed user of FractalVision software.** I want to receive a free newsletter by Dick Oliver, notification of updates to FractalVision, and free information on related products from Cedar Software.

(There is no charge to register unless you wish to order additional products at this time.)

____ **Send me the products selected below, on:**

   5.25" 360K disks   3.5" 720K disks   5.25" 1.2M disks   3.5" 1.4M disks

Please add a $5 shipping/handling fee to all North American product orders ($10 overseas), including orders for FRACTINT only.

Visa/MasterCard or U.S. check #: _____

Expiration date: _____   Sign here: _____

__ **FRACTINT Version 17.2   FREE**

A terrific complement to FractalVision, this free program by the famous "Stone Soup Group" displays over 60 types of mathematical fractals, with 3-D, color animation, fractal planets, and many other spectacular effects. (FRACTINT is also available from most BBS systems and shareware/freeware distributors for a small distribution fee.)

__ **Graphics Workshop by Alchemy Mindworks $39**

A handy utility which prints, scales, rotates, crops, dithers, and converts between many graphics file formats, including the PCX and GIF formats supported by FractalVision and FRACTINT.

__ **Full C source code for FractalVision $39**

For those who want to see the procedures from this book incorporated into two full-sized applications (The source code for FRACTINT is included free). Thousands of lines of commented C code, plus assembly language 32-bit integer math functions compatible with both programs (assembler not required). Compatible with all major C and C++ compilers.

__ **Dick Oliver's Fractal Grafics 3D $99**

Create true three-dimensional fractal models and export DXF files to any 3-D CAD, rendering, or animation software. Includes 3-D trees, ferns, mountains, galaxies, and many other models, as well as a Handbook of 3-D Fractal Design. This is a sophisticated system: expect to spend some time learning to use it.

(Inquire about educational site licenses and training workshops.)

Send this page to: Call 802-888-5275 or FAX 802-888-3009

 **Cedar Software**

Route 1, Box 5140
Morrisville, VT 05661

Although many personal computers use 3 1/2-inch disks to store information, some older computers use 5 1/4-inch disks for information storage. If your computer uses 5 1/4-inch disks, you can return this form to Sams Publishing to obtain 5 1/4-inch disks to use with this book. Complete the remainder of this form and mail to:

FractalVision,
First Edition
Disk Exchange
Sams Publishing
11711 N. College Ave., Suite 140
Carmel, IN 46032

We will send you, free of charge, the 5 1/4-inch version of the book software.

Name_____ Phone_____

Company_____ Title _____

Address_____

City_____ State _____ ZIP_____